PREPARATIVE
INORGANIC
REACTIONS

Volume 3

PREPARATIVE INORGANIC REACTIONS

Volume 3

Editor

WILLIAM L. JOLLY

Department of Chemistry
University of California
Berkeley, California

1966

INTERSCIENCE PUBLISHERS

a division of John Wiley & Sons
New York · London · Sydney

Library of Congress Catalog Card Number 64-17052

PRINTED IN THE UNITED STATES OF AMERICA

PREFACE

The principal aim of this series of books is to describe the rationale and theory behind the preparation of various important classes of compounds. The *rationale* generally consists of the recognition and extension of analogies, and the *theory* consists of the application of thermodynamic and kinetic principles.

The second aim of the series is to provide critical evaluations and comparisons of the various methods that have been used for preparing particular compounds. A few illustrative "recipes" are described, and references to analogous procedures are given.

Suggestions for future chapters are welcomed by the Editor.

WILLIAM L. JOLLY

CONTRIBUTORS TO VOLUME 3

John D. Corbett Institute for Atomic Research and Department of Chemistry, Iowa State University, Ames, Iowa

B. B. Cunningham Department of Chemistry and Lawrence Radiation Laboratory, University of California, Berkeley, California

R. A. Geanangel Department of Chemistry, The Ohio State University, Columbus, Ohio

John K. Ruff Redstone Research Laboratories, Rohm and Haas Co., Huntsville, Alabama

S. G. Shore Department of Chemistry, The Ohio State University, Columbus, Ohio

CONTENTS

Metal Halides in Low Oxidation States

JOHN D. CORBETT

*Institute for Atomic Research and Department of Chemistry, Iowa State University, Ames, Iowa**

CONTENTS

I. INTRODUCTION

As the references at the end of this chapter will attest, a very substantial fraction of what is known about halides of metals in low oxidation states has been published in the last ten or fifteen years. This is not to detract from the noteworthy pioneering efforts of earlier investigators, but is merely an observation that successful preparation of many of these compounds is either substantially improved or indeed made possible by advantages of techniques and methods not available to the earlier investigators. Certainly among the aids which should be counted as important are the ready availability of good vacuum and dry-box facilities, superior container and starting materials, especially metals, and x-ray and thermal analysis equipment for product char-

* Contribution No. 1809. Work was performed in the Ames Laboratory of the U.S. Atomic Energy Commission.

acterization. As a result not only are the products substantially purer, whatever their intended use, but also investigators are (or should be) becoming more informed and cautious concerning such pertinent details as containers, equilibrium relationships, and unusual phases. Among the last should be included phases which have substantial composition breadths ($NbCl_{3\pm}$, for example), which possess a stoichiometry not always described by a ratio of small, whole numbers ($TaCl_{2.33}$, $NbI_{1.83}$, $NdI_{1.95}$, $BiCl_{1.167}$), or which possess formidable kinetic limitations on their formation. In addition to the prerequisite characterization of lower oxidation states afforded by these preparations, more spectacular results, to some minds, have come from subsequent studies of them, particularly in the areas of spectra, metal–metal bonding, magnetic interactions, and structure in general. The present chapter will consider only that which must come first, the preparations, and the reactions, techniques, precautions, and the rationale behind them. A somewhat subjective evaluation of these is unavoidable.

The coverage in the present chapter will be limited to isolable compounds and hence will not include evidence for lower oxidation states afforded only by studies in dilute host crystals, in melts, or in the gas phase. Only chlorides, bromides, and iodides will be considered since many of the fluorides have already been dealt with in an earlier volume.[1] In addition, the high field and polarizing power of the fluoride ion makes it generally the poorest candidate among the halides for the preparation of low oxidation states, while stability differences among the heavier three, usually favoring the iodide, are substantially smaller. The unusual Ag_2F is an almost singular exception. At the other extreme, anions of even lower field and basicity, e.g., $AlCl_4^-$, will be included in the few cases where a new or less ambiguous product results. Halo-complexes of the oxidation states in question, i.e., double salts, are not considered nor are any of the more or less highly complexed derivatives with other ligands, the emphasis being rather on the "simple" halides.

The definition of a "lower" oxidation state is not so clear. In an incautious moment the author agreed that "lower" might include all halides made by reduction, thus eliminating only "normal" states and those obtained by strongly oxidative means. However, the well-known halides of iron(II), mercury(I), and tin(II), which might meet this criterion, are not covered.

II. TABULATION OF THE LOWER HALIDES AND THEIR PREPARATIVE METHODS

For purposes of reference as well as later example, the lower halides are compiled in Table I together with brief descriptions of the preparative methods, references, and a few comments. The collection is intended to include all valid, reduced phases but is probably unavoidably incomplete. Phases are generally identified by the experimentally observed halide-to-metal ratio even though these may seem rather strange in some situations. Further recourse to "whole-number research" to interpret these is generally not practicable without knowledge of a prototype structure or at least the density and size of the true unit cell. Some structural units are known, such as $Ta_6I_{12}I_2$ for $TaI_{2.33}$,[2] but it does not seem practical to include all of this information here. Also listed are a few evidently "metallic" phases, e.g., $La^{3+}(I^-)_2e^-$, which may not meet the definition of a lower oxidation state in the usual, localized sense.

In the second column of Table I is noted whether the compound melts congruently (C) or incongruently (I), if it is known and pertinent to the preparative method, as will be discussed in Section III.D. Only a brief description of the reaction and method is given, since, presumably, any laboratory preparation would be preceded by a more thorough investigation of the literature. Here T denotes a transport reaction and H–C denotes hot–cold (two-temperature) reaction condition; the significance of these will be considered later. In many instances only a leading reference to a recent publication is given. A valuable source frequently cited here is *Handbuch der Präparativen Anorganischen Chemie,* edited by Brauer,[3] where the method and the original literature are fully described. However, the sections in this vary widely in their coverage of recent work on low oxidation state halides, and so only those which are reasonably up to date have been included. Of the older literature, Sidgwick[4] is particularly good.

III. GENERAL CONSIDERATIONS

A. Quality

The impurity level which can be tolerated in a product depends on the particular compound, the intended use, and pride. Some products require less care, when used for a powder pattern, extraction of a single crystal, or certain subsequent reactions. On the other hand, some spectral investigations, melt studies, or determinations of the composition of a new phase, for example, require a great deal more care, and in some situations the purity may even be the controlling factor. Consequently, preparative shortcuts are usually not worth while. Literature sources are observed to vary widely with respect to probable quality of the products.

TABLE I
The Metal Halides in Low Oxidation States and their Preparative Reactions

Compound[a]	Melting behavior[b]	Reaction	Refs.	Comments or restrictions
$LaI_{2.42}$	I	LaI_3 + La(stoich.) (melt)	5	
LaI_2	C	LaI_3 + La(excess) (melt)	5	Metallic
$CeI_{2.42}$	I	CeI_3 + Ce(stoich.) (melt)	5	
CeI_2	I	CeI_3 + Ce(excess) (melt)	5	Metallic
$PrCl_{2.31}$	I	$PrCl_3$ + Pr(excess) (melt)	6	Stable above 594°
$PrBr_{2.38}$	I	$PrBr_3$ + Pr(excess) (melt)	7	
$PrI_{2.50}$	C	PrI_3 + Pr(stoich.) (melt)	5	
PrI_2	I	PrI_3 + Pr(excess)(melt)	5	
$NdCl_{2.37-2.33}$ or $NdCl_{2.27}$	I	$NdCl_3$ + Nd(stoich.) (melt)	8,9	
$NdCl_2$	I	$NdCl_3$ + Nd(excess) (melt)	8,9	
$NdI_{1.95}$	C	NdI_3 + Nd(excess) (melt)	8	Saltlike
$SmCl_{2.2}$	I	$SmCl_3$ + Sm(stoich.) (melt)	10	
$SmCl_2$	C	$SmCl_3$ + Sm(excess) (melt)	10	H_2 reduction is incomplete; attacks glass[11]
$SmBr_2$,SmI_2[c]	C ?	H_2 + SmX_3; dissoc. SmI_3	12,13	90% yield reported for dissociation
EuX_2[c]	C ?	H_2 + EuX_3; dissoc. EuI_3	14–16	
		$EuCl_3$ + Zn(stoich.), distil	11	
$GdCl_{1.6}$	I	$GdCl_3$ + Gd(excess) (melt)	17	
GdI_2	I	GdI_3 + Gd(excess) (melt)	17	Probably metallic
$DyCl_{2.1}$	I	$DyCl_3$ + Dy(stoich.) (melt)	18	
$DyCl_2$	I	$DyCl_3$ + Dy(excess) (melt)	18	
TmI_2	I ?	TmI_3 + Tm(excess) (melt)	19	
		HgI_2 + Tm		

(*continued*)

TABLE I (*continued*)

Compound[a]	Melting behavior[b]	Reaction	Refs.	Comments or restrictions
YbX_2[c]	C ?	$YbX_3 + H_2$; dissoc. YbI_3	20,21	
		$YbCl_3$ + Zn(stoich.) distil	11	
$ThBr_3$, ThI_3	I	ThX_4 + Th(stoich.) (melt)	22,23	
ThI_2	I	ThI_4 + Th(excess) (melt)	23,24	Metallic
UX_3	C	UX_4 + U(stoich.) (melt)	25	
		UCl_4 + Al, Zn, or H_2	26	
		UH_3 + HX	27	
$NpCl_3$, $NpBr_3$		$NpX_4 + H_2$ or NH_3	27	
		$NpO_2 + AlX_3$ + Al	27	
TiX_3		TiX_4 or X_2 + Ti(stoich.)	3	
		$TiCl_4 + H_2$(glow discharge)	28	Continuous, pyrophoric
		$TiCl_4$, $TiBr_4 + H_2$ (W filament)	3,29,30	Lower yield
		TiX_4(excess) + H_2	3	Lower yield
TiX_2		TiX_4 or X_2 + Ti(excess)	3,31	Glass attack Cl>Br>I
		Disprop. TiX_3	3	Some metal produced, ref. 3; however, see ref. 32
		$TiCl_4 + H_2$(excess) (electrodeless discharge)	3	Very finely divided
ZrX_3[d]		$ZrX_4 + H_2$(glow discharge)	34	Low yield, pyrophoric
		$ZrCl_4$, $ZrBr_4$(excess) + Zr pwdr, 40–60 atm	35,36	0.2–1% Zr in product
		ZrX_4(excess) + Zr pwdr, 15–18 atm; regrind and repeat	37,38	1–3% Zr in product
		$ZrCl_4$(excess) + Zr, 1 atm; screen to separate metal	39	45% yield, SiO_2 attack > 700°C
ZrX_2		ZrX_3 disprop[e]		
HfX_3		HfX_4(excess) + Hf pwdr, 5–18 atm, regrind and repeat	37,38	1–6% Hf in product
$HfI_{3.3}$		HfI_4(excess) + Hf foil, physical separation; equil. with HfI_4 or Hf for phase limits	42	30–40% yield; phase is of variable composition

(*continued*)

TABLE I (*continued*)

Compound[a]	Melting behavior[b]	Reaction	Refs.	Comments or restrictions
VX_2		VCl_3, VBr_3 + H_2(675°)	3	May contain some metal[f]
		Disprop. VCl_3, VBr_3	3,44	
		V + Br_2(stoich.)	3	
		V + I_2(excess) $\rightarrow VI_{2+} \xrightarrow{\Delta}$	45	
NbX_4		$NbCl_5$ + Nb(T[g])	3,46	See also ref. 47
		$NbBr_5$ (via Br_2) + Nb(T)	46,48	
	I	Dissoc. NbI_5	49	Should also result from NbI_5 + Nb (T)
$NbCl_{3\pm}$, $NbBr_{3\pm}$[h]		$NbCl_5$, $NbBr_5$(vary) + Nb foil(T)	3,48	
		$NbCl_5$, $NbBr_5$ + H_2 (vary T)	3,47	
		HCl + Nb 800° (∼lower limit-Nb_3Cl_8)	50	Slow
		$NbCl_5$ + Al	3	
		$NbCl_4$ disprop (∼upper limit)	3	Presumably for $NbBr_3$ too
NbI_3	I	NbI_4 disprop. (+ dissoc.)	49	Presumably also from higher iodide + Nb (stoich.), $t < 500°$
$NbI_{2.67}$		NbI_5 + Nb(excess, shot) 650–700°(T)	51,52	
		Disprop. NbI_3, NbI_4	51	Less satisfactory
$NbCl_{2.33}$		$NbCl_{2.67}$ + Nb	50, 52a	Earlier referred to as $NbCl_2$[53]
		$NbCl_3$, $NbCl_{2.67}$ + KCl (disprop.)	54	Products are K_2NbCl_6 and $NB_6Cl_{14}·4KCl$
$NbBr_{2.33}$		$NbBr_5$ + Al(+$AlBr_3$)	54	
$NbBr_2$		$NbBr_5$ + H_2 (electrodeless discharge)	55	$NbBr_{2.33}$?
NbI_2		NbI_3 + H_2, 300–400° (>400° → Nb)	56	$NbI_{1.83}$?
$NbI_{1.83}$		Higher I + Nb container, 800°(T)	57,58	
TaX_4	I	$TaCl_5$, $TaBr_5$ + Ta(T)	3,59–61	
		TaX_5 + Al(T)	3,59	Iodide slow
		$TaCl_5$, $TaBr_5$ + H_2 (electrodeless discharge)	3,55	
$TaCl_{3\pm}$, $TaBr_{3\pm}$[i]		TaX_5 + Ta(T)	60,61	

(*continued*)

TABLE I (*continued*)

Compound[a]	Melting behavior[b]	Reaction	Refs.	Comments or restrictions
$TaBr_{2.83}$	I	Disprop. $TaBr_4$ (equilibrium conditions)	62	Not found by transport[61]
$TaCl_{2.5}$		$TaCl_5 + Ta(T)$	60,61	
$TaBr_{2.5}$	I	$TaBr_{2.83} + Ta$	62	
$TaBr_{2.33}$, $TaI_{2.33}$		$TaX_5 + Al$ (H–C)[j]	62,63	
		Higher Br + Ta, > 640°	62	
		$TaI_5 + Ta(T)$	2, 63a	
CrX_2	C	$CrCl_3 + H_2 + HCl$	3,64	
		$Cr + HCl$	3	Free metal?[62]
		$CrCl_3 + Cr$(stoich.) (melt)	25	
	C ?	$CrBr_3 + H_2$	3	May need HBr
		$Cr + HBr + Br_2$	65	
	C	$Cr + I_2$(stoich.)	25	
		CrI_3 dissoc.	66	
		Cr(excess) + I_2	3	Slow, incomplete
$MoCl_4$		$MoCl_5 + C_6H_6$(reflux)	67	Some carbonaceous impurity
$MoBr_4$		$MoBr_3 + Br_2$, 60°	68	
MoX_3		$MoCl_5 + H_2$	3	T (see ref. 69)
		$MoCl_5 + H_2$ (>100 psi)	70	
		$Mo + Br_2$, 450–500°	3,71	
		$Mo + I_2$, 300°	72	
MoX_2		Disprop. $MoCl_3$	3	Contains $MoCl_3$ according to ref. 73
		$Mo + COCl_2$	3	Incomplete
		Dissoc. $MoBr_3$	3	
		$Mo + Br_2$, 600–650°	71	
		$MoCl_2$ + LiBr(melt)	74	Aqueous wash to remove LiBr; 0.9% Cl left; 50% yield
		$Mo + I_2$, 400–500°	75	MoI_3 at lower temp.[72]
		Dissoc. MoI_3	72,75	
		$MoCl_2$ + LiI(melt)	74	Aqueous wash to remove LiI; 82% yield
WCl_5		$WCl_6 + H_2$	3	Distil from lower chlorides
		Disprop. WCl_4	76	
WBr_5		Dissoc. WBr_6	76	
WCl_4		WCl_6(excess) + Al, H–C	76	

(*continued*)

TABLE I (*continued*)

Compound[a]	Reaction	Refs.	Comments or restrictions
WBr_4	WBr_5(excess) + Al, H–C	76	60–80% yield
	WBr_5 + W(T)	76	10% yield
WBr_3	WBr_2 + Br_2(excess), 50°	77	
WCl_2	Disprop. WCl_4	76	WCl_6 + Al possible[78] H_2 + WCl_6 unsatisfactory[79]
WBr_2	WBr_2(sl. excess) + Al foil	78	92–94% yield
	Disprop. WBr_4	76	See also ref. 77a
	WBr_5 + H_2(400–450°)	79	
$TcCl_4$	Tc_2O_7 + CCl_4 (bomb)	80	
ReX_3	Dissoc. $ReCl_5$	79,81	70% yield
	Re + Cl_2, sublime	3	
	Dissoc. $ReBr_5$, sublime	82	
	Dissoc. ReI_4	83,84	Rinse with CCl_4, EtOH, Et_2O
	Decomp., $(NH_4)_2ReI_6$ *in vacuo*, then I_2 at 200°	83	
	$HReO_4$ + HI(55%) + ethanol	85	60–70% yield
ReI_2	Dissoc. ReI_3	86	Wash off I_2
ReI	Dissoc. ReI_3	83,86	
$RuCl_3$	Ru + Cl_2(+ CO)	87	α form; T[88]
	$RuCl_6^{2-}$ + EtOH (reflux)	87	β form
	RuO_2 + Cl_2 + CO	89	
$OsCl_3$[k]	Dissoc. $OsCl_4$	90	
	Decomp. $(NH_4)_2OsCl_6$ + Cl_2	90	
$OsBr_3$	Dissoc. $OsBr_4$	91	97.6% pure
$OsCl_2$[k]	Disprop. $OsCl_3$, boil with HCl	90	
OsI_2	OsO_4 + 55% HI + EtOH, to dryness	86	(Oxyiodide?)
OsI	OsO_4 + 55% HI + EtOH, under CO_2	89	Amorphous
IrX_2[k]	Dissoc. IrX_3	92,93	
IrX[k]	Dissoc. IrX_2	92,93	
PtX_3	Dissoc. PtX_4	94–96	

(*continued*)

TABLE I (*continued*)

Compound[a]	Melting behavior[b]	Reaction	Refs.	Comments or restrictions
PtX_2		Decomp. H_2PtCl_4, water wash	97	No free Pt; Cl/Pt sl. high
		Dissoc. $PtCl_4$	98,94	Caution nec. to avoid free Pt
		Dissoc. $PtBr_4$	95	
		Decomp. H_2PtBr_4 or H_2PtBr_6	99	
		Dissoc. PtI_4	96,99	Difficult to get pure
PtCl, PtBr		Dissoc. PtX_2	94,95	Borderline stability
PtI?		Dissoc. PtI_2	96	X-ray evidence only
CuCl, CuBr	C	$Cu^{2+} + SO_3^{2-} + Cl^-(Br^-)$	3,100	Vacuum sublimation improves
		$Cu + X_2$	101	Also CuX_2(l) + Cu
AuCl		Dissoc. $AuCl_3$	102	Prolonged heating gives metal
		Dissoc. $HAuCl_4 \cdot 4H_2O$	3	Via $AuCl_3$ presumably
AuBr		Dissoc. $AuBr_3$	4,103	
$Cd_2(AlX_4)_2$	I	CdX_2 + Al(stoich.) (melt)	104	AlX_3 formed *in situ*
$GaCl_{2.25}$	I	$GaCl_3$ + Ga(stoich.) (melt)	105	
Ga_2X_4	C	GaX_3 + Ga(stoich.)	106–108	
		$GaCl_3$, $GaBr_3$(excess) + Ga, vaporize excess GaX_3, fractionally crystallize	109,110	Less convenient
GaBr, GaI	I	GaX_3 + Ga(excess)	107,108	Bromide difficult to obtain pure
$Ga(AlX_4)$	C	GaX_3 + Al(stoich.)	106,107	AlX_3 formed *in situ*
$InCl_2$[l]	I ?	$InCl_3$ + In(stoich.) (melt)	111	
$InBr_2$, InI_2	C	InX_3 + In(stoich.) (melt)	114–116	
		HgX_2 + In(stoich.) (melt)	113	See text
$InCl_{\sim 1.8}$[l]	~C	$InCl_3$ + In(stoich.) (melt)	111,112	
$InBr_{1.73}$	sl.I	$InBr_3$ + In(stoich.) (melt)	114,115	Latter ref. indicates C
$InCl_{1.50}$	C	$InCl_3$ + In(stoich.) (melt)	111,112	
		Hg_2Cl_2 + In(stoich.) (melt)	113	See text

(*continued*)

TABLE I (*continued*)

Compound[a]	Melting behavior[b]	Reaction	Ref.	Comments or restrictions
$InBr_{1.40}$	C	$InBr_3$ + In(stoich.) (melt)	114	Ref. 115 reports $InBr_{\sim 1.5}$
InX	C	$InCl_3$ + In(excess) (melt)	111, 112	
	C	$InBr_3$ + In(excess) (melt)	114, 115	
	C	InI_3 + In(excess) (melt)	116	
		HgX_2 or Hg_2X_2 + In	113	See text
$InAlCl_4$	C	Hg_2Cl_2 + In + Al (stoich.)	113	
$BiCl_{1.167}$	I	$BiCl_3$ + Bi(excess); remove unreacted $BiCl_3$ physically	117, 118	Reaction incomplete; the lower bromide and iodide[119] have not been characterized

[a] X is Cl, Br, or I.

[b] C denotes congruent; I denotes incongruent

[c] See text regarding container problems.

[d] Other reductants (e.g., Al) appear generally unsatisfactory.[33]

[e] Although several lines of evidence suggest ZrX_2 may be obtained in this way,[37,40,41] no substantial characterization of a zirconium(II) halide has been reported.

[f] Hydrogen reduction near 450° followed by disproportionation of last traces of VX_3 at 700° is better.[43]

[g] T is transport reaction (see text).

[h] Variable phase for Cl and Br, $2.67 < X/Nb \lesssim 3.1$, but not for I.

[i] Chloride and bromide are of variable composition.

[j] H–C is hot–cold, two-temperature synthesis (sealed tube).

[k] No recent studies.

[l] There is some disagreement as to the existence and melting character of $InCl_2$, the composition of the phase near $InCl_{1.8}$ (and near $InCl_{1.3}$), and the character of the melting of InCl.[111–113]

The problem of low molecular weight impurities in halides, particularly in those of the heavier elements, can be quite disturbing. For example, 0.5 wt % H_2O in LaI_3 corresponds to a product which when analyzed gives a reasonable 99.5% La + I, perhaps within the usual analytical uncertainty considering the difficulty of obtaining a sample weight of the material. Yet on reaction with, say, lanthanum metal to form LaI_2, the water impurity will consume a substantial amount of metal and drastically affect the purity of the product. In this instance

50% additional metal is required for the "reduction," assuming LaOI and LaH_2 are the products and the resultant material is only 83 mole % LaI_2, yet analysis shows 99.57 wt % La + I! Similarly, if the starting material contains 0.5 wt % oxygen as LaOI, the final product is only 89% LaI_2. Carbon and silica, other possible impurities in LaI_3, have a similar effect. The same problems arise with low atomic weight impurities in the metal. Although they are somewhat less serious in this instance because of the smaller quantity used, the impurities are usually far more difficult to remove. Although in some instances vacuum fusion and spectrographic facilities may be available to give approximate measures of these impurities, it is generally better to take exceptional precautions throughout to avoid their introduction. This means the use of high quality starting materials, e.g., a vacuum sublimed, higher halide, a good high vacuum facility (not 10 μ or a few torr as sometimes stated), a good *dry* box, and a technique which involves no transfers or apparatus changes in the air and no stoppers or corks in the apparatus. Manipulations and reactions are generally best carried out in sealed containers with no, or a minimum number of, joints, stopcocks, etc., and in extreme cases these must be baked out in a vacuum prior to use. This also presumes a completely inert container—a problem that cannot always be ideally solved. Under these conditions one can frequently obtain substantially quantitative yields, although problems of kinetics or of product stability may not be so easily overcome. Under these circumstances the reported 90–92% $SmCl_2$ from H_2 + $SmCl_3$, for instance, or 90% SmI_2 from dissociation of SmI_3, would be judged unsatisfactory, and in fact such apportionment of the analytical results into components requires some predisposition as to the identity of the latter.

B. Use of a Solvent

Although there are obvious exceptions, a great number of compounds listed in Table I cannot be obtained, or retained, in the presence of the usual molecular solvents. Some are too sensitive to disproportionation to tolerate even slightly basic solvents, whereas others reduce all such materials. Solvolysis may also be a problem, particularly for higher oxidation state precursors. Even without these detractions subsequent complete removal of solvent may be difficult and may lead to pyrolysis, cracking, etc. Sublimation may not always eliminate carbonaceous impurities because of either cosublimation or entrainment. These can be particularly troublesome reducing (or oxidizing) agents in solution studies where even trace amounts produce major perturbations, as has been noted with molten salt solutions of aluminum, cadmium, lead, and bismuth halides.[120–122] A better procedure is to avoid their introduction in the first place, which may mean synthesis from the elements rather than purification of commercial materials.

The use of salts as solvents offers definite advantages of stability and in the rapid attainment of equilibrium. One obvious choice, the halide of the metal in question in a higher oxidation state, can lead to very clean reactions. This is simply then a melt reaction in the molten system MX_n–MX_{n-y}. On the other hand, solvents of halides of other metals, e.g., the alkali metals, are generally less desirable since they (*1*) usually reduce the stability of a lower state, as discussed later under anion effects (Sect. IV.D), (*2*) often form double salts with the product, and (*3*) may introduce foreign impurities, as with water from the lithium halides in the metathetical reactions with MoX_2 (Table I). Even in the absence of these effects, it is usually difficult to impossible to remove the added salts from all but the least reactive products. Obvious exceptions occur when the latter is stable to the necessary solvent (MoX_2) or the solvent is volatile. In the second instance the added salt may serve as a useful flux, as with AlX_3 in the production of $NbBr_{2.33}$, $TaBr_{2.33}$, and $TaI_{2.33}$.[54,62] Likewise, where an aqueous solution of $NbCl_{2.33}$ ($\rightarrow Nb_6Cl_{12}^{2+} + 2Cl^-$) is of interest, the K_2NbCl_6 and excess KCl resulting from the reaction

$$15NbCl_{2.67} + 10KCl \rightarrow 2\ Nb_6Cl_{14}\cdot 4KCl + 3K_2NbCl_6$$

may be removed by conventional means.[54]

C. Choice of Reducing Agent

Generally the metal of the salt involved is the most obvious and suitable reducing agent, particularly for the lowest oxidation state when the product is only slightly stable to disproportionation. The special problems here and with intermediate states will be considered in Section IV. In some situations, as with the very refractory metals or with those unavailable in sufficient quantity or purity, other reducing agents may have to be employed. The choice is often simply based on thermodynamic relationships. Hydrogen is certainly one of the most widely used or tried. However, the free energy change for the couple H_2–HX is relatively small, even for the chloride, and in fact becomes negligible for HI; therefore hydrogen is most useful for the more easily reduced, higher chlorides (and fluorides), e.g., the trichlorides of V, Cr, Eu, and Yb. On the other hand, hydrogen reductions of $SmCl_3$ (SmF_3) and $TmCl_3$ (and not surprisingly, TmI_3) are unsatisfactory.[11,19,123] Complications may also result in systems with very stable metal hydride phases, as perhaps occurs with cerium.[17]

A foreign metal as the reducing agent of course produces a salt impurity which usually must be removed, so the systems are in this respect similar to those with salt solvents discussed earlier. This accounts for the frequent use of the good reducing agent aluminum, as its halides are relatively volatile. Here the aluminum may produce finely divided metal of the salt in question which then reacts with the excess halide. However, a specific solvent or fluxing action is also apparent in some systems as described earlier for niobium and tantalum. Some of the more ionic halides may actually react with AlX_3 to form lower melting tetrahaloaluminates, and this change in anion may then lead to a substantially greater stability of the reduced state; conversely, production of a more basic metal halide *in situ* by this means usually has the opposite effect (Sect. IV.D). Zinc is one of the few other metals that has been found to have some general utility as a reducing agent for the production of UCl_3, $EuCl_2$, and $YbCl_2$, but not $TiCl_3$. These are sufficiently stable to permit the use of the weaker reducing agent zinc, and the distillation of the $ZnCl_2$ produced.[11,26,28] Stable intermetallic phases obviously will interfere with this approach as well as the following method.

Metathetical reactions have a definite utility for the production of some lower halides and are especially useful when small amounts are desired, only the metal in question is available, or necessary dry box and vacuum facilities are not available. Dry mercury and silver halides, for example, are easily obtained and may be reacted with a more active metal M according to

$$Hg_2X_2 + M \rightarrow MX_2 + 2\ Hg$$

However, incomplete reaction may result if stoichiometric amounts are used, and the reaction proceeds via two liquid phases, metal and salt, as is usual. Under these circumstances complete reaction requires that the activities of M in Hg and of Hg_2X_2 in MX_2 both go substantially to zero. The lack of this condition may account for the high halide-to-metal ratios in the production of the indium(I) halides by this means (Table I); an excess of M in most cases would therefore appear desirable. If the desired product MX_2 is an intermediate rather than the lowest halide, stoichiometric proportions must be used, and the success of the method depends largely on the magnitude of the equilibrium constant for the above reaction.

D. Phase and Other Thermodynamic Relationships

Some preparations proceed with only gaseous and solid phases present and without the formation of liquid or solid solutions or intermediate

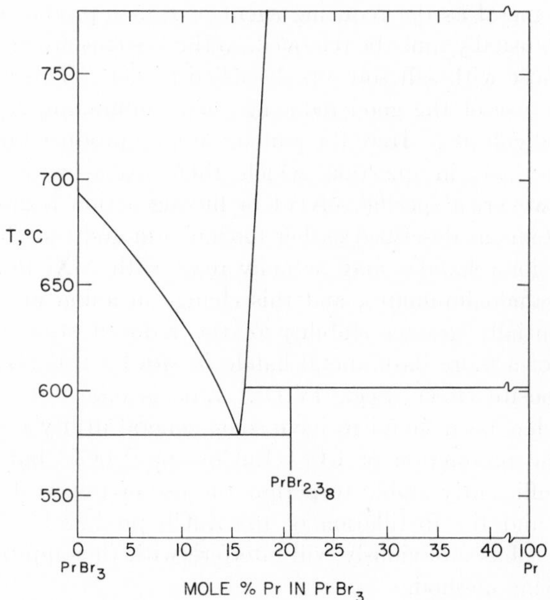

Fig. 1. Phase relationships of the compound $PrBr_{2.38}$ in the $PrBr_3$–Pr system.[7]

phases, so that condensed phase relationships do not pertain. Examples of a number of these are to be found in Table I. On the other hand, solid–solid reactions in systems with different volatility relationships may not proceed via a gaseous component at a sufficiently rapid rate, and the reactants must be heated to fuse the higher salt and/or the product. The former transition is, by and large, of no consequence in the present discussion and will simply accelerate the reaction. However, the character of the melting of the product, should this occur, is of paramount importance. Should the product melt with decomposition, i.e., peritectically, no reduction of the all-liquid system with metal and subsequent cooling will ever be successful in producing a pure phase. It appears that a number of incomplete reductions reported in the literature may have resulted from just this property.

The phase relationships of one of many such lower halides, $PrBr_{2.38}$, are shown in Figure 1. It is seen that reduction of $PrBr_3$ by excess Pr metal just above the melting point (601°) will only give a liquid of composition $PrBr_{2.52}$, so that reduction to the pure lower phase must be accomplished by reaction below 601°, preferably between the liquid phase $PrBr_{2.5+}$ and excess metal above the eutectic at 579°. The success of the preparation and, in fact, the identification of the phase composition in the first place, depends on the success of this equilibration and on the sensitivity of the method used to detect unreacted $PrBr_3$ (or finely divided Pr)—an x-ray powder pattern, optical examination, or the disappearance of the eutectic halt on thermal analysis (generally less sensitive). Very long equilibration times, if necessary, are the best procedure and temperature cycling should be avoided, especially through the peritectic temperature because of the formation of finely divided metal at that point. Physical separation of salt from unreacted metal prior to analysis requires that pieces rather than a powder be used. With extreme incongruency ($GdCl_{1.58}$), patience, luck, and a temperature-gradient (crystal-growing) procedure are helpful.

Intermediate phases which melt incongruently, as does $LaI_{2.42}$ (Fig. 2), of course, cannot be obtained using excess metal but rather require stoichiometric proportions. Identification of the composition in the first place requires adequate equilibration of samples ($734 < t < 750°$) followed by some technique of phase detection as described above.* It should be noted that samples for such equilibrations should first be quenched from the all-liquid region and then taken up to temperature in order to obtain a relatively homogeneous dispersion of phases rather than the segregated mixture which would probably result from slow cooling. It should also be observed that although $LaI_{2.00}$ melts congruently (Fig. 2) and can therefore be obtained from a direct melt reaction, further reaction of its melt with metal is usually endothermic, so that the limiting composition (slowly) increases in metal content with increasing temperature. Consequently a mixture of metal and the lowest halide may be obtained if the equilibration is carried out too far above the melting point of the salt, and the melt is then cooled rapidly.

It is not the purpose of this article to discuss methods of phase diagram determination, as vital as these may be to the characterization of a new system. Some descriptions of techniques applicable to melts, as well as leading references to the literature, have been given elsewhere.[124] A good example of their careful application is a recent study of the $InBr_3$–In system.[114]

It is certainly not possible to cite all the limits on the stability of lower halides which may be described by thermodynamic relationships. However, examples of upper and lower temperature limits to stability should be included as cautions to the investigator. An upper limit of stability for disproportionation or dissociation to a gaseous product which is dictated by the vapor pressure of the latter is analogous to a peritectic melting point. Here the decomposition pressure and the

* A comparison of x-ray and thermal analysis methods for this interpretation may be obtained from two studies[8,9] of the phases near $NdCl_{2.35}$ and $NdCl_{2.25}$.

higher vapor pressure of the product may converge (the latter often has a lower enthalpy change), in which case the solid halide cannot exist (is completely decomposed) above the intersection (quadruple point). For example, the pressure of $TaBr_5$(g) above $TaBr_4$(s) [and $TaBr_3$(s)] becomes equal to that of pure liquid $TaBr_5$ at about 330°, so that $TaBr_4$(s) does not exist above this temperature.[59]

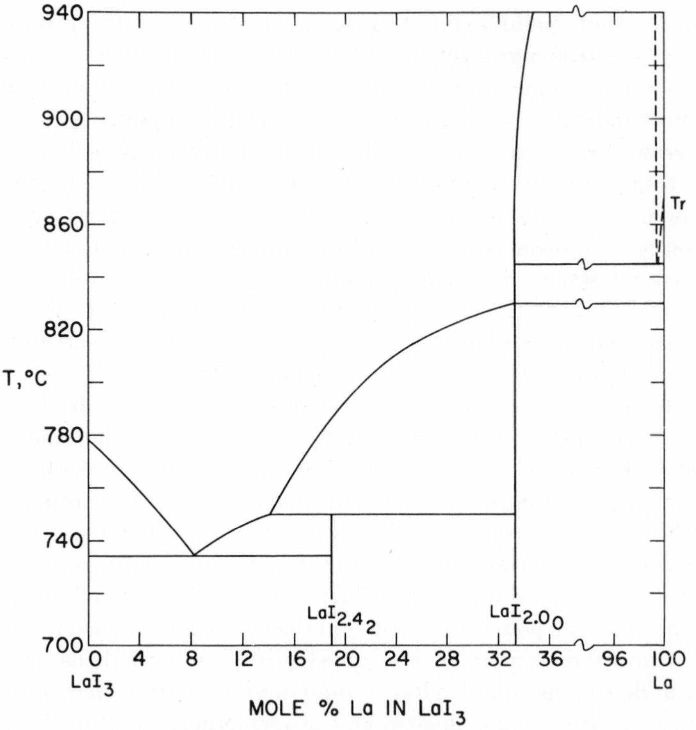

Fig. 2. The system LaI_3–La, with the incongruently melting intermediate $LaI_{2.42}$ and the congruently melting $LaI_{2.0_0}$.[5]

Although extrapolated thermodynamic data may predict a lower temperature limit for stability, e.g., for the disproportionation of AuBr,[103] this is seldom observed, presumably for kinetic reasons. A rare example (among halides) is the (exothermic) disproportionation of $PrCl_{2.31}$ into solids Pr and $PrCl_3$ below about 594°, which is about 60° below its incongruent melting point.[6] A reversal in $\Delta H°$ and thus the upper stability limit associated with melting is presumably brought about by the larger positive change in the enthalpy (and entropy) associated with fusion of the product $PrCl_3$.

An unusual property of some halides which should certainly be noted is their existence as phases of substantial composition breadth rather than as the usual "line" compounds. Although such a Berthollide behavior has long been known among sulfides, oxides, etc., its occurrence among the compounds considered here is substantially limited to the "trichlorides" and "tribromides" of niobium and tantalum[47,48,60,61,125] and to the triiodide of hafnium.[42] In the first instance there is a single, homogeneous phase extending from $NbCl_{3.13}$ to $NbCl_{2.67}$ (at about 366°), so that the trichloride is only an incidental composition in this region. Obviously the composition obtained in their preparations depends on the method and conditions (Table I). A similar variance in composition has been suggested for the "difluorides" of Sm, Eu, and Yb,[123] and a much smaller region has been found with $FeCl_3$, down to $FeCl_{2.9975}$ at 290°.[126] The investigator should certainly be cautious concerning the occurrence of a substantial range of homogeneity in other systems by comparing samples at the oxidized and reduced limit, i.e., in equilibrium with either the next higher or the next lower phase, and as a function of temperature.

E. Kinetic Difficulties

In opposition to what has been said concerning equilibrium systems, kinetic problems may make what should be well-defined relationships difficult if not impossible to attain. In addition to the general restrictions of slow diffusion, vaporization, etc., slow reactions are usually encountered in systems involving complex structures, refractory metals, or both. The formation of $BiCl_{1.167}$ is an example of the former; even though both of the reacting salt and metal phases are liquid, the highly viscous melt, the intermediate density of the product, and the complexity of the Bi_9^{5+}, $BiCl_5^{2-}$, and $Bi_2Cl_8^{2-}$ units formed may all interfere. As a result it is substantially impossible to convert even gram amounts of $BiCl_3$ into the pure compound on lengthy equilibration with excess metal. Identification of the product's composition by x-ray powder techniques following physical separation (sublimation or extraction of unreacted $BiCl_3$) is also not particularly accurate.[117,118]

The traditionally inert or refractory metals prove to be nearly that in many of their reactions and often require rather extreme conditions even in preparation of their normal valent halides. More to the point here is the fact that this property is frequently combined with substantial structural complexity in the lower halides, especially metal–metal bonding, so that synthesis reactions utilizing metal and a higher halide can be extremely slow and equilibrium very difficult to obtain. In fact, such metal–metal bonding (polynuclear structure) has been considered to be necessary for subhalide stability in order to recover part of the very substantial heats of sublimation of some metals, especially Nb, Ta, Mo, W, and Re.[53] The slowness with which one complex structure is converted into another is illustrated by the fact that $NbCl_{2.67}$ (which contains Nb_3 units) disproportionates in a thermobalance directly to metal (and $NbCl_4$) rather than to the equilibrium phase $NbCl_{2.33}$ which contains Nb_6Cl_{12} groups. Other reactions giving $NbCl_{2.33}$ also proceed extremely slowly and in some cases to an apparently amorphous product.[50] The apparently irreversible, incongruent melting of NbI_3 and the inability to form the equilibrium phase $NbI_{1.83}$ from $NbI_{2.67}$ and metal at a respectable rate below about 750–800°, are probably manifestations of structural complexity.[51,57] Tantalum forms somewhat analogous structures, and attainment of condensed phase equilibria in a reaction between, for example, $TaBr_4$, $TaBr_{2.33}$, and Ta is almost impossible.[62] In one case different products appear to be formed by equilibration and transport experiments, $TaBr_{2.83}$ and $TaBr_3\pm$, respectively,[61,62] perhaps for kinetic reasons. The situation can be one of extreme frustration unless one of the unreacted components or the product is volatile. Only a very few lower halides volatilize congruently, e.g., $YbCl_2$, $EuCl_2$, $TiCl_3$, so direct separations are usually not possible. Under these circumstances near-equilibrium production of the phase via incongruent vaporization or with the aid of another gaseous oxidation–reduction couple (transport reactions) can be invaluable, as will be described in Section IV.D.

IV. EQUILIBRIUM METHODS

Attainment of equilibrium or a condition close to it in a synthesis is generally preferable, especially for compounds close to disproportionation and for investigations of phase composition and homogeneity. This type of reaction is generally highly specific, in contrast to some non-equilibrium approaches, and in difficult cases is the most suitable for the preparation of high purity materials. This section will add to what has already been said some different considerations which apply to: (*1*) the synthesis of the lowest phase in a system compared to an intermediate phase, if any, (*2*) anion effects on lower oxidation states, and (*3*) a brief consideration of the near-equilibrium conditions of transport reactions.

A. The Lowest Phase

The mode of decomposition of the lowest phase is almost always by disproportionation, e.g.,

$$3MX_2(s) \rightarrow 2MX_3(s,l,g) + M(s,l)$$

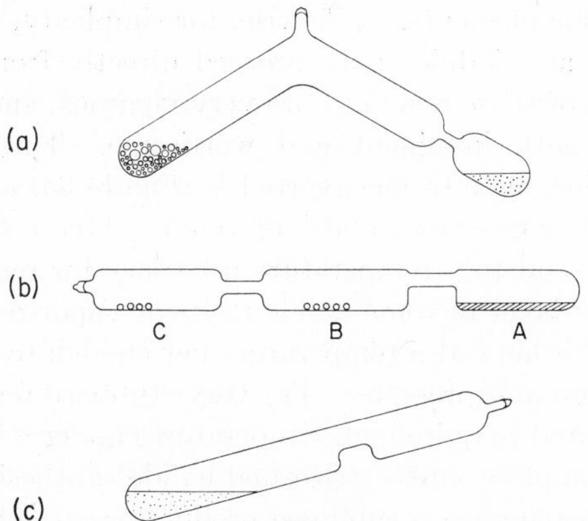

Fig. 3. (*a*) A simple, two temperature synthesis apparatus. (*b*) Two step synthesis of a lower halide from the elements via a higher halide. (*c*) A reaction container for vigorous, metathetical reactions.

Obviously extreme care must be taken, particularly with the less stable compounds, against temperature gradients favoring loss of the usually more volatile higher halide. The optimum reducing agent for the production of the phase is obviously the metal M itself, the reverse of the above equation. Generally all other reducing agents will either be weaker, and thus less suitable, or will be stronger than M and therefore produce M in the course of the reaction (as well as introduce a potential contaminant). Respectable rates of reaction often require a melt of pure MX_3, plus excess metal, the reaction proceeding to pure liquid or solid MX_2 depending on the phase relationships. However, the use of an excess of metal is inappropriate in a few instances, e.g., UX_3, $CrCl_2$, and $GaCl_2$, where the lowest solid halide is congruently melting and its melt can be further reduced. The limiting compositions of the salt melt in equilibrium with metal near the melting points of the respective salts are about $UBr_{2.88}$, $CrCl_{1.93}$, and $CaCl_{1.96}$, the halogen-to-metal ratio decreasing somewhat with increasing temperature.[25,136] This further reaction suggests reduction to a still lower halide which is stable only in the melt at reduced activity, such as

$$UX_3(l) + U(s) \rightarrow UX_2(soln)$$

This type of reaction, discussed elsewhere,[127] is not included in this article.

Compared to chlorides there are generally fewer methods for the preparation of normal-valent bromide and especially iodide reactants for the above reactions, so that these are frequently obtained directly by reaction of the elements. Likewise, for simplicity, the synthesis of lower bromides and iodides may proceed directly from the elements. Obviously some of these reactions are very vigorous, and the dangers of explosions are both imminent and worrisome. The familiar "hot–cold" tube in the shape of an inverted V, Figure 3*a*, or other variants enable a far milder reaction to be carried out. Metal, usually in excess, is heated in one end to a temperature necessary for reaction, often the point at which a layer of some halide melts or vaporizes, while halogen in the other end is kept at a temperature low enough to maintain only a moderate reaction and pressure. For very stubborn reaction the metal may thus be heated to quite high temperatures under a few atmospheres of halogen in complete safety. Normal halide synthesis by this means using excess halogen gives a sublimed product near the bend of the tube which is sealed off from the excess halogen. For lower halides the temperatures are inverted after the reaction is complete so as to sublime any higher halides back onto the metal, the former halogen reservoir is sealed off, and the product equilibrated for homogeneity if necessary. This method is far more desirable than any which attempts to carry out the reaction of the elements under isothermal conditions, a procedure frequently described as frightening and prone to explosion. The method is based on the assumption that excess metal can be used, as bromine and iodine are not easily handled in stoichiometric amounts in such a simple apparatus, and also that the glass container is inert to the metal and the product. Starting with sublimed higher halide of course gives an additional purification and may be somewhat easier to handle. The apparatus shown schematically in Figure 3*b* allows direct synthesis and a subsequent metal–metal halide reaction in a single apparatus. Here heated metal in part *C* reacts with halogen from *A*, a higher halide sublimes onto metal in *B*, the latter part is sealed off, and the components made to react, either isothermally or under transport conditions. A flow procedure with halogen in a carrier gas passing over heated metal is usually less tractable unless the initial, higher halide can be cleanly condensed in the neighborhood of a second batch of metal, and this portion sealed off and equilibrated.

Metathetical reactions mentioned earlier often may be very vigorous, e.g., In + HgX_2, Al + $BiCl_3$ or $CdCl_2$, particularly when the product is much more volatile, but they may be carried out safely in containers of ordinary wall thickness designed as in Figure 3*c* where the volatile product is initially allowed to escape from the reaction zone into the cooler end. Heating with a hand torch rather than a furnace is sometimes better as the reaction may be observed and cooled off if necessary with an air blast. After the reaction subsides the volatile products are sublimed back into A and the tube equilibrated isothermally. Splashing or sputtering of nonvolatile lower halides or metals into B must be avoided as these usually cannot be recombined readily. A related procedure applicable to the less vigorous aluminum reductions of niobium and tantalum halides allows the more volatile components to reflux into the cooler, upper portion.[54,59,62,63] None of these reactions is particularly convenient if a metal container must be used, and a higher halide is a better starting material.

B. Intermediate States

Synthesis of an intermediate phase presents problems of both phase relationships and the usual necessity of reacting stoichiometric proportions. As already considered in Section III.D, an incongruently melting MX_2 in an MX_3–MX system cannot be simply prepared by cooling a melt of the appropriate composition, as this usually gives a mixture of all three halides (see Fig. 2). The synthesis proceeds better by prolonged equilibration below the melting point of MX_2 of an intimate mixture secured by quenching the melt. The need for stoichiometric proportions of, for example, MX_3 and M is general unless the product is sufficiently stable so that excess MX_3 may be volatilized. For instance, the alternate synthesis of $GaCl_2$ or $GaBr_2$ from excess GaX_3 plus metal, followed by partial volatilization of GaX_3, and then repeated fractional crystallization of GaX_2 to a constant melting point (Table I)[128] is quite inconvenient. Other variations are no more practicable for excess metal yields GaX either in solution or as a solid, and even $GaCl_2$ distils with considerable decomposition.

All of these difficulties may be avoided by reacting a stoichiometric amount of higher halide or halogen with the metal. At times weighing these directly in the dry box is sufficiently accurate, although this not as feasible with small amounts or with a highly reactive component, (Br_2, I_2, TiX_4, AlX_3, GaX_3, etc.). Enclosure of this in a fragile, sealed ampule is very helpful in this circumstance as it allows the weight of a critical component to be determined before its transfer to the necessary amount of metal. The general technique is illustrated in Figure 4. First, an approximate amount of halide or halogen is sublimed or distilled into a bulb or tube A, sealed off, and weighed. This is then sealed into B, the bulb fractured with a glass-enclosed magnetic hammer, the contents completely sublimed into C, sealed off, and the glass fragments recovered from B and weighed. The requisite amount of metal is then put in a third piece at E, this sealed onto C at D, the separating bulb or diaphagm broken as before, the components combined in E, sealed off, and made to react. Both the amount and the composition are known

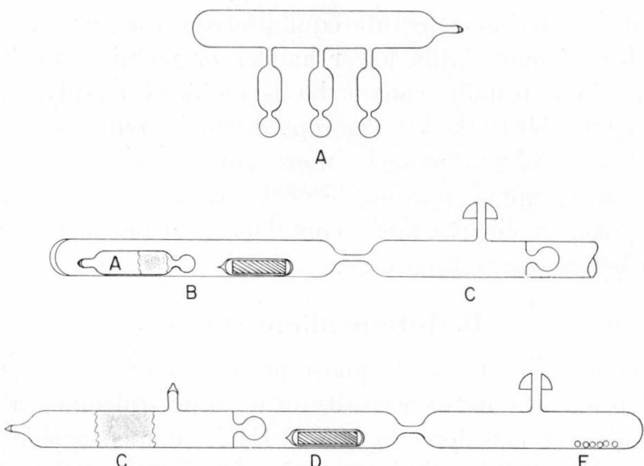

Fig. 4. An ampule technique for the reaction of known amounts of halogen or higher halide (*A*) with metal (*E*) (see text).

to a high precision by this method presuming buoyancy corrections are applied. The method was apparently first applied to the transfer of aluminum halides[129] and has been found to be useful in the synthesis of not only stoichiometric higher or lower halides, including synthesis by metathetical reactions,[106,108] but also double salts, intermediate compositions for phase analysis, and known amounts for solubility studies.

C. Anion Effects

An empirical generality of long-standing tradition is that the stability of the lowest halide with respect to disproportionation usually increases with increasing size of the anion. [Mercury(I) and cadmium(I) are exceptions, however.] Perhaps the most cogent observation on this effect has been that the rate of change of the lattice energy (and the heat of formation) between successive (increasing) oxidation states generally decreases from fluoride to iodide.[130] In other words, for the decomposition

$$3MX_2(s) \rightarrow 2MX_3(s) + M(s,l)$$

$$\Delta H^\circ = -3U_2 + 2I_3 - I_1 - I_2 - \Delta H_{subl}(M) + 2U_3$$

where U_2 and U_3 are the (experimental) lattice energies of MX_2 and MX_3, and the other terms have the usual meaning. Thus in the ionic limit the larger anion gives the smaller value of $2U_3 - 3U_2$ and hence a more positive ΔH°. Roughly comparable entropy changes for the reaction with different anions then lead to the observed stability order. Covalency will favor decomposition and will presumably be greatest for the iodide, though this factor seems less important [except perhaps with Hg(II) and Cd(II) again].

In condensed systems only the lattice terms in the above expression are subject to adjustment. An extension of the size observation with halides suggests that an even larger anion should be better for stabilization of new states.[104,106] A useful species here is AlX_4^-, generated *in situ* by

$$X^- + AlX_3 \rightarrow AlX_4^-$$

as the previous tabulation indicates for cadmium(I), gallium(I), and indium(I); additional examples are known for copper and bismuth. Tetrahaloaluminate salts of a number of other lower halides in already known oxidation states may be easily made by the last reaction. Gallium itself may also provide the large anion with gallium(I) salts,

$$GaX + GaX_3 \rightarrow Ga(GaX_4)$$

to form the so-called gallium dihalides. Some other large anions (PF_6^-, BPh_4^-) are not as tractable, particularly if one is to start with that salt of a higher oxidation state. Extension to a wider variety of metals is limited because of reduction of AlX_4^- by the more active metals and their lower states; GaX_4^- is even more susceptible.

An alternate interpretation for the above lattice energy effect may also be made in terms of melt interactions. For the general reduction

$$2M^{3+} + M = 3M^{2+} \text{ (melt)}$$

small anions interact with the M^{3+} ion more strongly than with M^{2+}, either by covalent or coulombic means, thereby limiting the reduction and giving the general reduction order $Cl < Br < I$. Excess halide of a cation less acidic than M^{3+} (e.g., NaX) is known to decrease the stability of M^{2+} even further. Conversely, introduction of a more acidic halide, which in the extreme amounts to substitution of a larger, less basic anion, substantially increases the stability of the lower state. In general these results also pertain to lower states stable only in melts.[127]

To avoid the need for weighing both the reactive AlX_3 and the metal halide in reasonably correct proportions, the anion may be generated *in situ*, e.g.,

$$4CdCl_2 + 2Al \rightarrow Cd(AlCl_4)_2 + 3Cd$$

followed by

$$Cd(AlCl_4)_2 + Cd \rightarrow Cd_2(AlCl_4)_2$$

below the product's melting point. The extent of the second reaction may in fact be determined from the weight of unreacted metal. Decomposition pressures of tetrachloroaluminates are naturally much less than that of pure $AlCl_3$; for example, $NaAlCl_4$ and $Cd(AlCl_4)_2$ may be handled in standard wall vessels to above 600 and 400°, respectively, although precautions should be taken against the unexpected. There is some evidence that excess $AlCl_3$ is incorporated as $Al_2Cl_7^-$.[131]

The effect of the structurally integral halide anions on the stability of the polynuclear compounds of niobium and tantalum is not as clear, although the heavier halides of the $M_6X_{12}^{2+}$ species appear to be less stable in aqueous solution.[54,63] On the other hand, other iodide phases of niobium and tantalum turn out to be rather different in composition from the chlorides and bromides (Table I).

D. Transport Reactions

It was noted earlier that nearly all of the substances of concern here disproportionate under the extreme conditions necessary for their possible sublimation or distillation. Nonetheless, it is often possible to obtain these materials as apparent sublimates condensing from the gaseous components produced by incongruent vaporization or by reaction with another oxidizing agent. These processes have been titled Chemical Transport Reactions; inasmuch as an excellent monograph by this title has recently appeared,[88] only the simplest considerations will be given here.

Consider one of the well-studied examples, $NbCl_3$,[25] which reacts with $NbCl_5$ to give the equilibrium

$$NbCl_3(s) + NbCl_5(g) = 2NbCl_4(g)$$

In a closed tube under a temperature gradient the product $NbCl_4$ will diffuse to the cooler portion of the container where this endothermic reaction will reverse and deposit $NbCl_3$. The $NbCl_5$ thereby produced then diffuses back to the hotter end to repeat the process. The actual temperatures used here are about 390° for "vaporization" and 355° for deposition, the choice, in part, depending on the gas pressure and the closeness of approach to equilibrium conditions desired. The process is thus controlled by diffusion, the $\Delta S°$ of the reaction, and the forward and reverse rates of the transporting reaction. Convection or flow transport conditions may also be used and an inert gas may be added to control the rate of diffusion.

In the particular case of $NbCl_3$, the trichloride is actually only a particular composition in a phase of remarkable breadth, $NbCl_{3.13}$ to $NbCl_{2.67}$ (at 355°). In this instance the composition of the transported product may be conveniently varied by the pressure of the $NbCl_5$

introduced. Alternately, the phase may be allowed to generate its transporting gas $NbCl_4$ and $NbCl_5$ by disproportionation, in which case one transports the lower phase limit $NbCl_{2.67}$ at 580°. Obviously synthesis and transport may both be accomplished in the same reaction vessel (Fig. 3*b*) and even in one step. For example, $TaBr_5$ at the coolest portion (~300°) may be reacted with Ta at the hottest part (~600°) to form $TaBr_4$(g), which diffuses to an intermediate zone. Here it may be deposited as such (310°) or disproportionated to $TaBr_3$ (350°) or to $TaBr_{2.5}$ (460°), depending on the indicated, intermediate temperature.[61] Such variations thus provide considerable information on the regions of stability of the various phases. In general a transport reaction is possible if only gaseous products are involved and if the equilibrium for the transport reaction is not extreme. Also the product of the transporting equilibrium cannot be the highest oxidation state unless conditions are such as to allow halogen dissociation, in which case it becomes a halogen transport reaction as with $FeI_2 + I_2$ and the familiar iodide metal process. Most of the systems noted in Table I which undergo transport (T) do so to lower temperatures, that is, the reaction is endothermic. Those few halide systems known to undergo transport in either direction involve dissociation of gaseous products ($Au_2Cl_6 \rightarrow Au_2Cl_2 + 2Cl_2$, $Cu_3Cl_3 \rightarrow 3CuCl$) or of the reactant ($I_2 \rightarrow 2I$) to bring about a change in sign of $\Delta H°$. Obviously the relative magnitudes of both $\Delta H°$ and $\Delta S°$ are important, and generalities have been developed in these terms.[88]

Transport reactions often prove to be extremely useful for the growth of well-formed crystals. The principal difficulty with synthetic applications is one of small yield per unit time; depending on the system and the conditions, the synthesis of 1 g of product may require from an hour to several weeks.

V. NON-EQUILIBRIUM METHODS

A. Dissociation and Disproportionation

Synthesis by dissociation (halogen loss) or by disproportionation, where applicable, are time-honored methods. Either of these may be carried out under near equilibrium conditions, as by diffusion or convection (transpiration), but the classification here applies to the reactions as carried out either under dynamic vacuum or in a sealed tube under extreme conditions of large temperature and pressure gradients. The extreme divergence from equilibrium here is the principal drawback of the methods, although there are certainly instances where they work reasonably well. Their success depends on substantial differences in successive equilibrium constants or rates. For disproportionation, a usable preparation of MX_2 by the reaction

$$2MX_3(s) \rightarrow MX_2(s) + MX_4(g)$$

requires that a subsequent step, e.g.,

$$3MX_2(s) \rightarrow 2MX(s) + MX_4(g)$$

have some combination of very low pressure of MX_4 (or MX_3) or a low rate at temperature in order to carry the first reaction to completion without a substantial amount of the second. In practice the latter is *never* zero but may still be sufficiently slight so as to not interfere. Care must be taken in the identification of the composition of a new product obtained by such means, however, as it is often possible to secure almost any desired result, irrespective of the pure phase compositions, by suitable adjustment of temperature and time.

Dissociation reactions present similar problems in that the reaction

$$MX_3(s) \rightarrow MX_2(s) + {}^1/_2X_2(g)$$

may be followed by a substantial amount of disproportionation as shown above. The low stabilities of PtCl and AuCl in the latter step significantly detract from the preparation of the pure materials by dissociative means.

In order to prevent subsequent decomposition the reactions sometimes must be conducted at as low a temperature as is feasible, which can mean extremely long reaction periods and hence greater chances for contamination, even from residual gases in a high quality vacuum. More important, products of some structural complexity which are poorly crystalline or even amorphous to x-rays may be obtained under these conditions, or they may be entirely bypassed for kinetic reasons. The lowest niobium chloride and iodide phases are in this category[51,53,57] (Sect. III.E). Finally, an inherent disadvantage of a disproportionation process is that a substantial fraction of what may be a very dear starting material is necessarily lost through formation of the higher halide.

In spite of these inherent difficulties, suitable precautions and suspicion concerning the results of the decomposition reactions can ameliorate some of the problems. For example, use of an inert gas atmosphere allows higher temperatures as well as a somewhat closer approach to equilibrium. In any case results should be checked by equilibrium reactions of annealing, flow or static measurements, or under transport conditions.

B. Reduction in Flow Systems

Reduction of a heated, higher halide by a flow of H_2, NH_3, etc. suffers some of the same problems as just noted as it is generally carried out rather far from equilibrium conditions. Again, such reductants are usually inferior to the metal itself and may lead to by-products such as stable hydrides and nitrides. Although the first step may proceed satisfactorily,

$$2MCl_3(s) + H_2 \rightarrow 2MCl_2(s) + 2HCl$$

the free energy change per equivalent for further reduction to metal

$$MCl_2(s) + H_2 \rightarrow M(s) + 2HCl$$

may not be very different, particularly when disproportionation (another problem) is possible. Furthermore the equilibrium pressure of HCl in the second reaction will *never* be zero, so further reduction by the usual flow of excess H_2 is possible. The more successful applications of this method therefore employ a mixture of H_2 and HCl (or HBr), as with $CrCl_2$ and $CrBr_2$, Table I. If a melt is reduced, the lowered activity of the reactant may mean either incomplete reduction ($SmCl_2$) or the possibility of overreduction to a still lower solute in solution ($CrCl_2$?). Either the first, or an enhanced attack of somewhat unsatisfactory containers may be the reason for the earlier recommendations that rare earth metal chlorides not be fused during their reduction to the dichlorides with hydrogen (as quoted in ref. 3).

The reverse of the last reaction, a hydrogen halide–metal synthesis step, may conversely involve excess oxidation to higher states than desired, although this may be less serious since these usually involve volatilization of the product to a cooler zone. In practice, impurities in commercial hydrogen halides may also lead to undesirable side reactions, producing carbides for example.

Some flow reactions have been described in which a higher halide is heated with H_2, Al, or the same metal, and the stream then rapidly quenched.[132–134] The latter step to some extent avoids other reactions which may occur on slow cooling. However, the procedure tends to give mixtures and, naturally, non-equilibrium products. Reactions at a heated filament (TiX_3, Table I) fall into this category.

C. Electric Discharges

Reduction with hydrogen, or other materials, may sometimes be brought to fruition by a high voltage discharge either between internal electrodes (glow discharge) or through the walls (electrodeless or silent). Such methods appear to fall into the general category of "brute force" methods, and they frequently depend on a subsequent, rapid quench to avoid other reactions. All appear generally less satisfactory for the preparation of pure, equilibrium materials, and their workability appears to be extremely unpredictable. The physical arrangement may be critical as well; the glow discharge suitable for TiX_3 does not yield ZrI_3 unless the electrodes are placed differently, while an electrodeless discharge is not at all workable.[33]

Yields by these methods are frequently rather small, and the products so finely divided as to be pyrophoric. The energies dissipated in the wall with an electrodeless arrangement may also bring about side reactions or physical contamination. For example, the reported preparation of AlI[135] by this means seems improbable. The product adhered tenaciously to the walls and amounted to only 72 mg (plus 28 mg of glass) after passage of 40 g of AlI_3 through the discharge. The material was too inert for AlI as well, judging from the behavior of the AlI_3–Al system,[136,137] and may have contained AlOI instead.

VI. CONTAINERS

The traditional use of glass as a container is of course a result of its attractive properties and ease of fabrication. Nonetheless, there are an increasing number of systems where it is either of marginal utility or is completely impractical. It should be realized that even some normal valent halides are unstable in glass by metathesis,

$$2MX_2 + SiO_2 \rightarrow 2MO + SiX_4(g)$$

The halides, particularly the iodides, of Al, Zr, Th, Cr(III), and the rare earth elements are of borderline stability by this reaction. More important is the state of the final oxide in the presence of silica; for example, the formation of $MgSiO_3$ just about compensates for the unfavorable ΔF°_{298} for the reaction of SiO_2 with MgI_2. However, kinetics may frequently make allowed reactions sufficiently slow so as to be untroublesome.

A more prevalent reaction is the reduction of siliceous materials by many subhalides or by the metals used in their preparations, particularly by those forming very stable silicides, oxides, or oxyhalides. This has been observed with at least some of the reduced halides of nearly all of the elements up through transition group VI (plus the inner transition metals), especially with the heavier members and the most reduced states which require use of higher temperatures. On the other hand the lower temperatures associated with the intermediate oxidation states of some of these do not result in contamination from glass. The direct attack of solid metal on glass is frequently very slight because of the limited contact. This is greatly enhanced, or observed at a much lower temperature, when a volatile lower halide, a melt, or other components are present which are capable of transporting metal or silica to the other phase. For example, the reaction of Ta or Nb with silica occurs readily at 800–1100° in the presence of halogen, where gaseous lower halides transport metal and/or silica, whereas reaction is unobservable in high vacuum at 1100°.[138]

The solution to many container problems, and in fact the only means by which many of the phases tabulated earlier may be obtained, has been the use of metal containers. Outstanding here are Mo, Ta, Nb, W, and the stainless steels. Fabrication of Mo and W is relatively difficult however, whereas Ta (and Nb) may be obtained as sheet or seamless tubing, containers may be fabricated at room temperature, and these welded to give gas-tight and relatively strong enclosures.[139] Tantalum, however, is a somewhat better reducing agent than Mo for salts of the more noble metals. Of course, all of these must in turn be enclosed in glass to protect them from the atmosphere. Care must be exercised that metals studied in these do not form intermetallics or, less likely, low melting alloys. As an example of the advantages of these metals, tantalum is perfectly satisfactory with all of the rare earth metal systems to at least 1100°. On the other hand, attack of these metals and their lower halides on Pt, Au, and SiO_2 containers used during early investigations was substantial because of the formation of very stable intermetallics, with the result that the lower salts were reported to be much less stable than they actually are.[140] Reported yields of 90–95% were no doubt a further reflection of these side reactions. Similar problems occur with the reduced melts contained in Al_2O_3.[141] There is no general solution to container problems, and only a circumspect and cautious attitude by the investigator in each particular case can be recommended.

Acknowledgments

The Author is indebted to R. E. McCarley and R. A. Potts for their numerous helpful comments and suggestions regarding this manuscript.

REFERENCES

1. E. L. Muetterties and C. W. Tullock, in *Preparative Inorganic Reactions*, Vol. 2, W. L. Jolly, Ed., Interscience, New York, 1965, Chap. 7.
2. D. Bauer, H. G. Schnering, and H. Schäfer, *J. Less-Common Metals*, **8**, 388 (1965).
3. G. Brauer, Ed., *Handbuch der Präparativen Anorganischen Chemie*, 2nd ed., Ferdinand Enke, Stuttgart, Germany, 1962.

4. N. V. Sidgwick, *The Chemical Elements and Their Compounds*, Oxford University Press, 1950.
5. J. D. Corbett, L. F. Druding, W. J. Burkhard, and C. B. Lindahl, *Discussions Faraday Soc.*, **32**, 79 (1961).
6. L. F. Druding, J. D. Corbett, and B. N. Ramsey, *Inorg. Chem.*, **2**, 869 (1963).
7. R. A. Sallach and J. D. Corbett, *Inorg. Chem.*, **2**, 457 (1963).
8. L. F. Druding and J. D. Corbett, *J. Am. Chem. Soc.*, **83**, 2462 (1961).
9. G. I. Novikov and O. G. Polyachenok, *Russ. J. Inorg. Chem.*, **8**, 545 (1963).
10. O. G. Polyachenok and G. I. Novikov, *Russ. J. Inorg. Chem.*, **8**, 1478 (1963).
11. O. G. Polyachenok and G. I. Novikov, *Russ. J. Inorg. Chem.*, **8**, 1378 (1963).
12. G. Jantsch and N. Skalla, *Z. Anorg. Allgem. Chem.*, **193**, 391 (1930).
13. W. Klemm and J. Rockstroh, *Z. Anorg. Allgem. Chem.*, **176**, 181 (1928).
14. E. Hohmann and H. Bommer, *Z. Anorg. Allgem. Chem.*, **248**, 383 (1941).
15. R. A. Coley and D. M. Yost, *Inorg. Syn.*, **2**, 71 (1946).
16. H. Bärnighausen, *J. Prakt. Chem.*, **14**, 313 (1961).
17. J. E. Mee and J. D. Corbett, *Inorg. Chem.*, **4**, 88 (1965).
18. J. D. Corbett and B. C. McCollum, *Inorg. Chem.*, **5**, 938 (1966).
19. L. B. Asprey and F. H. Kruse, *J. Inorg. Nucl. Chem.*, **13**, 32 (1960).
20. G. Jantsch, N. Skalla, and H. Jowurek, *Z. Anorg. Allgem. Chem.*, **201**, 207 (1931).
21. W. Klemm and W. Schuth, *Z. Anorg. Allgem. Chem.*, **184**, 352 (1929).
22. A. W. Wylie, private communication, 1964.
23. D. E. Scaife and A. W. Wylie, *J. Chem. Soc.*, 1964, 5450.
24. R. J. Clark and J. D. Corbett, *Inorg. Chem.*, **2**, 460 (1963).
25. J. D. Corbett, R. J. Clark, and T. F. Munday, *J. Inorg. Nucl. Chem.*, **25**, 1287 (1963).
26. J. F. Suttle, *Inorg. Syn.*, **5**, 145 (1957).
27. J. J. Katz and G. T. Seaborg, *The Chemistry of the Actinide Elements*, Methuen, London, 1957, pp. 161, 218.
28. T. R. Ingraham, W. K. Downes, and P. Marier, *Inorg. Syn.*, **6**, 52 (1960); *Can. J. Chem.*, **35**, 850 (1957).
29. J. M. Sherfey, *Inorg. Syn.*, **6**, 57 (1960).
30. W. L. Groeneveld, G. Leger, J. Wolters, and R. Waterman, *Inorg. Syn.*, **7**, 45 (1963).
31. P. Ehrlich, W. Gutsche, and H.-J. Seifert, *Z. Anorg. Allgem. Chem.*, **312**, 80 (1961).
32. D. G. Clifton and G. E. MacWood, *J. Phys. Chem.*, **60**, 311 (1956).
33. G. W. Watt and W. A. Baker, Jr., *J. Inorg. Nucl. Chem.*, **22**, 49 (1961).
34. I. E. Newnham and J. A. Watts, *J. Am. Chem. Soc.*, **82**, 2113 (1960).
35. H. L. Schläfer and H.-W. Wille, *Z. Anorg. Allgem. Chem.*, **327**, 253 (1964).
36. H. L. Schläfer and H. Skoludek, *Z. Anorg. Allgem. Chem.*, **316**, 15 (1962).
37. E. M. Larsen and J. J. Leddy, *J. Am. Chem. Soc.*, **78**, 5983 (1956).
38. L. F. Dahl, T. Chiang, P. W. Seabaugh, and E. M. Larsen, *Inorg. Chem.*, **3**, 1236 (1964).
39. B. Swaroop and S. N. Flengas, *Can. J. Chem.*, **42**, 1495 (1964).
40. J. Lewis, D. J. Machin, I. E. Newnham, and R. S. Nyholm, *J. Chem. Soc.*, **1962**, 2036.
41. H. L. Schläfer and H. Skoludek, *Z. Elektrochem.*, **66**, 367 (1962).
42. J. D. Corbett and A. W. Struss, to be published.
43. R. E. McCarley and J. W. Roddy, *Inorg. Chem.*, **3**, 60 (1964).

44. R. E. McCarley and J. W. Roddy, *Inorg. Chem.*, **3**, 54 (1964).
45. R. E. McCarley and K. O. Berry, to be published.
46. R. E. McCarley and B. A. Torp, *Inorg. Chem.*, **2**, 540 (1963).
47. H. Schäfer and F. Kahlenberg, *Z. Anorg. Allgem. Chem.*, **305**, 291 (1960).
48. H. Schäfer and K.-D. Dohmann, *Z. Anorg. Chem.*, **311**, 134 (1961).
49. J. D. Corbett and P. W. Seabaugh, *J. Inorg. Nucl. Chem.*, **6**, 207 (1958).
50. H. Schäfer and F. Liedmeier, *J. Less-Common Metals*, **6**, 307 (1964).
51. P. W. Seabaugh and J. D. Corbett, *Inorg. Chem.*, **4**, 176 (1965).
52. M. A. Kust and J. D. Corbett, unpublished research.
52a. A. Simon, H. G. Schnering, H. Wöhrle, and H. Schäfer, *Z. Anorg. Allgem. Chem.*, **339**, 155 (1965).
53. H. Schäfer and H. G. Schnering, *Angew. Chem.*, **76**, 833 (1964).
54. R. E. McCarley, P. B. Fleming, and L. A. Mueller, to be published.
55. V. Gutmann and H. Tannenberger, *Monatsh. Chem.*, **87**, 769 (1956).
56. M. Chaigneau, *Compt. Rend.*, **245**, 1805 (1957).
57. H. Schäfer, private communication, 1965.
58. L. R. Bateman, J. F. Blount, and L. F. Dahl, *J. Am. Chem. Soc.*, **88**, 1082 (1966).
59. R. E. McCarley and J. C. Boatman, *Inorg. Chem.*, **2**, 547 (1963).
60. H. Schäfer, H. Scholz, and R. Gerkin, *Z. Anorg. Allgem. Chem.*, **331**, 154 (1964).
61. H. Schäfer, R. Gerkin, and H. Scholz, *Z. Anorg. Allgem. Chem.*, **335**, 96 (1965).
62. R. E. McCarley and J. C. Boatman, *Inorg. Chem.*, **4**, 1486 (1965).
63. P. J. Kuhn and R. E. McCarley, *Inorg. Chem.*, **4**, 1482 (1965).
63a. D. Bauer, H. C. Schnering, and H. Schäfer, *J. Less-Common Metals*, **8**, 388 (1965).
64. A. B. Burg, *Inorg. Syn.*, **3**, 150 (1950).
65. H. Kühnl and W. Ernst, *Z. Anorg. Allgem. Chem.*, **317**, 84 (1962).
66. N. W. Gregory and L. L. Handy, *Inorg. Syn.*, **5**, 130 (1957).
67. M. L. Larson and F. W. Moore, *Inorg. Chem.*, **3**, 285 (1964).
68. R. E. McCarley, P. J. Carnell, and R. Hogue, *Inorg. Syn.*, **8**, in press.
69. H. G. Schnering and H. Wöhrle, *Naturwiss.*, **50**, 91 (1963).
70. D. E. Couch and A. Brenner, *J. Res. Natl. Bur. Std.*, **63A**, 185 (1959).
71. H. J. Emeléus and V. Gutmann, *J. Chem. Soc.*, **1949**, 2979.
72. J. Lewis, D. J. Machin, R. S. Nyholm, P. Pauling, and P. W. Smith, *Chem. Ind. (London)*, **1960**, 259.
73. J. C. Sheldon, *J. Chem. Soc.*, **1960**, 1007.
74. J. C. Sheldon, *J. Chem. Soc.*, **1962**, 410.
75. F. Klanberg and H. W. Kohlschütter, *Z. Naturforsch.*, **15b**, 616 (1960).
76. R. E. McCarley and T. M. Brown, *Inorg. Chem.*, **3**, 1232 (1964).
77. R. E. McCarley and T. M. Brown, *J. Am. Chem. Soc.*, **84**, 3216 (1962).
77a. R. Siepmann and H. Schäfer, *Naturwiss.*, **52**, 344 (1965).
78. R. E. McCarley and G. A. Murray, unpublished research.
79. H. J. Emeléus and V. Gutmann, *J. Chem. Soc.*, **1950**, 2115.
80. K. Knox, S. G. Tyree, Jr., R. D. Srivastava, V. Norman, J. Y. Bassett, Jr., and J. H. Holloway, *J. Am. Chem. Soc.*, **79**, 3358 (1957).
81. L. C. Hurd and E. Brimm, *Inorg. Syn.*, **1**, 182 (1939).
82. R. Colton, *J. Chem. Soc.*, **1962**, 2078.
83. R. D. Peacock, A. S. Welch, and L. F. Wilson, *J. Chem. Soc.*, **1958**, 2901.
84. G. W. Watt and R. J. Thompson, *Inorg. Syn.*, **7**, 187 (1963).
85. L. Malatesta, *Inorg. Syn.*, **7**, 185 (1963).

86. J. E. Fergusson, B. H. Robinson, and W. R. Roper, *J. Chem. Soc.*, **1962,** 2113.
87. K. R. Hyde, E. W. Hopper, J. Waters, and J. M. Fletcher, *J. Less-Common Metals,* **8,** 428 (1965).
88. H. Schäfer, *Chemical Transport Reactions* (trans. by H. Frankfort), Academic Press, New York, 1964.
89. H. Rémy and T. Wagner, *Z. Anorg. Allgem. Chem.*, **157,** 344 (1926).
90. O. Ruff and E. Bornemann, *Z. Anorg. Allgem. Chem.*, **65,** 454 (1910).
91. S. A. Shchukarev, N. I. Kolbin, and I. N. Semenov, *Russ. J. Inorg. Chem.*, **6,** 638 (1961).
92. L. Wöhler and S. Streicher, *Ber.*, **46,** 1577, 1591 (1913).
93. F. Krauss and H. Gerlach, *Z. Anorg. Allgem. Chem.*, **147,** 265 (1925).
94. S. A. Shchukarev, M. A. Oranskaya, and T. S. Shemyakina, *Zh. Neorgan. Khim.*, **1,** 17 (1956).
95. S. A. Shchukarev, T. A. Tolmacheva, M. A. Oranskaya, and L. V. Komandrovskaya, *Zh. Neorgan. Khim.*, **1,** 8 (1956).
96. S. A. Shchukarev, T. A. Tolmacheva, and G. M. Slavutskaya, *Russ. J. Inorg. Chem.*, **9,** 1351 (1964).
97. W. E. Cooley and D. H. Busch, *Inorg. Syn.*, **5,** 208 (1957).
98. A. J. Cohen, *Inorg. Syn.*, **6,** 209 (1960).
99. L. Wöhler and F. Müller, *Z. Anorg. Allgem. Chem.*, **149,** 377 (1925).
100. R. N. Keller and H. D. Wycoff, *Inorg. Syn.*, **2,** 1 (1946).
101. J. B. Wagner and C. Wagner, *J. Chem. Phys.*, **26,** 1597 (1957).
102. J. D. Corbett and L. F. Druding, *J. Inorg. Nucl. Chem.*, **11,** 20 (1959).
103. S. A. Shchukarev, M. A. Oranskaya, T. A. Tolmacheva, and L. L. Vanicheva, *Zh. Neorgan. Khim.*, **3,** 1478 (1959).
104. J. D. Corbett, W. J. Burkhard, and L. F. Druding, *J. Am. Chem. Soc.*, **83,** 76 (1961).
105. A. P. Palkin and N. V. Ostrikova, *Russ. J. Inorg. Chem.*, **9,** 1104 (1964).
106. R. K. McMullan and J. D. Corbett, *J. Am. Chem. Soc.*, **80,** 4761 (1958).
107. J. D. Corbett and A. Hershaft, *J. Am. Chem. Soc.*, **80,** 1530 (1958).
108. J. D. Corbett and R. K. McMullan, *J. Am. Chem. Soc.*, **77,** 4217 (1955).
109. N. N. Greenwood and I. J. Worrall, *J. Chem. Soc.*, **1958,** 1680.
110. N. N. Greenwood and I. J. Worrall, *Inorg. Syn.*, **6,** 33 (1960).
111. A. P. Palkin, N. V. Ostrikova, and T. N. Vigutova, *Russ. J. Inorg. Chem.*, **8,** 1344 (1963).
112. P. I. Fedorov and V. N. Fadeev, *Zh. Neorgan. Khim.*, **9,** 378 (1964).
113. R. J. Clark, E. Griswold, and J. Kleinberg, *J. Am. Chem. Soc.*, **80,** 4764 (1958); *Inorg. Syn.*, **7,** 18 (1963).
114. W. Morawietz, H. Morawietz, and G. Brauer, *Z. Anorg. Allgem. Chem.*, **316,** 220 (1962).
115. P. H. Walter, J. Kleinberg, and E. Griswold, *J. Inorg. Nucl. Chem.*, **19,** 223 (1961).
116. E. A. Peretti, *J. Am. Chem. Soc.*, **78,** 5745 (1956).
117. J. D. Corbett, *J. Am. Chem. Soc.*, **80,** 4757 (1958).
118. A. Hershaft and J. D. Corbett, *Inorg. Chem.*, **2,** 979 (1963).
119. S. J. Yosim, L. D. Ransom, R. A. Sallach, and L. E. Topol, *J. Phys. Chem.*, **66,** 28 (1962).
120. R. D. Barnes, R. A. Potts, and J. D. Corbett, to be published.
121. T. F. Munday and J. D. Corbett, *Inorg. Chem.*, **5,** 1263 (1966).
122. L. E. Topol, S. J. Yosim, and R. A. Osteryoung, *J. Phys. Chem.*, **65,** 1511 (1961).

123. L. B. Asprey and B. B. Cunningham, *Progr. Inorg. Chem.*, **2**, 267 (1960).
124. J. D. Corbett and F. R. Duke, in *Technique of Inorganic Chemistry*, Vol. 1, H. B. Jonassen and A. Weissberger, Eds., Interscience, New York, 1963, p. 110.
125. H. Schäfer and K.-D. Dohmann, *Z. Anorg. Allgem. Chem.*, **300**, 1 (1959).
126. H. Schäfer and L. Bayer, *Z. Anorg. Allgem. Chem.*, **272**, 265 (1953).
127. J. D. Corbett, in *Fused Salts*, B. R. Sundheim, Ed., McGraw-Hill, New York, 1964, Chap. 6.
128. N. N. Greenwood, *Advan. Inorg. Chem. Radiochem.*, **5**, 97 (1963).
129. H. C. Brown and H. Pearsall, *J. Am. Chem. Soc.*, **73**, 4681 (1951).
130. A. Van Arkel, *Research*, **2**, 307 (1949).
131. R. H. Moore, I. R. Morrey, and E. E. Voiland, *J. Phys. Chem.*, **67**, 744 (1963).
132. R. C. Young and J. H. Hastings, *J. Am. Chem. Soc.*, **64**, 1740 (1942).
133. R. C. Young, *J. Am. Chem. Soc.*, **53**, 2148 (1931).
134. C. H. Brubaker, Jr., and R. C. Young, *J. Am. Chem. Soc.*, **73**, 4179 (1951).
135. W. C. Schumb, and H. H. Rogers, *J. Am. Chem. Soc.*, **73**, 5806 (1951).
136. J. D. Corbett and S. v. Winbush, *J. Am. Chem. Soc.*, **77**, 3964 (1955).
137. J. Thonstad, *Can. J. Chem.*, **42**, 2739 (1964).
138. H. Schäfer, E. Schibilla, R. Gerken, and H. Scholz, *J. Less-Common Metals*, **6**, 239 (1964).
139. H. E. Miller, A. H. Daane, C. E. Haberman, and B. J. Beaudry, *Rev. Sci. Instr.*, **34**, 644 (1963).
140. L. Brewer, L. A. Bromley, P. W. Gilles, and N. L. Lofgren, in *The Chemistry and Metallurgy of Miscellaneous Materials—Thermodynamics*, L. L. Quill, Ed. McGraw-Hill. New York, 1950, p. 124.
141. H. R. Bronstein, A. S. Dworkin, and M. A. Bredig, *J. Phys. Chem.*, **66**, 44 (1962).

Sulfur Oxyfluorides and Related Compounds

JOHN K. RUFF

*Redstone Research Laboratories, Rohm and Haas Co., Huntsville, Alabama**

CONTENTS

I. INTRODUCTION

The application of new methods of synthesis and spectroscopy has resulted in the elucidation of some important principles in the chemistry of the sulfur oxyfluorides. The purpose of this chapter is to describe the general methods of synthesis of the sulfur oxyfluorides and their inorganic derivatives. For this reason a complete discussion of the structure and the physical and chemical properties of the compounds will be omitted. However, those physical properties which may aid in isolation and/or identification of a particular species are summarized in tables. References to the infrared and F^{19} NMR spectra of the compounds are also presented. In some cases where the F^{19} NMR spectra are simple, the value of the chemical shift (in ϕ units†) is also included.

* This work was carried out under Army Ordnance Contract No. DA-01-021 AMC-11536(Z).

† ϕ = ppm measured from CCl_3F.

An attempt will be made to cover most of the known inorganic sulfur oxyfluoride derivatives. These will include the two hypofluorite derivatives that have already been discussed[1] in this series. Additional information on many of these compounds can be found in two review articles which have recently been published.[2,3] A few compounds which have been obtained only in low yield and which lack complete characterization have been omitted, since it is felt that not enough is known about either their structure or their mode of formation to permit fruitful application of their method of synthesis to other materials. Furthermore only those reactions which are judged to be of synthetic utility will be included when several methods are available for the preparation of a given compound. The choice of synthetic method is sometimes difficult and should be based on several factors. The criteria used in this chapter, where a preference is expressed, are the difficulty in the experimental procedure, the availability of starting materials, the amount of product desired, and the author's experience or prejudice.

II. SULFUR(IV) OXYFLUORIDE DERIVATIVES

The number of sulfur(IV) oxyfluoride derivatives is quite limited in comparison to the wide variety of known sulfur(VI) oxyfluorides. This is a consequence of the lower valence state of the sulfur, in that it restricts the number of bonds of oxygen and fluorine to sulfur. The lower oxidation state, in general, also results in a greater reactivity of the sulfur(IV) derivative [in comparison to the corresponding sulfur(VI) derivative] since the sulfur is more accessible to attack by various chemical reagents. In some cases the sulfur(VI) compound appears to be more stable than the related sulfur(IV) derivative. Thus sulfur tetrafluoride can be converted to sulfur hexafluoride and sulfur by microwave excitation,[4] and potassium fluorosulfinate can be converted to potassium fluorosulfate and sulfur by heating.[5]

A. Covalent Sulfur(IV) Oxyfluorides

Thionyl fluoride, SOF_2, the most familiar example of a sulfur(IV) oxyfluoride, was first reported in 1896.[6] A large number of methods are now available for its preparation. Most of these are based on a fluorine–chlorine exchange reaction which utilizes thionyl chloride and some fluorine donor. The generalized reaction may be written as:

$$y\mathrm{SOCl_2} + \mathrm{M}_x\mathrm{F}_{2y} \rightarrow y\mathrm{SOF_2} + \mathrm{M}_x\mathrm{Cl}_{2y}$$

Antimony trifluoride, in the presence of catalytic amounts of antimony pentachloride, is one of the most convenient fluorinating reagents to use for this reaction in the laboratory.[7] All the reagents needed are commercially available* and the operation may be performed in standard Pyrex glassware. However, the mode of addition of the reagents is important in determining the purity of the crude product. If antimony trifluoride is added to thionyl chloride, which contains the antimony pentachloride, some thionyl chloride fluoride is also produced along with the thionyl fluoride.[7] Reverse addition serves greatly to decrease the amount of thionyl chloride fluoride formed.[8] A complete procedure for the preparation of thionyl fluoride by this method is given in *Inorganic Syntheses.*[8]

Anhydrous hydrogen fluoride can also be used to effect this exchange. The addition of anhydrous hydrogen fluoride to thionyl chloride, containing 10 wt % of antimony pentachloride, results in the rapid formation of thionyl fluoride and hydrogen chloride.[9] The latter compound may be removed by bubbling the product gases through ice water. Under these conditions only slight hydrolysis of the thionyl fluoride occurs and the hydrogen chloride is completely absorbed. The use of anhydrous hydrogen fluoride necessitates all metal or metal and plastic equipment. Therefore, unless the requisite equipment is readily available this procedure may not be as convenient as the one employing antimony trifluoride when relatively small amounts of thionyl fluoride are needed (<100 g). Many other reagents have also been used as fluorinating agents for converting thionyl chloride to thionyl fluoride. Several examples are arsenic trifluoride,[10] zinc fluoride,[6] iodine pentafluoride,[11] and potassium fluorosulfinate.[5] Potassium fluoride in refluxing acetonitrile is not effective and only a low yield of thionyl fluoride is obtained.

There is another exchange reaction capable of producing thionyl fluoride which employs either sulfur tetrafluoride or sulfur dioxide as a starting material. Fluorine–oxygen exchange can be achieved in certain cases. Thus when sulfur dioxide is treated with vanadium(V) fluoride, thionyl fluoride is formed in 98% yield.[12] The reaction of sulfur tetrafluoride with numerous oxygen-containing materials, including water, also produces thionyl fluoride.[13,14] Although this type of reaction has not been fully exploited, some application to other thionyl fluoride derivatives may be possible.

Thionyl chloride fluoride is the only other known inorganic covalent thionyl fluoride derivative. It results from partial fluorine–chlorine exchange in thionyl chloride by antimony trifluoride as discussed above. A better method, however, is the reaction of iodine pentafluoride with thionyl chloride.[11] If a 2.5-fold excess of thionyl chloride is slowly added to iodine pentafluoride contained in a quartz or polyethylene flask,

* In the United States.

thionyl chloride fluoride can be obtained in a 43% yield. The product, contaminated with chlorine, iodine trichloride, thionyl fluoride, and thionyl chloride, is evolved as the reaction proceeds and is collected in a glass trap. The first two contaminants are removed by shaking the crude mixture with mercury. The other impurities can be removed by low-temperature distillation.

Both thionyl fluoride and thionyl chloride fluoride are colorless gases which have irritating odors. Some of their physical properties are presented in Table I. Thionyl chloride fluoride is intermediate in chemical

TABLE I
Properties of the Covalent Sulfur(IV) Oxyfluorides

Compound	mp, °C	bp, °C	a[a]	b[a]	IR ref.	NMR ϕ Values	NMR Ref.
SOF_2	−129.5	−43.8	11.2	1908	19	−77.9	18
SOFCl	−139.5	11.4	7.83	1409	17	−78.6	18

[a] $\log p = a - b/T$.

reactivity between thionyl fluoride and thionyl chloride. Thionyl fluoride reacts slowly with water to form hydrogen fluoride and sulfurous acid and is inert to mercury, whereas thionyl chloride fluoride undergoes rapid hydrolysis and attacks mercury readily. Thionyl chloride fluoride is not stable and slowly disporportionates into thionyl fluoride and thionyl chloride at ambient temperature.

B. Ionic Sulfur(IV) Oxyfluorides

Fluorosulfinic acid, HSO_2F, can be regarded as a derivative of sulfurous acid, in which one of the hydroxyl groups has been replaced by fluorine.

$$\mathrm{HO}\overset{\overset{\displaystyle \mathrm{O}}{\|}}{\mathrm{S}}\mathrm{OH} \qquad\qquad \mathrm{HO}\overset{\overset{\displaystyle \mathrm{O}}{\|}}{\mathrm{S}}\mathrm{F}$$

The existence of the free acid has not been definitely established, although the compound $SO_2 \cdot HF$, mp −84°, exists at low temperature in the sulfur dioxide–hydrogen fluoride system.[5] The structure of this compound is not known, and the possibility that it is a molecular adduct held together by hydrogen bonding and not the true fluorosulfinic acid cannot be ruled out.

On the other hand, salts containing the fluorosulfinate ion, SO_2F^-, can be easily prepared[5] by the interaction of the alkali metal fluorides (except lithium fluoride) with sulfur dioxide.

$$MF + SO_2 \rightleftharpoons MSO_2F$$

For example, if potassium fluoride is stirred in an autoclave with excess liquid sulfur dioxide at 25° for several days, a product having the composition $KF \cdot 0.85\ SO_2$ is obtained. Tetramethylammonium fluorosulfinate can be made in a similar manner and will crystallize from a 3*M* solution in liquid sulfur dioxide at −6°. The larger the cation the more complete the conversion of fluoride to fluorosulfinate and the more stable the product. Although tetramethylammonium fluorosulfinate is the most stable salt reported, it exhibits a dissociation pressure of sulfur dioxide at room temperature. The salts do contain a discrete anion and are not simple solvates in as much as x-ray studies show that they are structurally related to the isoelectronic chlorate salts.

The fluorosulfinate salts have not been studied extensively. They show promise as intermediates in the preparation of sulfuryl fluoride derivatives (to be discussed later) or as a fluorinating agent for numerous chlorine-containing compounds. The following conversions have been reported.

$$SOCl_2 + 2KSO_2F \rightarrow 2KCl + 2SO_2 + SOF_2 \quad \text{(ref. 5)}$$

$$AsCl_3 + 3KSO_2F \rightarrow 3KCl + 3SO_2 + AsF_3 \quad \text{(ref. 5)}$$

$$POCl_3 + 3KSO_2F \rightarrow 3KCl + 3SO_2 + POF_3 \quad \text{(ref. 5)}$$

$$(PNCl_2)_4 + 8KSO_2F \rightarrow 8KCl + 8SO_2 + (PNF_2)_4 \quad \text{(ref. 15)}$$

Nitrosyl fluoride was found to react with sulfur dioxide in a manner analogous to that of alkali metal fluorides to form nitrosyl sulfuryl fluoride.[16]

$$NOF + SO_2 \rightleftharpoons NOSO_2F$$

Although the oxidation state of the sulfur in this compound is not known, its chemical behavior suggests that it should be considered as nitrosonium fluorosulfinate, $NO^{\oplus}\ SO_2F^{\ominus}$, and not as a derivative of sulfur(VI). The preparation of nitrosyl sulfuryl fluoride from nitrosyl fluoride and sulfur dioxide is the most convenient method available although several others are known.[16] A sufficient quantity of sulfur dioxide is condensed onto a frozen sample of nitrosyl fluoride in a metal reactor so that on warming the product is suspended in liquid sulfur dioxide. It may be separated from the excess sulfur dioxide by slow vacuum-line fractionation. Nitrosyl sulfuryl fluoride is obtained as a white crystalline compound which has a dissociation pressure of 2 mm Hg at −70° and is approximately 70% dissociated at 19°. It has a melting point of 8° under an autogeneous pressure of 3100 mm. Many of the chemical reactions of nitrosyl sulfuryl fluoride are analogous to those described for potassium fluorosulfinate, e.g.,

$$BCl_3 + 3NOSO_2F \rightarrow 3NOCl + 3SO_2 + BF_3$$

$$BF_3 + NOSO_2F \rightarrow NOBF_4 + SO_2$$

$$PCl_3 + 3NOSO_2F \rightarrow 3NOCl + 3SO_2 + PF_3$$

Although potassium fluorosulfinate behaves as an "active" form of potassium fluoride, the same relationship does not hold for nitrosyl sulfuryl fluoride, since it is much less reactive than nitrosyl fluoride.

III. THIONYL TETRAFLUORIDE AND RELATED COMPOUNDS

A. Thionyl Tetrafluoride

Thionyl tetrafluoride is the first of a large number of sulfur(VI) oxyfluoride derivatives to be discussed in this review. Its name is derived from the fact that only one oxygen is bound to the sulfur and can thus be considered as a derivative of thionyl fluoride. Thionyl tetrafluoride is unique among the sulfur(VI) oxyfluorides in that it is one of the few known examples of pentacoordinated sulfur. There is some experimental evidence that thionyl tetrafluoride can either gain or lose a fluoride ion, thus achieving either octahedral or tetrahedral coordination as is common to most of the sulfur(VI) oxyfluorides.

Thionyl tetrafluoride was probably first prepared by Moissan and Lebeau[20] who allowed thionyl fluoride to react with fluorine. They tentatively established its composition from pressure–volume–temperature measurements although they did not isolate the product. For almost fifty years the existence of this material remained unconfirmed. Then in 1951 the first characterization of thionyl tetrafluoride was reported although the work was done earlier.[11] There are two basic methods available for the synthesis of thionyl tetrafluoride: the oxidation of thionyl fluoride with a fluorine donor or the oxidation of sulfur tetrafluoride with an oxygen donor. In general, elemental fluorine has been used in the first method, although tetrafluorohydrazine can act as a fluorine donor when decomposed photolytically.[21]

Thionyl fluoride can be converted to thionyl tetrafluoride by fluorine under several conditions. The first attempt, in which the product was completely characterized,[11] was carried out in a nickel flow reactor at 150°. In this procedure an equimolar mixture of fluorine and thionyl fluoride is passed over a heated platinum gauze and the crude product is collected in a quartz trap. It consists of thionyl tetrafluoride contaminated with sulfur hexafluoride and sulfuryl fluoride. No thionyl fluoride is recovered. Cady and his co-workers[22] also studied the fluorination of thionyl fluoride in an effort to prepare pentafluorosulfur hypofluorite rather than thionyl tetrafluoride. Passage of a mixture of thionyl fluoride and excess fluorine over a silver fluoride catalyst at 200° results in a moderate conversion of the thionyl fluoride to pentafluoro-sulfur hypofluorite and in addition a low yield of thionyl tetrafluoride is formed.

A recent study of the fluorination of thionyl fluoride has shown[23] the importance of a catalyst in controlling the reaction. Active metal fluorides, such as the alkali fluorides, promote the formation of pentafluorosulfur hypofluorite whereas in an uncatalyzed reaction only thionyl tertafluoride is obtained. The uncatalyzed reaction of fluorine with thionyl fluoride in a static system therefore provides a convenient synthesis of thionyl tetrafluoride when relatively small amounts are needed.[23] The reaction is fairly slow at 25° and requires at least 30 hr. to go to completion. It may be performed in the following manner. A 20 mmole sample of thionyl fluoride is condensed into a 300-ml monel bomb with liquid nitrogen. While the bomb is still at −196°, an equimolar amount of fluorine is metered into the reactor. The bomb is allowed to warm to ambient temperature and stand for 30 hr. Then any excess fluorine is removed while the bomb is at −196°. The purity of the crude product is usually 95% or better. A further discussion of this fluorination procedure will be found in Section V.A. One other technique of fluorinating thionyl fluoride, which is particularly suitable if the silver fluoride catalytic fluorination apparatus is available, is to react pentafluorosulfur hypofluorite with thionyl fluoride at 190°.[24]

$$SF_5OF + SOF_2 \xrightarrow{AgF} 2SOF_4$$

The reaction occurs rapidly producing thionyl tetrafluoride in high purity.

The alternative method of preparation of thionyl tetrafluoride involves the oxidation of sulfur tetrafluoride by an oxygen donor. Several inorganic oxides, such as CrO_3 and NO_2, or salts, such as sodium nitrite or sodium nitrate, are capable of this conversion.[4] However, the yield of sulfur tetrafluoride obtained in such reactions is moderate to low and the crude product is generally contaminated with large amounts of sulfuryl fluoride, sulfur hexafluoride, and thionyl fluoride. A cleaner oxidation is obtained when elemental oxygen, in the presence of catalytic amounts of nitrogen dioxide, is used. Since no reaction occurs between oxygen and sulfur tetrafluoride in the absence of nitrogen dioxide, it is likely that the primary process is the oxidation of sulfur tetrafluoride by nitrogen dioxide.

$$SF_4 + NO_2 \rightarrow SF_4O + NO$$

The nitric oxide formed is reconverted to nitrogen dioxide by the oxygen present. The use of nitrogen dioxide alone, however, results in a low yield of thionyl tetrafluoride because of side reactions. The yield of thionyl tetrafluoride in the oxygen oxidation method is 75–80% and most of the impurities can be removed by selective absorption in dimethyl formamide.

Thionyl tetrafluoride is a colorless gas with a very sharp odor. Some of its physical properties are summarized in Table II. It reacts with water much more rapidly than either thionyl fluoride or sulfuryl fluoride which is perhaps a consequence of the unusual coordination state of the sulfur. In water it gives sulfuryl fluoride and hydrogen fluoride, while in sodium hydroxide solution fluoride and fluorosulfate ions are obtained.

TABLE II
Properties of Thionyl Tetrafluoride and Related Compounds

Compound	mp, °C	bp, °C	n_D^{25}	d_4, °C	IR ref.	NMR ϕValues	NMR Ref.
SF_4O	−99.6	−49	—	1.08 (−57°)	22	91	27
$HNSF_2$	—	43	1.3219	1.5216 (25°)	31	—	—
CH_3NSF_2O	—	39	1.3259	—	29	—	—
cis-$(NSOF)_3$	17.4	138.4	1.4169	1.92 (25°)	33	—	33
trans-$(NSOF)_3$	−12.5	130.3	1.4169	1.92 (25°)	33	—	33

Analysis of the infrared and Raman spectra of thionyl tetrafluoride suggests a molecule with C_{2v} symmetry.[25] This was confirmed by an electron diffraction study [26] in which thionyl tetrafluoride was found to exist as a slightly distorted trigonal bipyramid with the oxygen in one of the equatorial positions. Although there are two types of fluorine atoms in the molecule (the sulfur–fluorine bond distances are different for the apical and equatorial positions) the F^{19} NMR showed only one signal.[27] This presumably arises from a rapid equilibration of the different fluorine sites. No low temperature NMR studies have been reported which confirm this exchange.

There are no known inorganic substitution derivatives of thionyl tetrafluoride of the form $XSF_3{=}O$ although the organic derivative $C_6H_5NSF_3{=}O$ (with CH_3 attached below the N) has been reported.[28] The ionic derivative, $CsOSF_5$, formed by addition of cesium fluoride to thionyl tetrafluoride has been isolated but no experimental details were given.[4] When thionyl tetrafluoride is heated to 100° in the presence of excess cesium fluoride, it is completely absorbed.[23] However, it is not possible under these conditions to achieve complete conversion of the cesium fluoride to $CsOSF_5$, although the use of a suitable solvent will perhaps increase the conversion.

Because of this ability to accept a fluoride ion, thionyl tetrafluoride may be considered as an acid in a fluoride acid–base system.

Thionyl tetrafluoride can apparently behave as a weak base in this acid–base system since it forms addition compounds with several fluoride ion acceptors.[29] These complexes have been formulated as salts (SF_3O^+ MF^-_{x+1}) because of the known ability of the acid used to form very stable polyfluoroanions by combination with fluoride ion. Since the alternate formulation of these materials as molecular complexes, $SF_4O{\rightarrow}MF_x$, has not been eliminated more experimental evidence is necessary before the amphoteric behavior of thionyl tetrafluoride can be confirmed. The preparation of these complexes is best accomplished by direct combination of the constituents in a metal or quartz reactor. With boron trifluoride, an unstable complex is obtained which has a dissociation pressure of 760 mm at −39°. The complex $SF_5O \cdot AsF_5$ is considerably more stable (dissociation pressure = 7 mm at 20°) and can be sublimed in a closed system at 80°. Antimony pentafluoride forms the most stable complex with thionyl tetrafluoride and it shows no dissociation pressure at ambient temperature. The observed order of stabilities of these complexes is the same as the order of Lewis acidity of the metal fluorides.

B. Imino Derivatives of Thionyl Tetrafluoride

The imino derivatives represent a different type of derivative of thionyl tetrafluoride than those discussed in the previous section. They have the general form $-N{=}SF_2{=}O$ and in a sense can be considered as derivatives of sulfuryl fluoride. However, since they are in general prepared by reaction of amines with thionyl tetrafluoride they will be discussed here. The parent iminosulfur oxydifluoride, $HN{=}SF_2{=}O$, is prepared by the interaction of ammonia with thionyl tetrafluoride.[30] The reaction is performed in diethyl ether at −35° using a slight excess of thionyl tetrafluoride. A large excess of sodium fluoride is used to scavenge the hydrogen fluoride formed.

$$NH_3 + SF_3O + 2NaF \rightarrow HN{=}SF_2{=}O + 2NaHF_2$$

The product which is obtained as an azeotrope with ether has the composition $HNSF_2O \cdot 0.85(C_2H_5)_2O$. The addition of a stoichiometric amount of boron trifluoride to the azeotrope serves to remove the ether, and pure iminosulfur oxydifluoride can be isolated. If excess ammonia is present in the initial mixture the ammonium salt of the NSF_2O^- anion is obtained directly.[31]

Iminosulfur oxydifluoride is a stable colorless liquid which may be handled in glass apparatus. Some of its physical properties are presented in Table II. Relatively little has been reported about the chemical reactivity of iminosulfur oxydifluoride. One notable exception is its tendency to eliminate hydrogen fluoride and form poly(oxyfluorosulfur nitride).

$$n\mathrm{HN{=}SF_2{=}O} \xrightarrow{-n\mathrm{HF}} \left[\begin{array}{c} \mathrm{O} \\ \| \\ \mathrm{-N{=}S-} \\ | \\ \mathrm{F} \end{array} \right]_n$$

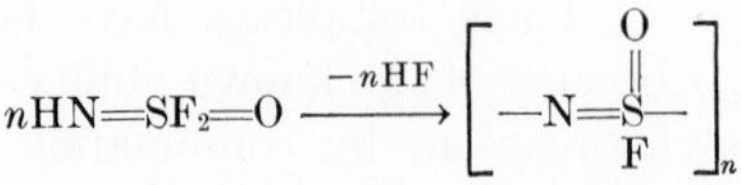

The use of cesium fluoride as a dehydrofluorinating agent gives a particularly clean polymer which precipitates as a tough, white rubber. The polymer prepared this way is soluble in phosphorus oxychoride or dimethyl formamide and has a minimal molecular weight of 20,000. Poly(oxyfluorosulfur nitride) may also be obtained directly from thionyl tetrafluoride by reaction with two equivalents of ammonia[32] or by the thermal decomposition of the ammonium salt of the $NSOF_2$ anion.[31] Since the sulfur–fluorine bond is susceptible to attack by nitrogen bases at elevated temperatures the poly(oxyfluorosulfur nitride) prepared from excess ammonia may be crosslinked to some extent.

Polymeric oxyfluorosulfur nitride also exists in a trimeric form.[33] This form is not prepared, however, by dehydrofluorination of iminosulfur oxydifluoride, but rather by a chlorine–fluorine exchange reaction. When the *trans* isomer of trimeric oxychlorosulfur nitride, $(NSOCl)_3$, is allowed to react with potassium fluoride in carbon tetrachloride solution at 145°, trimeric oxyfluorosulfur nitride is produced. The product is a mixture of the *cis* and *trans* isomers, which can be separated by vapor-phase chromatography.

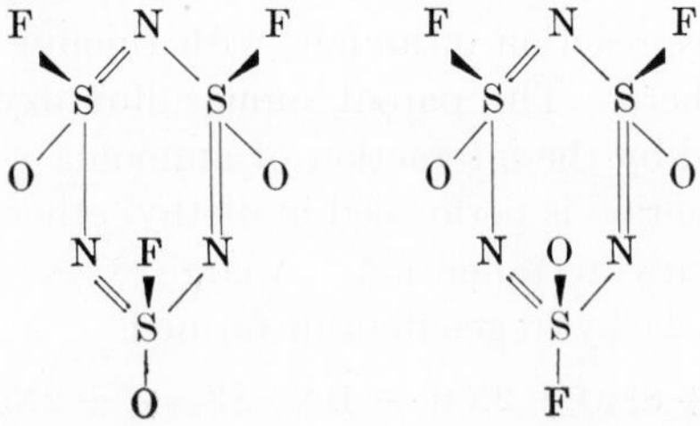

cis *trans*

Some of the physical properties of these isomers are given in Table II. Polymeric oxyfluorosulfur nitride in either its trimeric or higher molecular weight form is quite stable. No decomposition of the trimer was found at 350° alone or at 150° in hydrogen fluoride. Both forms appear to be more inert to hydrolysis than the isoelectronic PNF_2 polymers, but are decomposed at elevated temperatures in aqueous sodium hydroxide solutions.

IV. SULFURYL FLUORIDE AND RELATED DERIVATIVES

Sulfuryl fluoride, like thionyl fluoride, was one of the earliest examples of a sulfur oxyfluoride to be prepared.[20] Since then numerous compounds containing the SO_2F group have been synthesized. The organic compounds are generally named as derivatives of sulfonic acid (e.g., as sulfonyl fluorides), whereas the halogen-substituted compounds are named as derivatives of sulfuryl fluoride.[34] The organic derivatives will not be considered in this chapter with the exception of trifluoromethyl sulfonyl fluoride.

A. Sulfuryl Fluoride

There are several possible synthetic routes to sulfuryl fluoride. The most useful method is the fluorination of sulfur dioxide. Fluorine–chlorine exchange reactions and the addition of oxygen to thionyl fluoride have proved less fruitful as preparative means. An alternative method involving the thermal decomposition of a fluorosulfate salt has also been used. Fluorination of sulfur dioxide was the method used by Moissan and Lebeau[20] in the first reported preparation of sulfuryl fluoride. They combined elemental fluorine and sulfur dioxide in the presence of a hot platinum wire because direct mixing at room temperature often resulted in explosions. Since then other fluorination techniques have been developed which allow either a simple apparatus or better control over the reaction or both. An example is the fluorination of potassium fluorosulfinate in which a 1:1 mixture of fluorine and air is passed through a nickel tube packed with the salt.[5]

$$F_2 + KSO_2F \rightarrow KF + SO_2F_2$$

Sulfuryl fluoride is obtained in almost quantitative yield if the temperature of the reaction is kept below 60–70°. This method is adaptable to the preparation of relatively large amounts of sulfuryl fluoride. If small amounts are required the reaction is most conveniently performed in a static system.[23] The potassium fluorosulfinate is prepared directly in the reactor by addition of sulfur dioxide to potassium fluoride.[5] After removal of the excess sulfur dioxide the reactor is cooled to −196° and the desired amount of pure fluorine is metered into the metal bomb. The crude product obtained is usually 95% or better in purity if excess fluorine is avoided.[23]

Sulfuryl fluoride may also be prepared by the fluorination of sulfur dioxide with silver(II) fluoride.[35] The reaction is performed in a flow system at 180° by passing the sulfur dioxide through a column containing the fluorinating agent. The unconverted sulfur dioxide found in the product can be removed by low-temperature distillation.[36] Alternatively, the reaction may be carried out in a static system employing an excess of the silver(II) fluoride. Under these conditions the purity of the crude product is 95–98%.[18]

Another obvious approach to the preparation of sulfuryl fluoride is a fluorine–chlorine exchange reaction which utilizes sulfuryl chloride and some fluorine donor. However, reactions of this type do not generally give sulfuryl fluoride in good yields. The principal product is usually sulfuryl chloride fluoride since complete fluorination is difficult to achieve unless vigorous conditions are employed. Thus when sulfuryl chloride is treated with antimony(III) fluoride [in the presence of a catalytic amount of antimony(V) chloride] at 260° and 100 atm pressure, sulfuryl fluoride is formed in low yield.[35,37] The inert character of sulfuryl chloride fluoride to further exchange is in contrast with the ease in which thionyl chloride is converted to thionyl fluoride. However, by use of a high temperature and potassium fluoride, complete exchange can be achieved.[38] If sulfuryl chloride is passed, at a rate of 12 g/hr, through a column of potassium fluoride heated to 400°, an almost quantitative conversion to sulfuryl fluoride occurs. At 300° under the same flow conditions only a 23% conversion can be achieved.

The last method of preparation of sulfuryl fluoride to be discussed involves the thermal decomposition of metal fluorosulfates. This method was discovered by Traube[39] and later studied by other workers.[40,41] In general, a group II metal fluorosulfate is used and the decomposition is carried out at 500°. The product escapes from the reactor as it is formed and is condensed in a −78° trap. It may be purified by passage through an aqueous potassium permanganate solution and dried with sulfuric acid or phosphorus pentoxide.

$$M(SO_3F)_2 \xrightarrow{500^\circ} MSO_4 + SO_2F_2$$

Barium fluorosulfate is most commonly employed, although the strontium and zinc salts are suitable. Calcium fluorosulfate, however, gave only trace amounts of sulfuryl fluoride when heated to 500°.[41] Instead, a reversible decomposition of the salt was observed.

$$Ca(SO_3F)_2 \leftrightharpoons CaF_2 + 2SO_3$$

Sulfuryl fluoride is a colorless gas and it is remarkable that its boiling point was not known with accuracy until 1960.[42] A summary of its physical properties is presented in Table III. Chemically sulfuryl fluoride is quite inert. Only slow hydrolysis occurs in alkaline solution and no reactions are observed with the halogens. Organolithium reagents attack sulfuryl fluoride readily but no study has been made of the

TABLE III
Properties of Substituted Sulfuryl Fluoride Derivatives

Compound	bp (mp), °C	a[a]	b[a]	IR ref.	NMR ϕ Values	NMR Ref.
FSO_2F	−55.4	7.59	1023	43	−33.7	69
FSO_2Cl	7.1 (−124.7)	7.82	1385	56	−100.6	18
FSO_2NF_2	−18.2 (−110.5)	7.98	1703	51	−24.6 S—F	—
					−41.7 N—F	51
FSO_2N_3	38°, 215 mm	—	–	44	−61.5	44
FSO_2Br	40.0 (−86.0)	8.03	1610	56	−120.9	18
FSO_2CF_3	−21.7	7.74	1221	55	−37.8 (S—F)	18
FSO_2NCO	61.5	—	—	—	—	—

[a] $\log p = a - b/T$, approximate values of a and b.

products. The structure of sulfuryl fluoride is a distorted tetrahedron having C_{2v} symmetry.[43] The FSF angle is 96°7′ ± 10′ and the OSO angle is 123°58′ ± 12′. The S—F bond distance is slightly shorter (1.530 ± 0.003 Å versus 1.58 ± 0.02 Å) than that found for sulfur hexafluoride[43] and this is perhaps indicative of some π bonding between sulfur and fluorine.

B. Substituted Sulfuryl Fluoride Derivatives

The substituted sulfuryl fluoride derivatives to be discussed in this section have the general form XSO_2F where X is a halogen or an inorganic group. Several of the known examples contain inorganic groups which are bonded to sulfur through oxygen (e.g., FSO_2OF, FSO_2ONF_2, etc). These compounds, with the exception of the polysulfuryl fluorides, will be discussed in the next section under the heading of covalent fluorosulfate derivatives. The halogen substituted sulfuryl fluorides FSO_2Cl and FSO_2Br and two pseudohalogen derivatives FSO_2N_3 and FSO_2NCO are known (the iodide has not been reported). In addition several miscellaneous compounds will be considered.

No general method is available for the synthesis of such compounds, however, three approaches have been successfully used. They are, fluorination of a —SO_2— unit, substitution on the —SO_2F group, and radical reactions involving the $FSO_2^{\cdot}$ radical. When the right conditions are used, complete fluorination is avoided and SO_2X_2 can be cleanly converted to FSO_2X. An example of this approach, which was mentioned briefly above, is the preparation of sulfuryl chloride fluoride by fluorination of sulfuryl chloride. Several fluorinating reagents such as SbF_3,[37] NH_4F,[38] KF in CH_3CN,[44] and SbF_3Cl_2[35] are suitable. For example, if sulfuryl chloride and SbF_3Cl_2 are heated in an autoclave at 220–260° for 3 hr, sulfuryl chloride fluoride is produced in 72% yield.[35] Similar yields are reported for the reaction of ammonium fluoride with sulfuryl chloride at 80°.[38] This second reaction would probably be the method of choice if high pressure equipment is not available since standard laboratory glassware can be used. However, some variation of yield was reported which seemed to depend on the sample of ammonium fluoride used. Another example of this approach is the fluorination of sulfonyl isocyanate with fluorosulfuric acid. Fluorosulfuryl isocyanate is produced in good yield when an equimolar mixture of fluorosulfuric acid and sulfonyl isocyanate are heated together at 140° for 3 hr.[45] The product, which distils from the flask as the reaction proceeds, is obtained in 85% yield. The starting material is readily available from the reaction of sulfur trioxide and cyanogen bromide.[46]

Several successful substitution reactions on the $—SO_2F$ group are known. These do not, however, involve sulfuryl fluoride as a substrate for nucleophilic attack because of its inert chemical behavior. Pyrosulfuryl fluoride, $S_2O_5F_2$, on the other hand, has been found to be susceptible to cleavage by ionic nucleophiles.[44] The general reaction is:

$$S_2O_5F_2 + X^- \rightarrow FSO_2X + SO_3F^-$$

where X^- can be a variety of anions. This is apparently a general reaction and is applicable to the higher polysulfuryl fluorides. However for preparative purposes good yields of the substituted sulfuryl fluoride derivatives are obtained only when chloride or azide ions are used. The reaction is carried out in an aprotic polar organic solvent such as acetonitrile or nitromethane at 25°. The anion is present in slight excess and is usually used in the form of the sodium salt. The yields of sulfuryl chloride fluoride and sulfuryl azide fluoride are 96 and 65%, respectively. Since there are other equally good methods for the preparation of sulfuryl chloride fluoride from more readily available starting material, this reaction is probably most useful for the synthesis of sulfuryl azide fluoride.

An attempt to extend this reaction to the preparation of sulfuryl bromide fluoride and the unknown sulfuryl cyanide fluoride was not successful.[44] No substituted sulfuryl fluoride derivatives were isolated. Instead, the observed products of the two preparations are sulfur dioxide, sulfuryl fluoride, and either bromine or cyanogen, respectively. These products are believed to arise via the following sequence of reactions:

$$S_2O_5F_2 + CN^- \rightarrow FSO_2CN + SO_3F^-$$

$$FSO_2CN + CN^- \rightarrow FSO_2^- + (CN)_2$$

$$FSO_2^- + S_2O_5F_2 \rightarrow SO_2 + SO_2F_2 + SO_3F^-$$

The latter part of this scheme is confirmed by the formation of bromine from the reaction of bromide ion with sulfuryl bromide fluoride. This points out the futility of trying to convert XSO_2F to ZSO_2F by treatment with the anion, Z^-, when X is a group of relatively low electronegativity.

Ammonia or amines cleave pyrosulfuryl fluoride to produce aminosulfuryl fluoride derivatives.[47]

$$S_2O_5F_2 + 2R_2NH \rightarrow R_2NSO_2F + R_2NH_2{}^+SO_3F^-$$
$$R = H \text{ or } C_2H_5$$

The reaction is performed in ethyl ether at low temperature and a 40% yield of aminosulfuryl fluoride can be isolated. The yield of diethyl aminosulfuryl fluoride, however, is almost quantitative. The difference in yield is perhaps attributable to side reactions such as the intermolecular condensation of aminosulfuryl fluoride by loss of hydrogen fluoride. Aminosulfuryl fluoride can also be obtained by other methods such as the reaction of amino-sulfuryl chloride with either KF in refluxing acetonitrile[48] or arsenic trifluoride,[18] reaction of $PCl_3{=}NSO_2Cl$ with anhydrous fluoride,[49] or hydrolysis of $PCl_3{=}NSO_2Cl$ in arsenic(III) fluoride solution.[18] The yields in the latter two processes are 70 and 55%, respectively, and thus, they represent convenient methods of preparation of aminosulfuryl fluoride if a supply of pyrosulfuryl fluoride is not readily available. Aminosulfuryl fluoride is a colorless liquid which melts at 8° and is soluble in a variety of organic solvents. In aqueous solution it undergoes slow hydrolysis to form sulfamic acid and hydrogen fluoride.

The last basic approach to the formation of a substituted sulfuryl fluoride employs what are believed to be radical reactions in which the $FSO_2\cdot$ radical appears to be an important species. Complete proof of this concept is not available and the role of the $FSO_2\cdot$ radical must remain speculative. However, this is an important concept and its application may lead to the preparation of new compounds. The two derivatives which have been prepared using this approach are *N,N*-difluoraminosulfuryl fluoride and sulfuryl bromide fluoride. The evidence supporting the radical nature of the reaction is stronger in the first case than the second.

N,N-Difluoraminosulfuryl fluoride is prepared by reaction of sulfur dioxide with tetrafluorohydrazine. This reaction can be accomplished by either thermal or photolytic activation. The difluoramino radical is known to undergo photolytic decomposition according to the equation[50]:

$$NF_2 \xrightarrow{2537\ \text{A}} NF\cdot + F\cdot$$

and when tetrafluorohydrazine is photolyzed, nitrogen trifluoride and difluorodiazine are the principle products. If this photolysis is performed in the presence of sulfur dioxide, an 83% yield of *N,N*-difluoraminosulfuryl fluoride is obtained.[50] It is believed that $FSO_2\cdot$ radicals are produced by the interaction of sulfur dioxide with fluorine radicals formed in the photolysis. These radicals can then combine with either another fluorine radical or a difluoramino radical to give the observed products, FSO_2NF_2 or SO_2F_2. Alternately the preparation of *N,N*-difluoraminosulfuryl fluoride can be achieved by thermal means.[51] The exact nature of the mechanism of this reaction is not known, but it is probable that radical processes are also involved.

The synthesis of sulfuryl bromide fluoride is accomplished by the fluorobromination of sulfur dioxide. Bromine monofluoride has been suggested as the active species in the reaction but conclusive evidence is lacking.[11] The synthesis is performed by combining an equimolar mixture of bromine and bromine trifluoride (which is used as a source of bromine monofluoride) with excess sulfur dioxide in a metal pressure reactor. After the reactants are allowed to stand for several days, the crude product is passed through mercury, sodium fluoride, and finally through phosphorus pentoxide. Sulfuryl bromide fluoride is obtained in 88% yield. No mechanistic studies on this reaction are available to support the postulated radical nature. However, an alternative method for the preparation of sulfuryl bromide fluoride is almost certainly based on radical reactions. This method involves the controlled fluorination of sulfur dioxide in the presence of the radical trap—bromine. Thus when a mixture of sulfur dioxide, bromine, and difluorodiazine are heated together at a 100°, sulfuryl bromide fluoride is obtained in 85% yield.[52] If tetrafluorohydrazine is used as a radical trap instead of bromine, *N,N*-difluoraminosulfuryl fluorine is obtained in quantitative yield. The course of the reaction is believed to follow the equations:

$$2SO_2 + N_2F_2 \rightarrow 2FSO_2\cdot + N_2$$
$$2FSO_2\cdot + X_2 \rightarrow 2FSO_2X$$
$$X = Br \text{ or } NF_2$$

The chemical properties of sulfuryl bromide fluoride and *N,N*-difluoraminosulfuryl fluoride have not been extensively investigated.

Trifluoromethyl sulfonyl fluoride can be prepared by several routes. One method which has been widely applied to the preparation of alkyl and aryl sulfonyl fluorides is a fluorine–chlorine exchange reaction. An alternative method involves treatment of the anhydride of trifluoromethyl sulfonic acid with sodium fluoride.[44]

$$(CF_3)_2S_2O_5 + F^- \rightarrow CF_3SO_2F + CF_3SO_3^-$$

Both of these methods give a good yield of trifluoromethyl sulfonyl fluoride and are relatively simple to carry out. Unfortunately, the starting materials, CF_3SO_2Cl and $(CF_3)_2S_2O_5$, are not readily accessible in quantity because of a lack of a convenient source of trifluoromethyl sulfonic acid. Therefore when large amounts of trifluoromethyl sulfonyl fluoride are required, a better method to use is the electrochemical fluorination of methyl sulfonyl chloride in anhydrous hydrogen fluoride.[53–55]

$$CH_3SO_2Cl + 4[F] \xrightarrow{HF} CF_3SO_2F + HCl + 2HF$$

The yield obtained by this method is generally high (87%) although some variation has been noted. The electrochemical fluorination technique may also be used to prepare the higher perfluoroalkylsulfonyl fluorides. The yield of the product decreases, however, with increasing length and/or branching of the alkyl group.

No structural investigations have been reported on the substituted sulfuryl fluoride derivatives. The infrared and Raman spectra of sulfur chloride fluoride and sulfuryl bromide fluoride have been recorded.[56,57] A summary of some of the physical properties of these compounds is presented in Table III (p. 47).

C. Polysulfuryl Fluorides and Derivatives

Another type of derivative of sulfuryl fluoride which has been reported are the polysulfuryl fluorides. These can be considered as low molecular weight polymers of sulfur trioxide in which a fluorine atom and a FSO_2 group terminate the chain ($F[—SO_2O—]_nSO_2F$). Alternatively the polysulfuryl fluorides can be considered as anhydrides of the corresponding polyfluorosulfuric acids. The first member of the series, pyrosulfuryl fluoride, is thus the anhydride of fluorosulfuric acid and consequently converts to this acid upon hydrolysis. However, the dehydration of fluorosulfuric acid by conventional reagents such as phosphorus pentoxide does not yield pyrosulfuryl fluoride. Instead, fluorination of the phosphorus to phosphorus oxyfluoride occurs. Pyrosulfuryl fluoride can be obtained from fluorosulfuric acid by treatment with arsenic pentoxide[58] or cyanogen chloride.[59] Arsenic pentoxide is not satisfactory to use because of the slow rate of formation of pyrosulfuryl fluoride and its contamination with arsenic trifluoride. The use of cyanogen chloride for the preparation is preferred. The reaction is performed in a standard flask equipped with a gas inlet tube and a Dry Ice reflux condenser. The fluorosulfuric acid containing a small amount of aluminum chloride is heated to 100–110° and the cyanogen chloride is added until the mixture solidifies. The product is then distilled out of the mass and washed with 96% sulfuric acid. The yield obtained is 73%.

An alternative preparation of pyrosulfuryl fluoride, which may involve the salt of fluorodisulfuric acid as the active intermediate, has been reported.[41] Normally the reaction of sulfur trioxide with a group II metal fluoride produces the metal fluorosulfate salt. However, if calcium fluoride is treated with an excess of sulfur trioxide, a more complex solid product is formed. Hydrolysis of the product, obtained from the interaction of calcium fluoride and a ninefold excess of sulfur trioxide at 200°, with excess 92% sulfuric acid results in the formation of pyrosulfuryl fluoride in 72% yield.

$$CaF_2 + 4SO_3 \xrightarrow{200°} Ca(S_2O_6F)_2$$

$$Ca(S_2O_6F)_2 + H_2O \xrightarrow{H_2SO_4} CaSO_4 + H_2SO_4 + S_2O_5F_2$$

Pyrosulfuryl fluoride can also be obtained from the reaction of sulfur trioxide with the more covalent metal fluorides or in one case a nonmetal fluoride. Furthermore, higher polysulfuryl fluorides are also produced under the right conditions by this method. Some of the fluorides that have been used are SbF_5,[60] VF_5,[12] and IF_5.[61] In the first case antimony(V) fluoride is added to excess sulfur trioxide and the mixture is refluxed for several hours. The stoichiometry reported for the reaction,

$$2SbF_5 + 14SO_3 \rightarrow Sb_2O(SO_4)_4 + 5S_2O_5F_2$$

has not been verified and little is known about the solid product formed. The crude pyrosulfuryl fluoride is distilled from the mixture and washed with concentrated sulfuric acid to remove any unreacted sulfur trioxide. The use of antimony(V) fluoride rather than either vanadium(V) fluoride or iodine pentafluoride is perhaps more convenient because of the ease in handling the reagents in standard glassware.

When boron trifluoride is used to fluorinate sulfur trioxide, pyrosulfuryl fluoride is not the major product.[62] Instead a mixture consisting of several higher polysulfuryl fluorides is formed. The reaction is carried out by passing gaseous boron trifluoride over the surface of liquid sulfur trioxide until the mixture solidifies. Then an excess of 70% sulfuric acid is added and the product mixture separates as an oil. The F^{19} NMR spectrum of the crude product mixture indicates that several polysulfuryl fluorides are present. The following composition is believed to be typical: $S_2O_5F_2$, 25%; $S_3O_8F_2$, 50%; $S_4O_{11}F_2$, 16%; $S_5O_{14}F_2$, 5%; $S_6O_{17}F_2$, 3%; and $S_7O_{20}F_2$, 1%.[63] Isolation of all of the above polysulfuryl fluorides has not been accomplished and the presence of the two heavier members of the mixture, $S_6O_{17}F_2$ and $S_7O_{20}F_2$, has been inferred from the NMR data. Since the thermal stability of the polysulfuryl fluorides decreases with increasing molecular weight only the species up to $S_5O_{14}F_2$ can be separated by vacuum distillation. In fact, if the distillation is performed at atmospheric pressure only pyrosulfuryl fluoride and trisulfuryl fluoride are isolated.[62]

The general mode of thermal decomposition of the polysulfuryl fluorides can be represented by the equation:

$$S_nO_{3n-1}F_2 \rightarrow SO_3 + S_{n-1}O_{3n-4}F_2$$

Pyrosulfuryl fluoride is decomposed at 400° to sulfuryl fluoride and sulfur trioxide while trisulfuryl fluoride decomposes to pyrosulfuryl fluoride and sulfur trioxide at 150°.[41] The higher members apparently decompose below 120° but no complete studies have been reported. The polysulfuryl fluorides are toxic liquids which hydrolyze to sulfuric and fluorosulfuric acid. Some of their physical properties are listed in Table IV.

The only known substituted polysulfuryl fluoride derivatives are pyrosulfuryl chloride fluoride and trisulfuryl chloride fluoride. They cannot be prepared by a simple nucleophilic displacement reaction since S—O—S bond cleavage occurs instead. However, this reaction can be used to prepare a chlorine-substituted derivative which contains one less sulfur atom than the starting material.[44]

$$S_3O_8F_2 + Cl^- \rightarrow FS_2O_5Cl + SO_3F^-$$

$$S_4O_{11}F_2 + Cl^- \rightarrow FS_3O_8Cl + SO_3F^-$$

Only the first of these reactions is of preparative importance since the yield of trisulfuryl chloride fluoride is quite low.

TABLE IV

Properties of the Polysulfuryl Fluorides and Related Compounds

Compound	bp (mp), °C	IR ref.	NMR ϕ Values	NMR Ref.
$S_2O_5F_2$	51	12	−48.5	69
$S_3O_8F_2$	120	70	−49.9	63
$S_4O_{11}F_2$	57/6 mm	—	−50.4	63
$S_5O_{14}F_2$	65/1 mm	—	−50.6	63
FS_2O_5Cl	100	—	−49.0	18
FS_3O_8Cl	40/15 mm	—	—	
$HN(SO_2F)_2$	170	51	−58.5 (neat)	51
$FN(SO_2F)_2$	60.8	51	−44.9 SF 28.5 NF	51
$ClN(SO_2F)_2$	36/36 mm	18	−57.1	68a
$KN(SO_2F)_2$	(100)	67	−52.4 aq. soln.	67
$RbN(SO_2F)_2$	(95–96)	67	−52.4 aq. soln.	67
$CsN(SO_2F)_2$	(115–117)	67	−52.4 aq. soln.	67

An alternate method of preparation of these two compounds involves the use of silver(II) fluoride as a fluorinating agent.[64,65] Two moles of the corresponding polysulfuryl chloride are added to one mole of silver(II) fluoride. When pyrosulfuryl chloride is used, a vigorous reaction occurs on mixing and the product can be distilled after it subsides. The reaction is not as rapid when trisulfuryl chloride is employed and it is necessary to heat the mixture at 100° for 12 hr before isolating the product. These polysulfuryl chloride fluorides resemble the unsubstituted compounds in their appearance. Some of their physical properties are presented in Table IV.

The structures of the polysulfuryl fluorides and chlorides are not definitely known, but it has generally been assumed that they are linear chains involving a single S—O—S bridge. This is supported by Raman and infrared spectral studies on the pyrosulfuryl halides and the trisulfuryl halides.[65] Little evidence was found for a cyclic structure. Furthermore, from the number of polarized Raman lines observed, one of the two *trans* configurations rather than the *cis* configuration is indicated for the pyrosulfuryl compounds.

trans

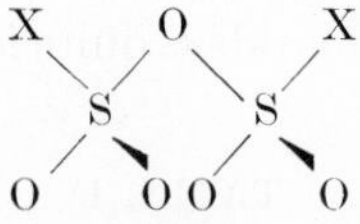

cis

D. Imidodisulfuryl Fluoride and Derivatives

Replacement of the bridging oxygen in pyrosulfuryl fluoride by a monosubstituted nitrogen results in another type of sulfuryl fluoride derivative—imidodisulfuryl fluoride. Several examples of compounds which contain the —$N(SO_2F)_2$ group, have been reported. The parent compound, imidodisulfuryl fluoride, $HN(SO_2F)_2$, can be prepared by the reaction of fluorosulfuric acid with urea in the following manner.[66] The stoichiometric amount of fluorosulfuric acid is slowly added to the urea so that the temperature remains below 100°. After the addition is complete, the mixture is held at 100° for several hours or until carbon dioxide evolution ceases. The crude product, contaminated with fluorosulfuric acid, is distilled from the mixture under reduced pressure. Further purification is difficult by distillation. However, by allowing the crude product to react with a suspension of sodium chloride in methylene chloride the fluorosulfuric acid can be removed. After distillation a yield of 30% is obtained.

$$NH_2CONH_2 + 3HSO_3F \rightarrow HN(SO_2F)_2 + CO_2 + NH_4SO_3F$$

Imidodisulfuryl fluoride can also be produced by reaction of fluorosulfuric acid with either fluorosulfuryl isocyanate or sulfonyl isocyanate at 160° in the absence of a solvent. In the latter case a 2:1 ratio of acid to sulfuryl compound is used since the first step of the reaction is the conversion of sulfonyl isocyanate to fluorosulfuryl isocyanate as discussed before.[45] The formation of imidodisulfuryl fluoride from fluorosulfuryl isocyanate follows the equation:

$$FSO_2NCO + HSO_3F \rightarrow HN(SO_2F)_2 + CO_2$$

The yield in both cases is about 70–75%. This is a better method than that which employs urea if the necessary starting materials are accessible.

Imidodisulfuryl fluoride is a colorless liquid of low volatility which behaves as a moderately strong monobasic acid in aqueous media. The potassium, rubidium, and cesium salts of imidodisulfuryl fluoride can be prepared by neutralization of the parent acid with the corresponding metal carbonates.[67] These salts are nonhygroscopic and are purified by recrystallization from ethanol. Silver imidodisulfuryl fluoride is best prepared by reaction of silver oxide with the parent acid in trifluoroacetic acid. Several other salts are also known. The stability of imidodisulfuryl fluoride ion in aqueous acid is much greater than that reported for the related imidodisulfonate ion $HN(SO_3^-)_2$.[68]

The imidodisulfuryl fluoride anion is isoelectronic with pyrosulfuryl fluoride and might be expected to have a similar structure (**1**). However, the fact that the group electronegativity of the imidodisulfuryl fluoride group is larger than that of either a SO_2F group or nitrogen suggests that considerable S—N π bonding occurs (**2**). The infrared spectrum of the anion also supports this assumption.

$$F{-}S({=}O)_2{-}\overset{\ominus}{N}{-}S({=}O)_2{-}F \qquad F{-}S({=}O)_2{-}N{=}S({=}O)(O^{\ominus}){-}F$$

(**1**) (**2**)

Covalent inorganic derivatives containing the $—N(SO_2F)_2$ group are also known. Fluorination of imidodisulfuryl fluoride at 25° produces *N*-fluoroimidodisulfuryl fluoride in almost quantitative yield.[51] The fluorination is carried out by passage of a 10–15% mixture of fluorine in helium over the surface of the imidodisulfuryl fluoride until the liquid disappears. The product is purified by distillation in standard Pyrex equipment. Chlorination of imidodisulfuryl fluoride, however, does not produce the corresponding *N*-chloro derivative although it can be obtained in about 60% yield by chlorination of the silver salt.[68a]

N-Chloroimidodisulfuryl fluoride appears to be more reactive than the *N*-fluoro compound and is thus useful for the preparation of other derivatives containing the imidodisulfuryl fluoride group. For example, photolysis of *N*-chloroimidodisulfuryl fluoride with a low-pressure mercury lamp produces hydrazino tetrasulfuryl fluoride in almost quantitative yield.[68a]

$$2ClN(SO_2F)_2 \xrightarrow{2537\ Å} Cl_2 + (FSO_2)_2NN(SO_2F)_2$$

V. FLUOROSULFATE DERIVATIVES

The compounds to be discussed in this section contain the fluorosulfate group, FSO_2O, either bonded through oxygen (FSO_2OX) or as the fluorosulfate anion. Fluorosulfate compounds have been divided into two broad types, ionic and covalent. The distinction is not rigorous since the former class includes some metal fluorosulfate derivatives that are probably covalent (in the sense that anhydrous aluminum chloride is covalent), while the latter class contains some ionic halogenfluorosulfate complexes. Fluorosulfuric acid, though predominantly covalent, is included in the first classification since it is a ready source of the fluorosulfate ion.

A. Fluorosulfuric Acid and Its Salts

Fluorosulfuric acid was the first known example of a compound containing the fluorosulfate group to be isolated.[71] Its relationship to sulfuric acid can be illustrated by replacing one of the hydroxyl groups with a fluorine atom. Replacement of the second hydroxyl group with fluorine results in the non-acidic molecule sulfuryl fluoride.

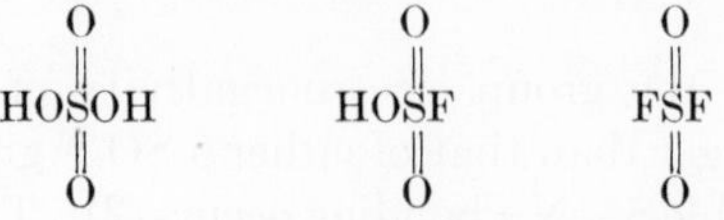

In practice, however, this type of replacement has never been used to prepare fluorosulfuric acid. Only two basic methods for its synthesis are known: the addition of hydrogen fluoride to sulfur trioxide or a fluorine–chlorine exchange reaction employing chlorosulfonic acid and a fluorine donor. The former method is more general and may be performed under a variety of experimental conditions, some of which do not employ hydrogen fluoride directly. The direct addition is best carried out by introducing liquid hydrogen fluoride, by means of a steel capillary tube, below the surface of sulfur trioxide at 35°.[72] After the addition is complete the mixture is heated to 100° to remove any unreacted hydrogen fluoride and sulfur trioxide before the residue is distilled. Since this procedure requires facilities for handling anhydrous hydrogen fluoride perhaps a more convenient laboratory preparation is the use of a metal fluoride or bifluoride in sulfuric acid as a source of hydrogen fluoride. The sulfuric acid also serves as a solvent for the sulfur trioxide. For example, ammonium fluoride,[73] calcium fluoride,[74] or potassium bifluoride[75] may be added with cooling to fuming sulfuric acid (containing approximately 60% sulfur trioxide).

$$CaF_2 + 2SO_3 + H_2SO_4 \rightarrow CaSO_4 + 2HSO_3F$$

This mixture is then heated to 100° before the product is distilled from the excess sulfuric acid. In general these reactions are performed in metal equipment although the crude fluorosulfuric acid may be redistilled in glass apparatus.

The other approach to the preparation of fluorosulfuric acid involves chlorosulfuric acid and a fluorine donor, such as ammonium fluoride or an alkali metal fluoride.[76] The reaction is performed by adding a slight excess of the solid fluoride to the acid and warming until all of the hydrogen chloride is evolved. The residue consists of a crude fluorosulfate salt which may be converted to fluorosulfuric acid by treatment with sulfuric acid.[77] Direct conversion of chlorosulfonic acid may be achieved at ambient temperature by addition of this acid to excess anhydrous hydrogen fluoride.[78] After evolution of hydrogen chloride ceases the crude mixture is heated to 100° in a stream of dry air to remove any unreacted hydrogen fluoride before distillation of the product.

Fluorosulfuric acid is a corrosive colorless liquid which fumes in moist air. In dilute aqueous solution it is completely ionized as shown by conductance studies.[79] Such solutions, however, are not stable and fluorosulfuric acid undergoes slow decomposition, into sulfuric acid and hydrogen fluoride. If only a little water is present, the equilibrium

$$HSO_3F + H_2O \rightleftharpoons H_2SO_4 + HF$$

is established. The specific conductivity of the anhydrous acid is 2.20×10^{-4} mho, a value intermediate between that of hydrogen fluoride and sulfuric acid.[80] The predominant mode of self-ionization of the acid is

$$2HSO_3F \leftrightharpoons H_2SO_3F^+ + SO_3F^-$$

Fluorosulfuric acid is one of the strongest acids ever studied and most oxygen-containing materials behave as bases when dissolved in it. In fact no simple protonic acids are known to exist in the pure acid. Many metal fluorides such as the trifluorides of arsenic, antimony, or bromine also behave as bases. One exception is antimony pentafluoride, which increases the acidity of fluorosulfuric acid.

An investigation of solutions of sulfur trioxide in fluorosulfuric acid by F^{19} NMR and Raman spectroscopy indicate the formation of polyfluorosulfuric acids,[81] e.g.

$$HSO_3F + SO_3 \rightarrow HS_2O_6F$$

However, a rapid exchange of the sulfur trioxide between the species in solution apparently occurs, and attempts to isolate individual polyfluorosulfuric acids have not been successful.

The fluorosulfate anion, being the anion of a strong acid, forms normal salts with the electropositive metals. Numerous mixed fluorosulfate–halide metal derivatives which appear to be double salts have also been reported. Since the fluorosulfate ion is isoelectronic with perchlorate and tetrafluoroborate ions many of its salts are isomorphous with the corresponding perchlorate and tetrafluoroborate salts.[82,83] Infrared[83] and Raman[84] spectral studies on the anion have been reported.

Salts of fluorosulfuric acid can be prepared by a variety of procedures. The simplest is probably either a metathetical reaction or neutralization of the aqueous acid with a suitable base. Traube[39] was able to isolate the alkali metal fluorosulfates by addition of the corresponding hydroxides to an aqueous solution of ammonium fluorosulfate. The solubility of these salts decreases from lithium to cesium so that the potassium, rubidium, and cesium salts precipitated from solution upon mixing. This approach is limited, in general, to the alkali metals or ammonium salts since decomposition of most other metal fluorosulfates occurs in water, especially if the metal involved forms an insoluble fluoride or sulfate. In certain cases complexation of the metal with ammonia or amines, to increase the size of the cation, permits isolation of the fluorosulfate salt.[82,85–87] A few examples of such salts are: $Ni(NH_3)_6(SO_3F)_2$, $Cu(NH_3)_4(SO_3F)_2$, $Cr(NH_3)_6(SO_3F)_3$, and $Cd(NH_3)_6(SO_3F)_2$.

Since the majority of the known metal fluorosulfate derivatives must be prepared in an anhydrous media some of the general methods available will be briefly mentioned before discussing particular compounds. Three of the more common reactions employed are illustrated by the following equations:

$$MF + SO_3 \rightarrow MSO_3F \qquad (1)$$

$$MF + HSO_3Cl \rightarrow MSO_3F + HCl \qquad (2)$$

$$MCl + HSO_3F \rightarrow MSO_3F + HCl \qquad (3)$$

These methods may also be used to prepare the alkali metal salts.

The alkaline earth fluorosulfates can be prepared by all three of the methods illustrated above. In the first method[41] heating stoichiometric quantities of the metal fluoride and sulfur trioxide at 200° for 24 hr in a steel autoclave results in a 92–99% conversion to the fluorosulfate salt. However, magnesium and beryllium fluoride do not react with sulfur trioxide and only partial conversion of either zinc or mercury fluorides can be obtained using these conditions. Alternate procedures involving the reaction of fluorosulfuric acid with the anhydrous metal chloride[40] or chlorosulfuric acid with the metal fluoride[77] also give good yields of the alkaline earth fluorosulfate salts. Unlike the method employing sulfur trioxide, magnesium fluorosulfate can be obtained from magnesium chloride and fluorosulfuric acid.[88]

In carrying out the reaction between either the alkaline earth or alkali metal fluorides and sulfur trioxide, an excess of the latter reagent should be avoided since these fluorides are capable of combining with more than one equivalent of sulfur trioxide. Potassium fluoride, for example, when allowed to react with excess sulfur trioxide for 24 hr at ambient temperature forms a new fluorosulfate derivative.[89] If the excess sulfur trioxide is removed at a pressure of 13 mm of mercury, the composition of the residue is KS_2O_6F. At higher temperatures (or lower pressures) potassium fluorodisulfate loses another equivalent of sulfur trioxide and converts to potassium fluorosulfate. Calcium fluoride apparently behaves similarly when heated to 200° in the presence of a large excess of sulfur trioxide.[41] The complete characterization of these materials which may contain the discrete fluorodisulfate ion, $S_2O_6F^-$, is lacking.

Fluorosulfate derivatives of the heavier metals can be prepared by methods similar to those just discussed, although in most cases complete replacement of the halogen by fluorosulfate groups is not achieved. The interaction of fluorosulfuric acid with a large number of anhydrous chlorides has been investigated by Hayek and co-workers.[88] They were able to obtain the compounds $TiCl_2(SO_3F)_2$, ZrF_3SO_3F, $TaCl_3(SO_3F)_2$, and $SbCl_4SO_3F$ by the addition of the chloride to an excess of fluorosulfuric acid. Several other metal chlorides gave less well-defined products when treated with fluorosulfuric acid (e.g., the thorium tetrachloride and tin tetrachloride reaction products appear to be mixtures).

Although the reaction of antimony trichloride and fluorosulfuric acid does not produce antimony(III) fluorosulfate, a product which approaches this composition is obtained from the interaction of antimony trifluoride and sulfur trioxide at 120°.[41] Arsenic trifluoride behaves in a completely different manner when treated with sulfur trioxide. A liquid product having the composition $2AsF_3 \cdot 3SO_3$ is formed.[41] The structure of this material is not known but its F^{19} NMR spectrum[90] suggests structure **3**.

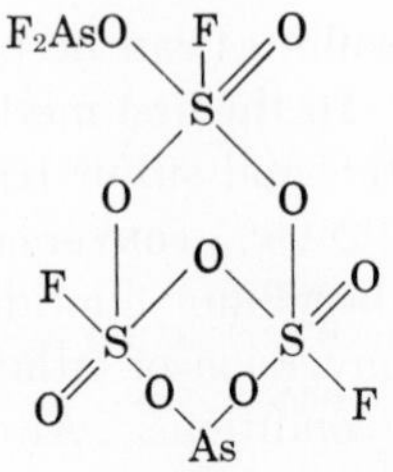

(3)

Sulfur trioxide also reacts with tungsten hexafluoride,[91] niobium pentafluoride, tantalum pentafluoride, and vanadium pentafluoride.[12] The materials obtained from a room temperature reaction in the first three cases appear to be fluorosulfate derivatives having the compositions $WF_2(SO_3F)_4$, $NbF_3(SO_3F)_2$, and $TaF_{2.5}(SO_3F)_{2.5}$. All three are viscous oils which react vigorously with water. Vanadium pentafluoride does not form a stable fluorosulfate derivative under these conditions. The reaction observed in this case is:

$$VF_5 + 2SO_3 \rightarrow VOF_3 + S_2O_5F_2$$

A recently developed method that can be used for the preparation of metal fluorosulfate compounds consists of the reaction of peroxydisulfuryl difluoride with an easily oxidized metal or an anhydrous metal chloride. Mercury(II) fluorosulfate is obtained by simple mixing of the constituents.[92]

$$Hg + FSO_2OOSO_2F \rightarrow Hg(SO_3F)_2$$

Using similar conditions peroxydisulfuryl difluoride reacts with tin tetrachloride, chromyl chloride[93] and molybdenum hexacarbonyl (or molybdenum metal),[94] to yield $SnCl(SO_3F)_3$, $CrO(SO_3F)_2$, and $MoO_2(SO_3F)_2$, respectively, in almost quantitative yield. These reactions are carried out at ambient temperature in a glass system by allowing an excess of the peroxide to react with the substrate. This method should be capable of extension to many other systems.

The two nonmetallic fluorosulfate salts, nitrosonium fluorosulfate and nitronium fluorosulfate, can be prepared by several methods. Nitrosonium fluorosulfate was first obtained, although not in the pure form, by reaction of dinitrogen trioxide with excess fluorosulfuric acid.[85]

$$N_2O_3 + 2HSO_3F \rightarrow 2NOSO_3F + H_2O$$

Two alternate procedures give a pure product. The first consists of the fluorination of $(NO)_2S_2O_7$ (produced by the reaction of nitrogen dioxide with sulfur dioxide) with excess bromine trifluoride at 25°.[95]

$$3(NO_2)S_2O_7 + 2BrF_3 \rightarrow 6NOSO_3F + Br_2 + 1.5O_2$$

After removal of the excess fluorinating agent an analytically pure product remains. The second method involves the interaction of nitric oxide and peroxydisulfuryl difluoride at 25°.[92]

$$S_2O_6F_2 + 2NO \rightarrow 2NOSO_3F$$

Simple mixing of the two reagents in an evacuated bulb results in a quantitative yield of the salt. Although this method is the most convenient of the two to carry out, peroxydisulfuryl difluoride is not as accessible as some of the other reagents.

Nitronium fluorosulfate is best prepared by the reaction of dinitrogen pentoxide with fluorosulfonic acid.[96]

$$N_2O_5 + HSO_3F \rightarrow NO_2SO_3F \downarrow + HNO_3$$

The acid is added to a solution of dinitrogen pentoxide in nitromethane at −10°. The nitronium salt precipitates as it is formed and may be removed by filtration. Alternatively, nitronium fluorosulfate can be obtained by the reaction of bromine trifluoride and sulfur trioxide in excess nitrogen dioxide.[95]

B. Covalent Fluorosulfate Derivatives

In addition to the ionic fluorosulfate compounds just discussed, a large number of covalent derivatives are known. The first examples of this class of compounds were organic fluorosulfonates, $ROSO_2F$, which were prepared from fluorosulfuric acid and either olefins or ethers. However, only several perfluoroalkyl fluorosulfonates will be included in this discussion since they cannot be obtained by classical organic procedures. The number of covalent inorganic fluorosulfate derivatives is not large and many of the known examples contain halogen.

The parent compound in this class, peroxydisulfuryl difluoride, is formally derived from peroxydisulfuric acid by replacement of the two hydroxyl groups with fluorine. As is true for fluorosulfuric acid, the preparation of peroxydisulfuryl difluoride cannot be accomplished by this approach. However, it may be obtained by a method which is analogous to that commonly used to prepare peroxydisulfuric acid. The electrolysis of fluorosulfuric acid containing a small amount of potassium fluorosulfate (as a supportiug electrolyte) produces peroxydisulfuryl difluoride with a current efficiency of 55%.[97] In order to minimize the reduction of the peroxide by nascent hydrogen it is necessary to use a divided cell with two exits and to run the reaction under vacuum at −23°. This permits the continuous removal of the products while retaining the fluorosulfuric acid in the cell.

An alternative approach to the preparation of peroxydisulfuryl difluoride involves the fluorination of either sulfur trioxide or the fluorosulfate anion. In general, most fluorination procedures lead to a mixture of the peroxide and fluorine fluorosulfate, FSO_2OF, so that some comments relative to the preparation of the latter compound are appropriate here. The catalytic fluorination of sulfur trioxide at 180° first produced fluorine fluorosulfate along with small amounts of the peroxide.[98] By altering the experimental conditions the peroxide can be obtained as the major product.[99] Complete details of this preparation of the peroxide are given in *Inorganic Syntheses*.[100] An alternative fluorination procedure involves passing fluorine over nickel(II) fluorosulfate or copper(II) fluorosulfate at 200°.[97] The mixed products are obtained in 75% yield, but the relative proportions of the peroxide and hypofluorite were not reported. The alkali metal fluorosulfates are not as suitable as the copper or nickel salts. In a static system, fluorination of the alkali metal fluorosulfates fails to produce fluorine fluorosulfate because of a subsequent reaction.[23]

$$2FSO_2OF + F^- \rightarrow OF_2 + SO_2F_2 + SO_3F^-$$

The fluoride present is formed in the fluorination.

The fluorination of sulfur trioxide can also be accomplished by photolysis using light of wavelength of 3650 Å.[101] The reaction was studied over the temperature range of 18–40° and with various ratios of fluorine to sulfur trioxide. This fluorination procedure gives results quite different than those already discussed, in that only peroxydisulfuryl difluoride is obtained even when an excess of fluorine is used. The kinetics of the reaction and the quantum yield data support the following mechanism:

$$F_2 + h\nu \rightarrow 2F\cdot$$

$$SO_3 + F\cdot \rightarrow FSO_3\cdot$$

$$2FSO_3\cdot \rightarrow S_2O_6F_2$$

The composition of the product mixture obtained from thermal fluorination procedures generally depends on the relative amounts of fluorine and sulfur trioxide present in the reaction zone and, to a lesser extent, the temperature of the reactor. As expected, excess fluorine favors the formation of fluorine fluorosulfate. This is probably due to reaction between a fluorosulfate radical and fluorine since the fluorosulfate radical is likely to be the primary fluorination product of either sulfur trioxide or the fluorosulfate anion. Originally it was reported that peroxydisulfuryl difluoride reacts directly with fluorine at 250° to produce fluorine fluorosulfate in almost quantitative yield.[70] Later investigations showed that under these conditions the peroxide is extensively dissociated into fluorosulfate radicals.[102] This dissociation is reversible up to 600°K and two methods were used to evaluate the enthalpy change. The temperature dependence of the ultraviolet spectrum of the radical (the radical absorbs over the range of 450–600 mμ while peroxydisulfuryl difluoride does not) and pressure–temperature measurements at constant volume gave values for the enthalpy of dissociation of 23.3 kcal/mole and 22.0 kcal/mole at 298°K, respectively. The use of higher temperatures in the catalytic fluorination appears to favor the formation of fluorine fluorosulfate[99] which is due perhaps to an increase in the concentration of fluorosulfate radicals.

The decision as to which method to choose for the preparation of peroxydisulfuryl difluoride depends on the availability of elemental fluorine, the amount of product desired, and other factors such as fabrication facilities. If only small amounts are needed (on the order of millimoles) the photolytic fluorination of sulfur trioxide is best. For larger amounts the catalytic fluorination of sulfur trioxide is probably more convenient than the electrolysis procedure, although it usually requires several runs before the optimum experimental conditions are found. This method has the added advantage in that it can be used to prepare fluorine fluorosulfate.

Peroxydisulfuryl difluoride is a colorless liquid which can be handled in a glass vacuum line (provided Kel-F 90 or some similar fluorochlorocarbon stopcock grease is used). It is a strong oxidizing agent which attacks most organic solvents. With water it reacts according to the equation,

$$S_2O_6F_2 + H_2O \rightarrow 2HSO_3F + O_2$$

The F^{19} NMR spectrum[69] of the peroxide shows only one type of fluorine and the infrared spectrum[99] is also in accordance with the proposed structure. Some of its physical properties are noted in Table V.

Because of the facile dissociation of peroxydisulfuryl difluoride into relatively stable free radicals, most of its reactions are probably reactions of the fluorosulfate radical. Thus, addition to ethylenic double bonds or replacement of chlorine from various inorganic and organic substrates occurs upon treatment with peroxydisulfuryl difluoride.[94] Reaction of the peroxide with the halogens yields a number of different halogen fluorosulfate derivatives. Simple addition of a halogen to produce compounds of the type $XOSO_2F$ or oxidation of the halogen to a higher valance state are the principle types of reactions that have been observed. The occurrence of the more highly oxidized states is found for bromine and iodine only, and consequently fluorine fluorosulfate and chlorine fluorosulfate are the only known derivatives containing these two halogens.

The halogen(I) fluorosulfates of fluorine, chlorine, and bromine are all obtained by direct reaction of excess halogen with peroxydisulfuryl difluoride. The reaction with fluorine can be performed at 250° in a flow system, however the previously discussed catalytic fluorination of sulfur trioxide is preferred. Chlorine fluorosulfate, which is more reactive than fluorine fluorosulfate, can be prepared in a high pressure

TABLE V

Properties of Some Covalent Fluorosulfate Derivatives

Compound	bp, °C	a[a]	b[a]	IR ref.	NMR ref.
HSO_3F	163.0	—		Salts 83	81
$S_2O_6F_2$	67.1	8.43	1873	99	69
FSO_3F	−31.3	8.03	1539	98	69
FSO_3Cl	45.1	8.14	1674	103	103
FSO_3Br	120.5	8.30	2126	—	—
FSO_3NF_2	−2.5	7.65	1287	107	107
FSO_3OF	0°	6.78	1063	109	69
$FSO_3CF_3\cdot$	−4.2	7.88	1339	115	115
FSO_3OCF_3	12.9	7.92	1440	115	115
$FSO_3C_2F_5$	22.1	7.98	1505	103	103
$FSO_3C_2F_4NF_2$—	52.3	7.88	1625	113	113
$FSO_3C_2F_4Cl$	55.4	8.11	1719	103	103
$(FSO_3)_2C_2F_4$	102.7	8.19	1995	94	94

[a] $\log p = a - b/T$, approximate values of a and b.

monel bomb by heating an excess of chlorine with the peroxide at 125° for five days.[103] After cooling the reactor to −78°, the excess chlorine is removed by evacuation and the purity of the product which remains is quite high. The analogous bromine compound, $BrOSO_2F$, can be prepared in glass at ambient temperature.[104] The yields of $XOSO_2F$ in all three preparations are very high, and separation of the excess halogen from the product is easily accomplished by simple fractionation. All three of the halogen(I) fluorosulfates are reactive and should be handled only in an inert atmosphere or in a vacuum line. Chlorine fluorosulfate is especially sensitive to traces of moisture which makes it difficult to handle in a glass apparatus. Some of the physical properties of these materials are listed in Table V.

When the reaction between bromine and peroxydisulfuryl difluoride is carried out using an excess of the latter reagent, bromine(III) fluorosulfate is quantitatively formed.[104]

$$Br_2 + 3S_2O_6F_2 \rightarrow 2Br(SO_3F)_3$$

The reaction of iodine with excess peroxydisulfuryl difluoride is completely analogous and an equally good yield of iodine(III) fluorosulfate can be achieved.[104] No purification of the product is necessary, in either case, other than the removal of the excess peroxide under vacuum. The bromine compound is an orange hydroscopic solid (mp 59°) which liberates bromine when treated with water

$$4Br(SO_3F)_3 + 6H_2O \rightarrow 2Br_2 + 3O_2 + 12HSO_3F$$

The iodine(III) fluorosulfate is also a nonvolatile solid (mp 32.2) and hydrolyzes with water according to the equation:

$$5I(SO_3F)_3 + 9H_2O \rightarrow I_2 + 3HIO_3 + 15HSO_3F$$

Two closely related bromine and iodine fluorosulfate derivatives can be prepared by reaction of excess peroxydisulfuryl difluoride with potassium bromide at 50° or with potassium iodide at 25°. Instead of displacement of the halogen as is found with potassium chloride,[94] oxidation of the bromine or iodine to a halate(III) species occurs.[93]

$$KX + 2S_2O_6F_2 \rightarrow KX(SO_3F)_4$$
$$X = I \text{ or } Br$$

Little is known about the physical and chemical properties of these salt-like materials.

In addition to the above discussed iodine fluorosulfate derivatives several other examples have recently been reported. Although the trivalent state is the highest oxidation state formed in the oxidation of iodine by peroxydisulfuryl difluoride, a fluorosulfate derivative of iodate(V) can be synthesized by the room temperature reaction of iodine with excess fluorine fluorosulfate.[105]

$$I_2 + 6FSO_3OF \rightarrow 2IF_3(SO_3F)_2 + S_2O_6F_2$$

The product is obtained in a quantitative yield by removal of the peroxide and excess hypofluorite. Attempts to volatilize this material result in decomposition. The F^{19} NMR spectrum of iodine trifluoride bisfluorosulfate shows two different fluorine environments as would be expected. At 25° the fluorines bound to the iodine appear as a broad band, which at −10° splits into two peaks whose area ratio is 2:1.[106] The non-equivalency of these fluorines unfortunately does not distinguish the *cis* and *trans* isomers of iodine trifluoride bisfluorosulfate if a tetragonal pyramidal structure is assumed.

Iodine(I) fluorosulfate can be obtained by reaction of iodine with the stoichiometric amount of peroxydisulfuryl difluoride at 60°.[106] It is a nonvolatile, diamagnetic solid (mp 51.5°) which is covalent in the solid sate. Upon dissolution in fluorosulfuric acid, ionization into I^+ and SO_3F^- ions occurs as shown by ultraviolet spectral studies. If excess iodine is employed in the reaction a material having the composition I_3SO_3F is formed.

$$3I_2 + S_2O_6F_2 \rightarrow 2I_3SO_3F$$

This result may best be accomplished by using a slight excess of iodine over that required by the above equation. The mixture is then slowly heated to 85° to complete reaction. Triiodine fluorosulfate is a hydroscopic solid, melting at 92° with the liberation of iodine. When it is dissolved in fluorosulfuric acid, dissociation into I_3^+ and SO_3F^- ions can be observed spectroscopically. The related compound, dichloro fluorosulfato iodine, ICl_2SO_3F, is obtained by treatment of iodine(I) fluorosulfate with chlorine at −50°. It is difficult to obtain in high purity. The preparation of pure iodine(I) fluorosulfate requires careful attention to the amount of iodine used since either a difficiency or excess will result in the formation of other nonvolatile materials.

The number of covalent nonhalogen-containing fluorosulfate derivatives is quite limited. Several examples of such materials contain either a SF_5 group or a $—SF_4—$ group and these will be discussed in the next section. Three examples which will be considered here are *N,N*-difluorohydroxylamine *O*-fluorosulfate, NF_2OSO_2F; peroxysulfuryl difluoride, FSO_2OOF; and chloryl fluorosulfate, ClO_2SO_3F. The first two are formed by what appear to be radical reactions. *N,N*-difluorohydroxylamine *O*-fluorosulfate is produced in quantitative yield from the interaction of tetrafluorohydrazine and peroxydisulfuryl difluoride at ambient temperature.[107] The reaction probably involves the recombination of two radicals since tetrafluorohydrazine exists in equilibrium with the difluoramino radical.[108] The preparation of peroxysulfuryl difluoride is accomplished by the photolytic addition of oxygen difluoride to sulfur trioxide[109] or peroxydisulfuryl difluoride.[69] The use of light having a wavelength of 3650 Å is necessary in order to excite only the oxygen difluoride if a high yield of product is to be obtained. Under these conditions the yield is nearly quantitative when sulfur trioxide is used. Previous work on the photodissociation of oxygen difluoride suggests that the initial step in the reaction is[110]

$$OF_2 + h\nu \rightarrow OF\cdot + F\cdot$$

This is probably followed by radical addition to the sulfur trioxide.

$$SO_3 + F\cdot \rightarrow SO_3F\cdot$$

$$OF\cdot + SO_3F\cdot \rightarrow FSO_2OOF$$

Alternatively the irradiation of a mixture of oxygen difluoride and peroxydisulfuryl difluoride produces fluorine fluorosulfate and peroxysulfuryl difluoride.[69] Some of the physical properties of these two compounds are presented in Table V. The last example, chloryl fluorosulfate, is synthesized by mixing sulfur trioxide and chloryl fluoride in the absence of a solvent.[111,112] The reaction is quite vigorous and because of the corrosive nature of chloryl fluoride it should be carried out in quartz or metal if a high purity product is desired. Chloryl fluorosulfate is a red liquid at ambient temperature which upon cooling solidifies to a red solid which then turns yellow on cooling to liquid nitrogen temperature. Nothing is known about the transformations occurring during cooling or about the chemical properties of chloryl fluorosulfate.

The reaction of a number of covalent monofluorosulfate derivatives, $XOSO_2F$, with perfluoroolefins yields various substituted perfluoroalkyl fluorosulfonates. The general reaction is:

$$XOSO_2F + \;>C{=}C< \;\rightarrow\; >\underset{\displaystyle X}{\underset{|}{C}}{-}C{<}^{OSO_2F}$$

The fluorosulfate derivatives that have been successfully employed include fluorine fluorosulfate,[103] chlorine fluorosulfate,[103] bromine fluorosulfate,[103] and *N,N*-difluorohydroxylamine *O*-fluorosulfate.[113] In the case of the halogen fluorosulfates the reaction is rapid at ambient temperature and is generally performed by allowing the reactants to mix slowly by diffusion in a vacuum. When the hydroxylamine derivative is employed a smooth addition to the olefin occurs at 85–95°. None of the symmetrically substituted products are obtained. A closely related reaction used to prepare bisfluorosulfonate derivatives occurs when peroxydisulfuryl difluoride is treated with a perfluoroolefin. Examples of this class of compounds include octafluoro bis(fluorosulfato) cyclopentane,[94] tetrafluoro bis(fluorosulfato) ethane,[94] hexafluoro bis(fluorosulfato) propane[114] and hexafluoro bis(fluorosulfato) cyclobutane.[114] The syntheses are carried out by slow addition of the peroxide to the olefin at room temperature.

Although fluorosulfate derivatives which contain a trifluoromethyl group cannot be synthesized by the above methods, the reaction of fluoroxytrifluoromethane with either sulfur trioxide or sulfur dioxide produces several such materials. The reaction with sulfur trioxide is carried out at 250°, either in a nickel bomb or in a metal flow system and trifluoromethyl peroxyfluorosulfonate can be isolated in low yield.

$$CF_3OF + SO_3 \rightarrow CF_3OOSO_2F$$

The major product in this reaction is peroxydisulfuryl difluoride formed by fluorination of the sulfur trioxide. The reaction of fluoroxytrifluoromethane with sulfur dioxide is more complex. When a flow system operating at 170–185° is employed, several new compounds are formed. The product mixture can be rectified by using the fractional codistillation, technique[116] and contains the materials CF_3OSO_2F, $CF_3OSO_2OSO_2F$, $CF_3OSO_2OCF_3$, and $CF_3OSO_2OSO_2OCF_3$.

The physical properties of some representative perfluoroalkyl fluorosulfonate derivatives are included in Table V. Their chemical behavior has not been extensively investigated.

VI. OXYGEN-CONTAINING DERIVATIVES OF SULFUR HEXAFLUORIDE

The compounds to be discussed in this section can formally be considered as derivatives of sulfur hexafluoride in which one or two of the fluorine atoms have been replaced by singly bonded oxygen. They will thus contain SF_5O— or —OSF_4O— groups. Included in the discussion are several examples in which both groups are incorporated in the same molecule. The synthesis of compounds of this class from sulfur hexafluoride has not been reported, which is undoubtedly due to its inert chemical behavior. In general, most of the reported preparative methods appear to involve radical reactions in which the radicals $SF_5\cdot$, $SF_5O\cdot$, or $ROSF_4\cdot$ are important species. Therefore in choosing a method of synthesis for this type of material, possible sources for these radicals should be considered. As is true for many radical reactions a large number of products are often obtained and the yield of the desired material may be quite low. Therefore yields will be quoted when known. Improvement in the yield of the desired material is often possible since relatively small changes in the experimental conditions of a given reaction may well result in a large change in the product distribution.

A. Compounds Containing the SF_5O— Group

The first report of a compound containing a SF_5O— group in which complete experimental details were presented came from Cady and his co-workers.[22] By employing the catalytic fluorination technique, previously discussed in Section III. A, thionyl fluoride can be converted to pentafluorosulfur hypofluorite in 50% yield by using excess fluorine. A low yield of thionyl tetrafluoride is also obtained in the fluorination. The exact nature of the catalyst and its effect on the reaction is not clear. A later study has shown that the alkali metal fluorides, and cesium fluoride in particular, also behave as catalysts in the fluorination of thionyl fluoride.[23] The reactions in the later study were performed in a static system at ambient temperature. In the absence of the metal fluoride only thionyl tetrafluoride is formed even in the presence of excess fluorine. However, when the fluorination is carried out in the presence of cesium fluoride, under the same experimental conditions, pentafluorosulfur hypofluorite can be isolated in better than 95% yield by using a slight excess of fluorine. Similarly thionyl tetrafluoride can be converted to pentafluorosulfur hypofluorite in equally high yield if the catalyst is present. The fluorination of thionyl fluoride thus appears to consist of two steps and the catalyst is required only in the last one.

$$SOF_2 + F_2 \rightarrow SOF_4$$

$$SOF_4 + F_2 \xrightarrow{CsF} SF_5OF$$

The first step is slower than the catalyzed step since the product mixture obtained from the catalytic fluorination which uses only one equivalent of fluorine consists of a nearly equimolar mixture of pentafluorosulfur hypofluorite and unreacted thionyl fluoride contaminated with a small amount of thionyl tetrafluoride.

It has been suggested that the active species in the catalyzed step of the fluorination is the $SF_5O^{\ominus}$ ion formed by reaction of the metal fluoride with thionyl tetrafluoride. Fluorination of the known salt, $CsOSF_5$,[4] under these conditions produces pentafluorosulfur hypofluorite in high yield. Therefore the metal fluoride appears to be responsible for the catalytic activity, and the catalytic action observed in the earlier study is possibly due to silver(I) fluoride and not silver(II) fluoride which is assumed to be present under the experimental conditions. Although a complete understanding of the interaction of thionyl tetrafluoride or thionyl fluoride with the metal fluoride is still lacking, this method of synthesis of pentafluorosulfur hypofluorite is convenient to use and the purity of the crude product is sufficiently high for many applications. The procedure previously described for the synthesis of thionyl tetrafluoride can be used if an excess of the catalyst is added to the metal reactor. Finely ground cesium fluoride has proved to be the best catalyst and its activity can be increased by prior treatment with thionyl tetrafluoride at 100°, followed by fluorination. The regenerated cesium fluoride is more active than that obtained by grinding.[23]

Pentafluorosulfur hypofluorite is one of the more useful intermediates for the syntheses of compounds containing the SF_5O group. In many of its reactions the $SF_5O\cdot$ radical is an important species. This radical is not as stable as the fluorosulfate radical because of the decomposition reaction:

$$SF_5O\cdot \rightarrow SF_4O + F\cdot$$

Therefore, the yields in these reactions are generally lower and more by-products are formed than in corresponding reactions involving the fluorosulfate radical. Dimerization of the $SF_5O\cdot$ radical does, however, lead to the stable peroxide SF_5OOSF_5. This can be accomplished by photolysis of pentafluorosulfur hypofluorite with a high-pressure mercury lamp.[24] An equilibrium is apparently extablished in this system

$$2SF_5OF \leftrightharpoons SF_5OOSF_5 + F_2$$

since the yield of bispentafluorosulfur peroxide does not continue to increase with increasing irradiation after reaching a limit of somewhat above 25%. However a prolonged photolysis (140 hr) results in a 70% yield of the peroxide since the fluorine formed is apparently removed by reaction with the reactor. The peroxide also undergoes slow decomposition under the photolysis conditions.

The reaction of pentafluorosulfur hypofluorite with either thionyl tetrafluoride or sulfur tetrafluoride also yields bispentafluorosulfur peroxide. In the first case, an equimolar mixture of pentafluorosulfur hypofluorite and thionyl tetrafluoride (or a 3:1 mixture of SF_5OF and SOF_2) are heated to 168° for 12 hr in a small volume copper reactor.[24] The yield of isolated peroxide is 33%. Alternately a 26% yield of bispentafluorosulfur peroxide is obtained from the reaction of pentafluorosulfur hypofluorite with sulfur tetrafluoride in the liquid state at 75°.[117] The yield of peroxide decreases to 16% when this reaction is run at 140° in the gas phase.[118] Bispentafluorosulfur peroxide in these systems can generally be purified by distillation.

One of the major side products in the reaction of pentafluorosulfur hypofluorite with sulfur tetrafluoride is bispentafluorosulfur oxide, SF_5OSF_5. It is formed in the liquid state reaction in 33% yield[117] and in 8% yield when the reaction is carried out at 140°.[118] Bispentafluorosulfur oxide can also be synthesized in 40% yield by the oxidation of pentafluorosulfur chloride with elemental oxygen.[119] The oxidation is performed by ultraviolet irradiation of a 3:1 mixture of pentafluorosulfur chloride and oxygen at atmospheric pressure for 6 hr. Some bispentafluorosulfur peroxide is also formed. Both bispentafluorosulfur oxide[120] and bispentafluorosulfur peroxide[121] have been reported as by-products in the fluorination of sulfur but this method does not have synthetic utility.

The chemical reactivity of these three derivatives varies markedly. Pentafluorosulfur hypofluorite is a highly reactive gas which attacks

TABLE VI
Properties of Compounds Containing SF_5O or OSF_4O Groups

Compound	bp (mp), °C	a[a]	b[a]	IR ref.	NMR ref
SF_5OF	−35.1 (−86.0)	7.84	1173	22	125
SF_5OOSF_5	49.4 (−95.4)	7.89	1611	24	123
SF_5OSF_5	31	7.40	1375	119	123
SF_5OSO_2F	39.6	8.34	1682	126	124
SF_5OOSO_2F	54.1	7.76	1594	127	123, 127
SF_5ONF_2	−10.8	7.82	1300	129	129
$(SF_5O)_2SO_2$	101.9	8.08	1947	127, 128	123, 127
SF_5OCF_3	−11.0	7.75	1276	131	123, 131
$SF_5OC_2F_5$	15.0	7.82	1424	118	123
SF_5OOCF_3	7.7	7.84	1391	127	123, 127
$SF_4(SO_3F)_2$	116.6	7.96	1937	94	94
$SF_4(OSF_5)_2$	94	7.66	1747	127	123, 127
$SF_4(OCF_3)_2$	29.1	7.86	1506	131	131
$CF_3OSF_4NF_2$	29.3	7.68	1447	132	132
$SF_5OSF_4OOSF_4$	99	—	—	117	—
$SF_5OSF_4OOSF_4OSF_5$	59, 20 mm	—	—	117	—
$CF_3OSF_4OSF_5$	78	—	—	117	—
$CF_3OSF_4OOSF_4OCF_3$	102	—	—	117	—
$CF_3OSF_4OOSF_5$	125	—	—	117	—

[a] $\log p = a - b/T$, approximate values of a and b.

mercury and dissolves in aqueous base liberating oxygen. Both bispentafluorosulfur oxide and bispentafluorosulfur peroxide are uneffected by alkaline solutions except under drastic conditions. The reactivity of the former compound is undoubtedly enhanced by the presence of an O—F bond. Some of the physical properties of these materials are summarized in Table VI. The structures of bispentafluorosulfur peroxide[121] and pentafluorosulfur hypofluorite[122] have been determined by electron diffraction. The sulfur in each compound is in an octahedral environment surrounded by five fluorines and one oxygen. The SF and SO bond lengths in both compounds are almost identical [1.53 and 1.56 Å (SF) and 1.66 and 1.67 Å (S—O) for SF_5OF and SF_5OOSF_5, respectively]. The O—O bond length in the peroxide is the same as that found in hydrogen peroxide and the configuration of the SF_5 groups around the two oxygens is also similar to that of the hydrogens in hydrogen peroxide. The F^{19} NMR spectra of compounds containing a SF_5 group are generally complex. There are two magnetically non-equivalent types of fluorine in the SF_5 group; the apical fluorine and four equatorial fluorines. In most cases the ratio of the coupling constant of the two types of fluorine to their chemical shift is such that the spectrum of the SF_5 group appears as an AB_4 spectrum. The analysis of the F^{19} NMR spectra of the SF_5

group in a variety of compounds in terms of an AB_4 group has been reported.[123–125]

In addition to the three SF_5O derivatives discussed above several other simple compounds containing the SF_5O group have been reported. The syntheses of these materials generally utilize pentafluorosulfur hypofluorite or bispentafluorosulfur peroxide as a source of the SF_5O group. For example reaction of pentafluorosulfur hypofluorite with excess sulfur dioxide produces pentafluorosulfur fluorosulfate, SF_5OSO_2F. The reaction can be performed either in the liquid state at 50° for 10 hr,[117] or by photolysis, using a GE AH4 Floodlamp, in Pyrex equipment.[23] The yield in the former case is 21% while that obtained by photolysis is 30%. Although pentafluorosulfur fluorosulfate can also be produced by the photochemical reaction of sulfur dioxide with either disulfuryl decafluoride or bispentafluorosulfur peroxide,[126] it is felt that the best method for its preparation involves the use of pentafluorosulfur hypofluorite because of the relative availability of this material. Two related compounds, pentafluorosulfur peroxyfluorosulfate, SF_5OOSO_2F, and bispentafluorosulfur sulfate, $SF_5OSO_2OSF_5$, are also known. The first is prepared by the reaction of bispentafluorosulfur peroxide with peroxysulfuryl difluoride.[127]

$$SF_5OOSF_5 + FSO_2OOSO_2F \rightarrow 2SF_5OOSO_2F$$

The reaction is performed by photolyzing an equimolar mixture of the two peroxides for an extended length of time. The yield of the mixed peroxide is almost quantitative although only a 50% conversion is obtained. Complete separation of the pentafluorosulfur peroxyfluorosulfate from the peroxydisulfuryl difluoride is difficult by distillation. However, the latter can be removed by reaction with iodine. Bispentafluorosulfur sulfate is formed in low yield by the reaction of bispentafluorosulfur peroxide with sulfur dioxide at 225° either in a closed nickel reactor[127] or in a flow system.[128] A large amount of the sulfur dioxide employed in the reaction is oxidized to sulfur trioxide by the active oxygen formed from the decomposition of the peroxide.

Pentafluorosulfur hypofluorite reacts with tetrafluorohydrazine at ambient temperature to produce *N,N*-difluorohydroxylamine *O*-sulfur pentafluoride.[129] The reaction is carried out by allowing an equimolar mixture of the reactants to stand in glass for 10 hr. Numerous side products are formed and the yield of product is difficult to reproduce. However, yields as high as 85% have been achieved by using an aged reactor (i.e., a reactor which had been used several times before). Purification of *N,N*-difluorohydroxylamine *O*-sulfur pentafluoride can be accomplished by vacuum line fractionation.

A number of fluoroalkyl and perfluoroalkyl derivatives containing the SF_5O— group are readily accessible. The two carbon or higher homologs are most simply obtained by the addition of pentafluorosulfur hypofluorite to a carbon–carbon double bond.[118,130]

$$\rangle C{=}C\langle + SF_5OF \rightarrow FC{-}COSF_5$$

In general the reaction is performed by allowing a slight excess of the olefin to react with the hypofluorite at 25° in a glass apparatus. Care is necessary in the initial mixing of the reactants since the reaction is quite vigorous. If the olefins have an appreciable vapor pressure, as in the cases of C_2H_4, C_2F_4, and C_2H_3Cl, some control is obtained by diluting the olefin with nitrogen gas. The yield of the addition reaction is nearly quantitative. Trifluoromethoxyl sulfur pentafluoride, which cannot be synthesized by the above reaction, is formed by the interaction of sulfur tetrafluoride and fluoroxytrifluoromethane.

$$CF_3OF + SF_4 \rightarrow CF_3OSF_5$$

The best yield (88%) of trifluoromethoxy sulfur pentafluoride is obtained when a mixture containing a threefold excess of sulfur tetrafluoride is allowed to react in the liquid state at 75° for 10 hr.[117] If the reaction is carried out in the vapor phase at 100° only a 35% yield of the desired material is realized.[131]

The related mixed peroxide, pentafluorosulfur trifluormethylperoxide, CF_3OOSF_5, is prepared by reaction of two symmetrical peroxides.[127] Photolysis of an equimolar mixture of bispentafluorosulfur peroxide and bistrifluoromethyl peroxide for seven days produces the mixed peroxide about 30% yield.

$$SF_5OOSF_5 + CF_3OOCF_3 \rightarrow 2CF_3OOSF_5$$

Very little information concerning the chemical reactivity of SF_5OSO_2F, $SF_5OSO_2OSF_5$, SF_5OOSO_2F, SF_5ONF_2, and the alkyl derivatives is available. Some of their physical properties are presented in Table VI. The F^{19} NMR spectra of some of these materials have been analyzed and are in agreement with their formulation as SF_5 derivatives.[123,124,129]

B. Compounds Containing the —OSF_4O— Group

Among the products obtained in several of the reactions discussed in Section A are materials which contain a —OSF_4O— group. Some of these materials can be represented by the simple formula $ROSF_4OR$, while others are more complex in that they contain both SF_5O— and —OSF_4O— groups and consist of chains of alternating sulfur and oxygen atoms. The simple $ROSF_4OR$ derivatives will be considered first. One approach to the preparation of this type of compound is the reaction of an alkoxy free radical, RO·, with sulfur tetrafluoride. This has been accomplished in several cases. One interesting feature of this reaction is that only the *cis* isomer is formed. This suggests (assuming a stepwise addition of the radicals) that the most stable configuration of the intermediate radical, $ROSF_4$·, is

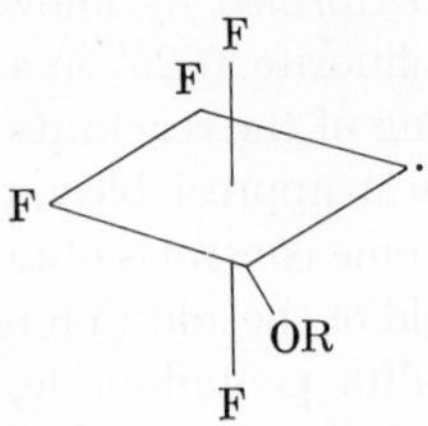

rather than a distorted octahedral with the unpaired electron in one of the *trans* positions. The structural assignment is based upon the F^{19} NMR spectra.

The compound, *cis*-tetrafluoro bis(fluorosulfonato) sulfur(VI), $SF_4(OSO_2F)_2$, can be synthesized by the addition of peroxydisulfuryl difluoride to sulfur tetrafluoride.[94]

$$SF_4 + S_2O_6F_2 \xrightarrow{128°} (FSO_2O)_2SF_4$$

The reaction is best performed in a metal system because of the slow hydrolysis of sulfur tetrafluoride in glass. The addition begins at 85° and is rapid at 128°. The product is formed in 86% yield and is easily purified by distillation. In a similar fashion bispentafluorosulfur peroxide will add to sulfur tetrafluoride to yield *cis*-bis(pentafluorosulfoxy) sulfur tetrafluoride, $SF_5OSF_4OSF_5$.[127] The reaction conditions are critical. For example, neither thermal nor photolytic reactions, when carried out in the gas phase, produce the desired material in other than trace amounts. However, ultraviolet irradiation of an equimolar mixture of the two reactants in the liquid state produces a 70% yield of the adduct. Another example of the difference in product distribution between reactions when carried out in the gas and liquid phases is the related system SF_4—SF_5OF. As discussed before, the gas phase reaction at 140° produces only sulfur hexafluoride, thionyl tetrafluoride, bispentafluorosulfur peroxide, and bispentafluorosulfur oxide.[118] However, in the liquid state at 75°, *cis*-bis(pentafluorosulfoxy) sulfur tetrafluoride is formed in addition to the above products.[117]

Another variable in the reaction between pentafluorosulfur hypofluorite and excess sulfur tetrafluoride which has been investigated is the effect of oxygen.[117] If oxygen is present during the liquid phase reaction, two other compounds, $SF_5OSF_4OOSF_5$ and $SF_5OSF_4OOSF_4OSF_5$, are formed along with the products obtained in the absence of oxygen. Purification of the various liquid products is accomplished either by distillation or vapor phase chromatography. The former compound, $SF_5OSF_4OOSF_5$, reacts with sulfur dioxide at 125° to yield $SF_5OSO_2OSF_4OSF_5$.[128] Some of the physical properties of these complex materials are summarized in Table VI.

Compounds which are similar to those discussed above, except that a pentafluorosulfur group has been replaced by a trifluoromethyl group, are also known. The procedures used to prepare these materials are analogous to many of those above except that fluoroxytrifluoromethane or trifluormethyl peroxide is used in place of pentafluorosulfur hypofluorite or bis-pentafluorosulfur peroxide. A good example is the reaction of sulfur tetrafluoride with fluoroxytrifluoromethane. The thermal reaction produces only trifluoromethoxy sulfur pentafluoride in significant yield. However under photolytic conditions *cis*-bis(trifluoromethoxy) tetrafluorosulfur(VI) is formed as well as the pentafluorosulfur derivative. Alternatively trifluoromethyl peroxide can be used in place of the hypofluorite. The yield of *cis*-bis(trifluoromethoxy) tetrafluorosulfur(VI), in either case, is only about 10%.[131] Only the *cis* isomer is obtained as is found for most of the other addition reactions of sulfur tetrafluoride. Some indication for the presence of the intermediate radical, $CF_3OSF_4\cdot$, is perhaps obtained when the reaction is performed in the presence of tetrafluorohydrazine. The *cis* addition product, $CF_3OSF_4NF_2$, can be isolated in 14% yield.[132] Several other examples of tetrafluorohydrazine behaving as a radical trap for sulfur-containing free radicals have already been discussed in Section IV.B.

The presence of oxygen during the reaction between sulfur tetrafluoride and fluoroxytrifluoromethane has the same effect on the product distribution as it does on the reaction between sulfur tetrafluoride and pentafluorosulfur hypofluorite.[117] Thus when a mixture of sulfur tetrafluoride and fluoroxytrifluoromethane containing a 25% excess of the former reactant is heated to 75° in the presence of oxygen, the new compounds, $CF_3OSF_4OSF_5$, $CF_3OSF_4OOSF_4OCF_3$, and $CF_3OSF_4OOSF_5$ are formed along with bispentafluorosulfur peroxide, trifluoromethoxy sulfur pentafluoride, and other more volatile products.

This type of reaction which involves the interaction of sulfur in a lower oxidation state, such as in sulfur tetrafluoride or sulfur dioxide with a hypofluorite like SF_5OF, FSO_2OF, or CF_3OF in the presence of oxygen, may be capable of extension to the preparation of even longer chains of sulfur and oxygen atoms. However the available evidence indicates that compounds containing bridging SF_4 groups are not as stable as the corresponding materials which contain bridging SO_2 groups.

REFERENCES

1. S. M. Williamson, in *Preparative Inorganic Reactions*, Vol. 1, W. L. Jolly, Ed., Interscience, New York, 1964, p. 239 ff.
2. H. L. Roberts, *Quart. Rev.*, **15**, 30 (1961).
3. H. J. Emeléus and A. G. Sharpe, *Advances in Inorganic Chemistry and Radiochemistry*, Vol. II, Academic Press, New York, 1960, p. 105 ff.
4. W. C. Smith and V. A. Engelhardt, *J. Am. Chem. Soc.*, **82**, 3838 (1960).
5. F. Seel and L. Riehl, *Z. Anorg. Allgem. Chem.*, **282**, 293 (1955).
6. M. Meslans, *Bull. Soc. Chim. France*, **15**, 391 (1896).
7. H. S. Booth and F. C. Mericola, *J. Am. Chem. Soc.*, **62**, 640 (1940).
8. W. C. Smith and E. L. Muetterties, *Inorganic Synthesis*, Vol. VI, McGraw-Hill, New York, 1960, p. 162.
9. U. Wannagat and G. Mennicken, *Z. Anorg. Allgem. Chem.*, **278**, 310 (1955).
10. H. Moissan aud P. Lebeau, *Compt. Rend.*, **130**, 1436 (1900).
11. H. Jonas, *Z. Anorg. Allgem. Chem.*, **265**, 273 (1951).
12. H. C. Clark and H. J. Emeléus, *J. Chem. Soc.*, **1958**, 190.
13. W. R. Hasek, W. C. Smith, and V. A. Engelhardt, *J. Am. Chem. Soc.*, **82**, 543 (1960).
14. A. L. Oppegard, W. C. Smith, E. L. Muetterties, and V. A. Engelhardt, *J. Am. Chem. Soc.*, **82**, 3835 (1960).
15. F. Seel and J. Langer, *Angew. Chem.*, **68**, 461 (1956).
16. F. Seel and H. Massat, *Z. Anorg. Allgem. Chem.*, **280**, 186 (1955).
17. J. K. O'Loare and M. K. Wilson, *J. Chem. Phys.*, **23**, 1313 (1953).
18. J. K. Ruff, unpublished results.
19. F. A. Cotton and W. D. Horrocks, *Spectrochim. Acta*, **16**, 358 (1960).
20. H. Moissan and P. Lebeau, *Compt. Rend.*, **132**, 374 (1901).
21. M. Lustig, C. L. Bumgardner, and J. K. Ruff, *Inorg. Chem.*, **3**, 917 (1964).
22. F. B. Dudley, G. H. Cady, and D. F. Eggers, Jr., *J. Am. Chem. Soc.*, **78**, 1533 (1956).
23. J. K. Ruff and M. Lustig, *Inorg. Chem.*, **3**, 1422 (1964).
24. C. I. Merrill and G. H. Cady, *J. Am. Chem. Soc.*, **83**, 298 (1961).
25. P. L. Goggin, H. L. Roberts, and L. A. Woodward, *Trans. Faraday Soc.*, **57**, 1877 (1961).
26. K. Kimura and S. H. Bauer, *J. Chem. Phys.*, **39**, 3172 (1963).
27. F. B. Dudley, J. N. Shoolery, and G. H. Cady, *J. Am. Chem. Soc.*, **78**, 568 (1956).
28. R. Cramer and D. D. Coffman, *J. Org. Chem.*, **26**, 4010 (1961).
29. F. Seel and O. Detmer, *Z. Anorg. Allgem. Chem.*, **301**, 113 (1959).
30. G. W. Parshall, R. Cramer, and R. E. Foster, *Inorg. Chem.*, **1**, 677 (1962).
31. F. Seel and G. Simon, *Angew. Chem.*, **72**, 709 (1960).
32. R. Cramer, U. S. Pat. 3,017,240 (1962).
33. F. Seel and G. Simon, *Z. Naturforsch.*, **196**, 355 (1964).
34. IUPAC, Report on Symbolism and Nomenclature, *J. Am. Chem. Soc.*, **82**, 5517 (1960).
35. H. J. Emeléus and J. F. Wood, *J. Chem. Soc.*, **1948**, 2183.
36. E. L. Muetterties, *Inorganic Syntheses*, Vol. VI, McGraw-Hill, New York, 1960, p. 158.
37. H. S. Booth and C. V. Herrman, *J. Am. Chem. Soc.*, **58**, 63 (1936).
38. M. M. Woyski, *J. Am. Chem. Soc.*, **72**, 919 (1950).
39. W. Traube, J. Hoerenz, and F. Wunderlic, *Ber.*, **52**, 1272 (1935).
40. M. Trautz and K. Ehrmann, *J. Prakt. Chem.*, **142**, 79 (1935).

41. E. L. Muetterties and D. D. Coffman, *J. Am. Chem. Soc.*, **80**, 5914 (1958).
42. F. S. Bockhoff, R. V. Detrella, and E. L. Pace, *J. Chem. Phys.*, **32**, 799 (1960).
43. E. R. Hunt and M. K. Wilson, *Spectrochim. Acta*, **16**, 570 (1960).
44. J. K. Ruff, *Inorg. Chem.*, **4**, 567 (1965).
45. R. Appel and H. Rittersbacher, *Ber.*, **97**, 849 (1964).
46. R. Graf, German Pat. 940,351 (1956).
47. R. Appel and G. Eisenhauer, *Z. Anorg. Allgem. Chem.*, **310**, 90 (1961).
48. R. Appel and W. Senkpiel, *Angew. Chem.*, **70**, 572 (1958).
49. L. K. Huber and H. C. Mandell, Jr., *Inorg. Chem.*, **4**, 919 (1965).
50. C. L. Bumgardner and M. Lustig, *Inorg. Chem.*, **2**, 662 (1963).
51. M. Lustig, C. L. Bumgardner, F. A. Johnson, and J. K. Ruff, *Inorg. Chem.*, **3**, 1165 (1964).
52. M. Lustig, *Inorg. Chem.*, **4**, 104 (1965).
53. T. S. Brice and P. W. Trott, U. S. Pat. 2,732,398 (1958).
54. J. Burdon, I. Farazmand, M. Stacy, and J. C. Tatlow, *J. Chem. Soc.*, **1957**, 2574.
55. T. Gramstad and R. N. Hazeldine, *J. Chem. Soc.*, **1956**, 173.
56. R. J. Gillespie and E. A. Robinson, *Spectrochim. Acta*, **18**, 1473 (1962).
57. R. J. Gillespie and E. A. Robinson, *Can. J. Chem.*, **39**, 2171 (1961).
58. E. Hayek, A. Aignesberger, and A. Engelbrecht, *Monatsh.*, **86**, 735 (1955).
59. R. Appel and G. Eisenhauer, *Ber.*, **95**, 1756 (1962).
60. E. Hayek and W. Koller, *Monatsh.*, **82**, 942 (1951).
61. W. Schmidt, *Monatsh.*, **85**, 452 (1954).
62. H. A. Lehmann and L. Kolditz, *Z. Anorg. Allgem. Chem.*, **272**, 73 (1953).
63. R. J. Gillespie, J. V. Oubridge, and E. A. Robinson, *Proc. Chem. Soc.*, **1961**, 428.
64. A. Engelbrecht, *Z. Anorg. Allgem. Chem.*, **273**, 269 (1953).
65. R. J. Gillespie and E. A. Robinson, *Can. J. Chem.*, **39**, 2179 (1961).
66. R. Appel and G. Eisenhauer, *Ber.*, **95**, 246 (1962).
67. J. K. Ruff, *Inorg. Chem.*, **4**, 1446 (1965).
68. H. H. Sisler and L. F. Audrieth, *J. Am. Chem. Soc.*, **60**, 1947 (1938).
68a. J. K. Ruff, *Inorg. Chem.*, **5**, 732 (1966).
69. G. Franz and H. Neumayr, *Inorg. Chem.*, **3**, 921 (1964).
70. J. E. Roberts and G. H. Cady, *J. Am. Chem. Soc.*, **81**, 4166 (1959).
71. T. E. Thorpe and W. Kirman, *J. Chem. Soc.*, **61**, 921 (1892).
72. British Pat. 479,450 (1938), *Chem. Abstr.*, **32**, 5165[3] (1938).
73. W. Traube, *Ber.*, **46**, 2513 (1913).
74. O. Ruff and H. J. Braun, *Ber.*, **47**, 646 (1914).
75. H. J. Meyer and G. Schramm, *Z. Anorg. Allgem. Chem.*, **206**, 25 (1932).
76. R. K. Iler, U. S. Pat. 2,312,413 (1943).
77. W. Traube, *Ber.*, **46**, 2525 (1913).
78. H. Weichert, *Z. Anorg. Allgem. Chem.*, **261**, 310 (1950).
79. A. A. Woolf, *J. Chem. Soc.*, **1954**, 2840.
80. A. A. Woolf, *J. Chem. Soc.*, **1955**, 433.
81. R. J. Gillespie and E. A. Robinson, *Can. J. Chem.*, **40**, 675 (1962).
82. E. Wilke-Döfurt, G. Balz, and A. Weinhardt, *Z. Anorg. Allgem. Chem.*, **185**, 417 (1930).
83. D. W. A. Sharp, *J. Chem. Soc.*, **1957**, 3761.
84. H. Siebert, *Z. Anorg. Allgem. Chem.*, **289**, 15 (1957).
85. W. Lange, *Ber.*, **60**, 962 (1927).
86. E. Wilke-Döfurt and H. G. Mureck, *Z. Anorg. Allgem. Chem.*, **184**, 121 (1929).
87. E. Wilke-Döfurt and K. Niederer, *Z. Anorg. Allgem. Chem.*, **184**, 145 (1929).

88. E. Hayek, J. Puschmann and A. Czaloun, *Monatsh. Chem.*, **85**, 359 (1954).
89. H. Lehmann and L. Kolditz, *Z. Anorg. Allgem. Chem.*, **272**, 69 (1953).
90. R. J. Gillespie and J. V. Oubridge, *Proc. Chem. Soc.*, **1960**, 308.
91. H. C. Clark and H. J. Emeléus, *J. Chem. Soc.*, **1957**, 4778.
92. J. E. Roberts and G. H. Cady, *J. Am. Chem. Soc.*, **82**, 353 (1960).
93. M. Lustig and G. H. Cady, *Inorg. Chem.*, **1**, 714 (1962).
94. J. M. Shreeve and G. H. Cady, *J. Am. Chem. Soc.*, **83**, 4521 (1961).
95. A. A. Woolf, *J. Chem. Soc.*, **1950**, 1053.
96. D. R. Goddard, E. D. Hughes, and C. K. Ingold, *J. Chem. Soc.*, **1950**, 2559.
97. F. B. Dudley, *J. Chem. Soc.*, **1963**, 3407.
98. F. B. Dudley and G. H. Cady, *J. Am. Chem. Soc.*, **79**, 513 (1957).
99. F. B. Dudley, G. H. Cady, and D. F. Eggers, Jr., *J. Am. Chem. Soc.*, **78**, 290 (1956).
100. J. M. Shreeve and G. H. Cady, *Inorganic Syntheses*, Vol. VII, McGraw-Hill, New York, 1963, p. 124.
101. E. H. Staricco, J. E. Sicre, and H. J. Schumacher, *Z. Physik. Chem. (Frankfurt)*, **35**, 122 (1962).
102. F. B. Dudley and G. H. Cady, *J. Am. Chem. Soc.*, **85**, 3375 (1963).
103. W. P. Gilbreath and G. H. Cady, *Inorg. Chem.*, **3**, 496 (1963).
104. J. E. Roberts and G. H. Cady, *J. Am. Chem. Soc.*, **82**, 352 (1960).
105. J. E. Roberts and G. H. Cady, *J. Am. Chem. Soc.*, **82**, 354 (1960).
106. F. Aubke and G. H. Cady, *Inorg. Chem.*, **4**, 269 (1965).
107. M. Lustig and G. H. Cady, *Inorg. Chem.*, **2**, 388 (1963).
108. F. A. Johnson and C. B. Colburn, *J. Am. Chem. Soc.*, **83**, 3043 (1961).
109. R. Gatti, E. H. Staricco, J. E. Sicre, and H. J. Schumacher, *Z. Physik. Chem. (Frankfurt)*, **36**, 211 (1963).
110. R. Gatti, E. H. Staricco, J. E. Sicre, and H. J. Schumacher, *Z. Physik. Chem. (Frankfurt)*, **35**, 343 (1962).
111. A. A. Woolf, *J. Chem. Soc.*, **1954**, 4113
112. M. Schmeisser and F. L. Ebenhoch, *Angew. Chem.*, **66**, 230 (1954)
113. M. Lustig and J. K. Ruff, *Inorg. Chem.*, **4**, 1441 (1965).
114. M. Lustig and J. K. Ruff, *Inorg. Chem.*, **3**, 287 (1964).
115. W. P. Van Meter and G. H. Cady, *J. Am. Chem. Soc.*, **82**, 6005 (1960).
116. G. H. Cady and D.P. Siegwarth, *Anal. Chem.*, **31**, 618 (1959).
117. G. Pass and H. L. Roberts, *Inorg. Chem.*, **2**, 1016 (1963).
118. S. M. Williamson and G. H. Cady, *Inorg. Chem.*, **1**, 673 (1962).
119. H. L. Roberts, *J. Chem. Soc.*, **1960**, 2774.
120. B. Cohen and A. G. MacDiarmid, *Inorg. Chem.*, **1**, 754 (1962).
121. R. B. Harvey and S. H. Bauer, *J. Am. Chem. Soc.*, **76**, 859 (1954).
122. R. A. Crawford, F. B. Dudley, and K. Hedberg, *J. Am. Chem. Soc.*, **81**, 5287 (1959).
123. C. I. Merrill, S. M. Williamson, G. H. Cady, and D. F. Eggers, Jr., *Inorg. Chem.*, **1**, 215 (1962).
124. R. K. Harris and K. J. Packer, *J. Chem. Soc.*, **1961**, 4736.
125. C. I. Merrill and G. H. Cady, *J. Am. Chem. Soc.*, **84**, 2260 (1962).
126. H. J. Emeléus and K. Packer, Jr., *J. Chem. Soc.*, **1962**, 771.
127. C. I. Merrill and G. H. Cady, *J. Am. Chem. Soc.*, **85**, 909 (1963).
128. G. Pass, *J. Chem. Soc.*, **1963**, 6047.
129. J. K. Ruff, *Inorg. Chem.*, **4**, 1788 (1965).
130. S. M. Williamson, *Inorg. Chem.*, **2**, 421 (1963).
131. L. C. Duncan and G. H. Cady, *Inorg. Chem.*, **3**, 850 (1964).
132. L. C. Duncan and G. H. Cady, *Inorg. Chem.*, **3**, 1045 (1964).

Compounds of the Actinides

B. B. CUNNINGHAM

Department of Chemistry and Lawrence Radiation Laboratory
University of California, Berkeley, California

CONTENTS

I. INTRODUCTION

The actinides are the series of elements of atomic number 89 (actinium) through 103 (lawrencium). The series is essentially of the inner transition of "*f*" types, analogous in many respects to the lanthanide, or rare earth, series, but showing much greater variability with respect to oxidation–reduction behavior.

Present knowledge of the chemical properties of the individual members of the series presents an extreme contrast; few elements in the periodic system have been the subject of such intensive investigation as have thorium, uranium, and plutonium (the actinides of technological importance), while the chemical properties of elements 99 through 103 are largely unknown.

In the United States the production and distribution of the elements is controlled by the U.S. Atomic Energy Commission and most actinide research has been done in the federally supported AEC laboratories. The synthesis of even microgram amounts of the heavier actinide elements is highly expensive, and much effort has been directed toward the development of methods of research which utilize minimal amounts of material.

The radioactivity of the materials being dealt with complicates their investigation not only because of the hazard presented to the investigator, but also for purely chemical reasons. The energy released in radioactive decay is so enormous compared to chemical bond energies that both the sample and its milieu are subject to continuous and severe chemical damage. Radiolysis of aqueous or non-aqueous media produces free radicals and other active species that may lead to unexpected side reactions, while the layer of air adjacent to the surface of a radioactive solid contains dissociated and excited gases, which can produce reactions similar to those observed in discharge tubes.

A. Nuclear Stability

All isotopes of the actinide elements are appreciably radioactive, but the variation in nuclear stability from one end of the series to the other is enormous. As shown in Table I the half-lives of the most stable known isotopes range from 1.4×10^{10} years (${}_{90}Th^{232}$) to a few seconds (${}_{103}Lw^{257}$).

TABLE I
Half-Lives of the Most Stable Known Isotopes of the Actinide Elements[a]

Atomic number	Element	Mass number of most stable isotope	Principal mode of decay[b]	Half-life[c]
89	Ac	227	β^-	2.12×10^1 y
90	Th	234	α	1.41×10^{10} y
91	Pa	231	α	3.25×10^4 y
92	U	238	α	4.51×10^9 y
93	Np	237	α	2.14×10^6 y
94	Pu	244	α	7.6×10^7 y
95	Am	243	α	7.65×10^3 y
96	Cm	248	α	4.7×10^5 y
97	Bk	247	α	$\sim 10^4$ y
98	Cf	251	α	$\sim 8 \times 10^2$ y
99	Es	254	α	480 d
100	Fm	257	α	79 d
101	Md	256	EC	1.5 h
102	No	255	α	~ 15 s
103	Lw	257	α	8 s

[a] The data are from *Chart of the Nuclides* issued by the General Electric Company, Schenectady, New York. Revised March 1965.

[b] β^-, decays by emission of a negative electron; α, decays by emission of a He^4 nucleus; EC, decays by orbital electron capture.

[c] Symbols: y, years; d, days; h, hours; s, seconds.

B. Sources

The half-lives of $_{90}Th^{232}$, $_{92}U^{238}$, and $_{92}U^{235}$ are comparable to the age of the earth; hence significant amounts of these isotopes exist as an inheritance from the formative period of the earth.

The decay chain:

$$_{92}U^{235} \xrightarrow[7.1 \times 10^8\text{ y}]{\alpha} {}_{90}Th^{231} \xrightarrow[1.06\text{ d}]{\beta^-} {}_{91}Pa^{231} \xrightarrow[3.4 \times 10^4\text{ y}]{\alpha} {}_{89}Ac^{227} \xrightarrow[21.7\text{ y}]{} \cdots$$

leads to a secular equilibrium which provides a natural source for both actinium and protactinium; their steady-state concentrations are 2.18 μg and 340 mg, respectively, per ton of natural uranium. Micrograms of actinium and grams of protactinium have been recovered from the processing of uranium ores, but in the case of actinium it is more economical to prepare the element synthetically by exposing radium to the high neutron fluxes provided by fission reactors[1]:

$$_{88}Ra^{226}(n,\gamma)_{88}Ra^{227} \xrightarrow[41.2\text{ m}]{\beta^-} {}_{89}Ac^{227}$$

The abundance of thorium in the crust of the earth is estimated[2] to be 12 ppm, only slightly less than the abundance of lead (16 ppm). The most important commercial source is the mineral monazite, a rare earth thorium orthophosphate having a variable thorium content which averages about 10%.

Although the crustal abundance of uranium is only about 4 ppm,[2] the figure exceeds that of such familar elements as silver and bismuth. More than two dozen uranium minerals are known, of which the more important are uranite (UO_2), pitchblende ($UO_{2.2-2.67}$), autunite [$Ca(UO_2)_2(PO_4)_2 \cdot nH_2O_4$], and carnotite [$K_2(UO_2)_2(VO_4)_2 \cdot nH_2O$].

Contemporary nuclear power reactors derive their energy almost entirely from the fission of ${}_{92}U^{235}$ which is present to the extent of 0.71% in natural uranium. It is of interest to note that projections of world power requirements predict the exhaustion of this isotope in about a century[3] if it were to remain the sole source of nuclear power.

In their natural state uranium ores are subject to a continuous neutron flux of very low intensity which arises in part from the spontaneous fission of ${}_{92}U^{238}$, and in part from the neutrons generated by the reaction of uranium α-particles with light element impurities. As a consequence, natural uranium contains trace amounts of neptunium, plutonium, and possibly higher transuranium elements, formed by reactions such as:

$$ {}_{92}U^{238}(n,2n){}_{92}U^{237} \xrightarrow[6.75\text{ d}]{\beta} {}_{93}Np^{237} $$

and

$$ {}_{92}U^{238}(n,\gamma){}_{92}U^{239} \xrightarrow[2.3\text{ h}]{\beta^-} {}_{93}Np^{239} \xrightarrow[2.3\text{ d}]{\beta^-} {}_{94}Pu^{239} $$

Identifiable quantities of both neptunium[4] and plutonium[5] have in fact been isolated from such natural sources, but the amounts are too small to be of practical significance.

The production of research quantities of the transuranium elements rests almost entirely on the utilization of the very high flux of neutrons provided by fission reactors. Samples of uranium, plutonium, or higher elements exposed to high neutron fluxes for long periods of time undergo a sequence of neutron captures and β^- decays leading to the formation of isotopes of higher and higher atomic number.

$$ {}_{94}Pu^{239}(n,\gamma){}_{94}Pu^{240}(n,\gamma){}_{94}Pu^{241} \xrightarrow[13.0\text{ y}]{\beta^-} {}_{95}Am^{241}(n,\gamma){}_{95}Am^{242} $$

$$ \begin{cases} \xrightarrow{\beta^-(90\%)} {}_{96}Cm^{242} \quad \cdots \\ \xrightarrow{\text{EC}(10\%)} {}_{94}Pu^{242} \end{cases} $$

Unfortunately, destruction of the heavy element isotopes by fission predominates over the capture and decay sequence. This is illustrated by the data of Table II which show the yields of the various elements (including major fission product elements) obtained from a typical processing of neutron irradiated americium.[6]

TABLE II
Products Formed by the Irradiation of 2.5 g of $_{95}Am^{241}O_2$ for Five Years at an Integrated Neutron Flux of 6×10^{22} Neutrons cm^{-2}

Fission product	Amount formed, mg	Actinides	Amount formed, mg
Zr	550	Pu	Several
Mo	305	Am^{241}	30
Ru	230	Cm^{244}	215
Ce	170	Bk^{249}	6.5×10^{-3}
Te	155	Es^{253}	2×10^{-4}
Y	115		
Rh	93		
Nd	70		
Pm	60		
Sr	125		

The amounts of the various isotopes, generated during lengthy neutron irradiations, rise and fall with time in a complicated manner that is sensitive to the half-lives of the isotopes, the intensity of the neutron flux, and to the neutron energy.

The time required for the formation of a given amount of an isotope which is n mass units heavier than the target material is often inversely proportional to the nth power of the neutron flux.

In order to provide for a substantial increase in the supply of transcurium isotopes the United States Atomic Energy Commission authorized the construction of a special high flux isotope reactor (HFIR) together with appropriate processing facilities (TRU).[7]

This installation, located at Oak Ridge, Tennessee, is expected within a few years to provide gram amounts of californium, milligrams of einsteinium, etc. for research purposes.

The half-lives of the isotopes of Md, No, and Lw are short in comparison with processing times for neutron-irradiated materials, and they cannot be recovered efficiently from such sources.

These elements have been produced by charged-particle bombardments of target materials spread on a thin foil backing.[8–10] The foil is inserted with its "unbuttered" side facing the oncoming beam of accelerated ions. The beam energy and foil thickness are such that the foil is essentially transparent to the bombarding particles. If a bombarding particle strikes a target nucleus, enough momentum is imparted to the struck nucleus to effect its physical transfer to an adjacent catcher foil. The product nucleus is thus instantly separated from the target material.

A moving belt arrangement is used to move the catcher foil quickly in front of a detector in order to establish the decay characteristics of the product isotope.

C. Recovery, Separation, and Purification

1. General Methods

In general the recovery, separation, and purification of the individual actinide elements is an integral part of any program of preparative chemistry, since (*1*) the primary source materials are often highly impure, (*2*) the isotopes are self contaminating through radioactive decay and, (*3*) many of the elements are so expensive to produce that recovery and reuse is economically mandatory.

The most widely used methods for the recovery, separation, and purification of the elements fall into three general classes: (*1*) precipitation methods, (*2*) solvent extraction, and (*3*) ion exchange.

Precipitation methods are generally used for crude separations from bulk impurities; "carrier" substances which form slightly soluble precipitates are often added to insure complete coprecipitation of trace amounts of the actinides.

Important slightly soluble salts of the 3^+ and 4^+ ions are the hydroxides, fluorides, oxalates, and iodates. Under the practical conditions of most separations procedures (high ionic strength, relatively short equilibration times) apparent solubilities are of the order of 0.5 mg/liter for hydroxides, 10 mg/liter for fluorides, and 100–200 mg/liter for oxalates and iodates.

Alternate hydroxide and fluoride precipitations will separate the actinides from most other elements except the rare earths, particularly if one or more hydroxide precipitations are carried out in ammoniacal solution.

Iodate (or phenylarsonate) precipitation from strongly acid solution is a useful method of separating 4^+ from 3^+ ions. For example, the solubility of $Th(IO_3)_4$ in $0.1M$ IO_3^-–$6M$ HNO_3 is only about 100 mg of Th per liter, whereas the solubility of $Am(IO_3)_3$ under these conditions is many grams per liter.

A very valuable precipitation process for the purification of plutonium is represented by the reaction:

$$Pu^{4+} + \frac{(3 + x)}{2}H_2O_2 + (1 - x)A^- + 2H_2O = PuO_{3+x}A_{1-x}2H_2O(s) + (3 + x)H^+ \quad (1)$$

where $A^- = Cl^-, NO_3^-, HO^-$, etc.

The solid peroxide is composed of layers of plutonium and peroxide oxygen atoms which are held together by interpolated layers of anions. In 1*M* HNO_3–10% H_2O_2 the peroxide solubility is about 200 mg/liter.

Only a few other elements (Th, Zr, Pa) form peroxides of comparably low solubility.

The separation of protactinium from niobium (a common troublesome contaminant) is represented by the reaction:

$$PaF_x^{5-x} + (7 - x)HF + 2K^+ = K_2PaF_7(s) + (7 - x)H^+ \quad (2)$$

Precipitation of the slightly soluble K_2PaF_7 is effected by adding a stoichiometric amount of KCl to a solution of the Pa(V) complex fluoride in 5% HF solution.

Ions of the type MO_2^{2+} are uniquely characteristic of the actinides, and the precipitation reaction

$$MO_2^{2+} + Na^+ + 3OAc^- = NaMO_2(OAc)_3(s) \quad (3)$$

leads to an effective purification from many other elements, including the tripositive rare earths.

Although a number of other slightly soluble actinide compounds have been prepared, the ones mentioned are most commonly used for preliminary separations from bulk impurities. Subsequent purification is then achieved by solvent extraction or ion exchange.

A variety of solvent-extraction methods for the recovery and separation of the actinide elements are based on the formation of complexes of their ions with β-diketones, organophosphates, or tertiary amines. Separation of the individual elements can often be achieved by careful regulation of the pH of the aqueous medium, or by altering the concentration of the complexing agent.

Both cationic and anionic exchange methods play an extremely important role in the separation and final purification of the individual elements.

Most of the exchange methods involve competing equilibria between the actinide ion, its aqueous complex with a carboxylic acid, and a sulfonic acid type cation exchange resin, or else the actinide ion, its chloro or nitrato anion complex, and a tertiary amine type anion exchange resin. Some anionic exchange methods are able to effect group separations between the lanthanide and actinide elements.

In the final stages of purification of small amounts of the actinides, great care must be taken to use specially purified reagents and resins; plastic or pure quartz columns should be used in place of glass.

The scheme used for the recovery, separation, and purification of the actinides, obtained by the neutron irradiation described in the Section I.B, provides an example of the use of some of the methods described above.[6] The important steps were:

1. Dissolution of the aluminum capsule containing the irradiated product in NaOH solution. The aqueous phase containing Al, Zn, etc. was discarded.

2. Treatment of the precipitate with HCl. The insoluble residue consisting of metallic Mo, Ru, Os, Te, and Rh (formed under the strongly reducing conditions of step 1) was discarded.

3. Anion-exchange separation of the lanthanide elements from the actinides by elution with 10*M* LiCl. The rare earths were discarded.

4. Separation of curium from the transcurium isotopes by a second LiCl column. The curium fraction was held for further purification.

5. Collection of the transcurium elements from LiCl solution by adding Fe^{3+} carrier, followed by an excess of NaOH. The aqueous fraction was discarded.

6. Dissolution of the $Fe(OH)_3$ plus actinide hydroxides in 10*M* HCl and passage of the HCl solution through a Dowex AG-1 column. Fe and Zr were retained by the column, which was discarded.

7. Evaporation of the HCl solution and redissolution of the actinide chlorides in 0.05*M* HCl; transfer to a Dowex 50 column and elution with 2*M* HCl. The actinide fraction, separated from common impurities such as Al, Fe, Ca, and Mg, was held for further purification.

8. Separation of the individual actinide elements by elution with α-HO isobutyric acid solution from a Dowex 50 column.

The separated and partially purified actinide elements were then subjected to rigorous purification by repeating the rare-earth and common-impurities separations, using specially purified reagents and small quartz columns which had been preleached with HCl to remove soluble trace constituents such as Al, Fe, Na, and Ca.

2. *Special Methods*

Special processes have been devised for the purification of actinium, protactinium, and berkelium.

a. Actinium. The product formed by exposing gram amounts of radium to neutron fluxes of the order of 10^{14}–10^{15} neutrons per cm^2 per sec for several months contains Ra, Rn, Ac, Pb, Bi, Tl, Th, and Po. The high level of penetrating γ-radiation associated with this material requires remote-control handling behind heavy shielding.

Separation and purification of the actinium[1] is conveniently effected by extracting an aqueous solution of the impure radium–actinium mixture in $0.1M$ HCl with twice its volume of $0.25M$ thenoyltrifluoroacetone (TTA) in benzene. Thorium and bismuth are extracted into the benzene phase which is discarded. The pH of the aqueous phase is adjusted to 5.5–6.0 by the addition of base. Fresh benzene–TTA is added and the extraction repeated. Actinium and lead are extracted, leaving radium and other impurities in the aqueous phase. The actinium and lead are stripped from the benzene–TTA phase by shaking with $0.1M$ HCl. After adding a small amount of inactive lead as carrier, the lead is separated from the actinium by precipitation as the sulfide.

Although freshly purified actinium is relatively safe to handle since it emits only soft β-radiation, its decay results in the buildup of hard γ-emitting daughter isotopes, which in a few days render it hazardous for most chemical preparations.

b. Protactinium. The residues from the processing of uranium ores represent the most economical sources of supply. The recovery of about 100 g of Pa^{231} from such a source has been described recently by Collins, Hillary, Nairn, and Phillips.[11]

Although protactinium constituted only $4 \times 10^{-4}\%$ of the starting material, which consisted mainly of uranium, iron, barium, zirconium, molybdenum, and calcium as nitrates, as well as considerable amount of silica, protactinium was recovered efficiently, principally by an $8M$ HNO_3 leach followed by extraction of the uranium with tributylphosphate, and protactinium extraction with diisobutylketone. The final product contained a few per cent of niobium.

Protactinium may be separated from niobium by precipitation as K_2PaF_7 from 5% HF solution.[12]

c. Berkelium. Berkelium may be oxidized to the 4^+ state by BrO_3^- or Ag^{2+}. The tetrapositive berkelium may then be extracted quantitatively from aqueous solutions by shaking with an equal volume of $0.15M$ hydrogen diethylhexylorthophosphoric acid (HDEHP) in heptane.[13]

In practice, the berkelium is dissolved in $10M$ HNO_3 and shaken with the HDEHP. The impurities extracted by the organic phase are discarded. The aqueous solution is then made $0.1M$ in $KBrO_3$ and again extracted with HDEHP in heptane. The Bk^{4+} now passes into the organic phase from which it is removed by shaking with $8M$ HNO_3 containing about $1.5M$ H_2O_2 (to reduce the berkelium to the 3^+ state).

This procedure will separate berkelium from almost all other elements except cerium.

D. Storage

Stocks of the purified actinide elements usually are stored in the form of nitrate solutions containing 1–3M excess nitric acid. Chloride stock solutions are sometimes preferred, but in these solutions radiolysis causes a gradual rise in pH, with eventual precipitation of an actinide hydroxide.

Storage containers for solutions must be vented because of the radiolytic formation of oxygen and other gases. An aqueous solution containing 1 g of $_{94}Pu^{239}$ ($t_{1/2}$ = 24000 y 5.2 meV α) evolves about 1 cm^3 (STP) of gas per day. (The rate of radiolysis is roughly proportional to the amount of the radioisotope, its decay energy, and the inverse of its half-life.)

Containers of glass or quartz subjected to radiation eventually exhibit surface cracking and loss of mechanical strength; plastics undergo gradual embrittlement. Transfer of solutions of radioisotopes to new containers is necessary from time to time.

It is standard practice to place the stock bottle in a secondary container which in turn is surrounded by lead shielding.

Stock solutions for which there is no immediate use are stored away from the laboratory working area.

Regardless of the method of storage the solutions are subject to contamination by dissolution of material from the container walls. Organic impurities are less objectionable than the inorganic substances derived from glass or quartz containers, since carbonaceous materials may be eliminated by ignition.

Unusual care must be taken to prevent contamination of microgram or submicrogram samples, since a single particle of dust may represent such gross contamination as to render the material useless.

A satisfactory method of storage on this scale is to adsorb the purified actinide ion on one or more beads of cation exchange resin of the sulfonic or carboxylic acid type having an exchange capacity only slightly in excess of the amount of material to be stored.[14] At resin saturation the concentration of (trivalent) actinide ions is about 2M. The cation exchange beads are readily manipulated mechanically without loss of material to contacting surfaces, and they may be washed in water or very dilute acid to remove particulate contamination, again with no loss of adsorbed material.

When the beads are heated in air the organic material is destroyed, leaving as residue an actinide sulfate, oxysulfate, or oxide depending on the ignition temperature. At 1200° complete conversion to an oxide occurs within a few minutes.

The ash content of purified cation exchange resins may be reduced below 10 ppm. Since at saturation the beads contain about 10 wt-% actinide element, bead storage introduces only negligible chemical contamination.

Although considerable volume change occurs on ignition the product oxide remains as a single coherent particle which possesses considerable mechanical strength and therefore can be transferred without loss to a suitable container for compound synthesis.

The storage of actinide compounds in the form of fine powders usually is avoided because of the possible formation of radioactive aerosols.

The actinide metals should be stored in vacuum or in a helium or argon atmosphere; exposure to air results in the formation of a surface coating of oxide or nitride.

Short-lived isotopes need frequent repurification because of self-contamination arising from decay.

E. Experimental Methods

1. Safety Aspects

With the exception of a few isotopes having very long half-lives the actinides are regarded as extreme physiological poisons. The maximum permissible body burden for the α-emitting isotopes is about 0.4 μcuries[15] (approximately 6 μg in the case of $_{94}Pu^{239}$).

Most of the actinide isotopes of chemical interest decay by emission of α-particles, with but little accompanying γ-radiation. Since α-particles have little penetrating power the α-emitting isotopes may be safely handled in a gloved enclosure maintained at a negative pressure with respect to the laboratory atmosphere and equipped with a filter to remove air-borne radioactivity from the exhaust. Transfer into or out of such a box affords an opportunity for the escape of radioactivity; this possibility should be checked by an immediate radiation survey of the suspect area.

Sharp objects, such as fine tweezers, scalpels, scissors, or glass micropipets, should either be absent from the enclosure or, if their presence is essential, they should be provided with a safe storage location where there is no possibility of inadvertent piercing of a glove.

Certain isotopes require additional protective measures; for example α-decay of $_{95}Am^{241}$ is accompanied by emission of a 40 keV γ-ray. Hence lead shielding should be used when working with milligram or larger amounts of this isotope. The isotope $_{98}Cf^{252}$ has a relatively short partial half-life for decay by spontaneous fission; neutron shielding is essential for work with even microgram samples.

As a final precaution, work with high levels of radioactivity should not be undertaken unless at least one other person is readily available in case of emergency.

2. *Preparative Techniques*

The techniques used for the preparation of multimilligram quantities of the actinide compounds generally resemble those of conventional inorganic preparative methods aside from the modifications that are necessary to insure adequate protection from the associated radiation.

Departures from conventional methods become increasingly necessary with diminution in sample size. The actinide metals and many of their compounds are reactive to the atmosphere. Where brief exposure of a large sample to air might result in only negligible surface contamination, a small sample might be converted to an entirely different compound.

Vacuum-line methods are employed, using systems capable of producing and maintaining vacua of 10^{-6} mm or better, and provided with feed lines for flushing with very pure helium or argon to protect the system when it is open. Samples are generally prepared *in situ* in quartz capillaries which are subsequently sealed for x-ray diffraction investigation.

Since transfer losses become prohibitively great for most solid samples on a milligram or smaller scale, transfer operations are held to a minimum. Frequently it is possible to convert a starting material into a succession of different compounds, all in the same capillary. Thus, an actinide oxide sample may be successively converted to an oxychloride, an anhydrous trichloride, and various trichloride hydrates, each of which may be subjected to x-ray diffraction study. If desirable, the sequence may then be reversed to obtain the original compound. Other possible sequences include iodides, bromides, chlorides, and fluorides.

The equipment and techniques used are described in detail in various publications.[16–18]

3. *Methods of Identification*

The identification of milligram or smaller quantities of actinide compounds by conventional methods of chemical analysis usually is out of the question; most identifications are made from x-ray diffraction patterns. A full description of the identification of submicrogram samples of $CfCl_3$ and Cf_2O_3 is given by Green.[18]

4. Determination of Sample Purity

Detection limits in the range from 0.05 to 0.01 μg may be realized for some 35 elements by spectrographic emission analysis.[16]

Detection of impurities at the picogram level is possible by isotopic dilution and mass analysis.[19]

A recently developed method of activation analysis for O, C, and N by $_2He^3$ bombardment promises to be extremely useful for analyzing samples of the actinide metals for trace amounts of these common impurities.[20]

5. Thermodynamic Measurements

Heat capacity, entropy, and enthalpy functions for uranium and thorium metals and for a number of their compounds have been determined to low temperatures by conventional methods.

Attempts to determine these functions at low temperatures for other actinide compounds have been successful only in the case of neptunium dioxide.

Basic difficulties arise because of radioactive heating and lattice damage when the half-life of the actinide isotope is too short. Thus meaningful low temperature heat capacity measurements could not be obtained with $_{94}Pu^{239}$ ($t_{1/2}$ = 24,300 y)[21] but could be obtained with $_{93}Np^{237}O_2$ ($t_{1/2} = 2 \times 10^6$ y).[22]

Heats of formation of $_{94}Pu^{239}O_2$ and $Pu^{239}C$ have been determined on the multigram scale by combustion calorimetry. The heats of formation of a number of compounds and aqueous ions of plutonium, americium, and curium have been obtained by measurements employing a heat of solution calorimeter having a sensitivity of about 0.0001 cal.[23]

Thermodynamic data have also been obtained from measurements of the potentials of aqueous couples and the temperature coefficients of the potentials.[24]

It is possible in some cases to measure the equilibrium constant of a reaction as a function of temperature with very limited amounts of material.

For example, the equilibrium constant for the reaction

$$AmCl_3(s) + H_2O(g) = AmOCl(s) + 2HCl(g) \tag{4}$$

which is equal to $P^2_{HCl(g)}/P_{H_2O(g)}$, may be determined by careful adjustment of the composition of a mixture of HCl(g) and H_2O(g) in contact with the trichloride.[25] Reversal of the reactions may be detected by weight change (if the sample is suspended from the arm of a sensitive balance) or by x-ray diffraction.

Equilibrium solubility data are readily obtained, even at very low solubilities, by using radiometric methods to assay the solution in equilibrium with a solid phase, and vapor pressure measurements by the Knudsen technique are possible at very low vapor pressures if the isotope employed has a high specific activity.

6. *Magnetic Susceptibility Measurements*

Bulk magnetic susceptibility measurements provide valuable information about metallic valences, electron configurations, and coupling schemes in the $5f$ series. Susceptibility equipment suitable for use with submicrogram samples is described by Marei.[26]

7. *Spectroscopic Measurements*

Optical emission, absorption, and fluorescence spectroscopy, as well as paramagnetic resonance spectroscopy, have played a major role in determining the nature of the $5f$ as compared to other transition series.

Absorption spectra have been of particular interest to chemists as an analytical tool, as an indication of liquid field effects, and in connection with heat capacities and entropies of the actinide ions.

Absorption spectra have been determined with submicrogram samples of solid compounds,[18] and with as little as 0.002 μl of solution.[27]

II. GENERAL PROPERTIES OF THE ACTINIDE ELEMENTS

A. Electronic Configurations

The ground-state electronic configurations of the neutral gaseous atoms of the lanthanide and light actinide elements have been determined by spectroscopic and atomic beam resonance methods.[28–42]

These configurations are shown in Figure 1 along with the relative energies of alternative d and f configurations for the elements near the beginning of each series.

The d configuration is more stable for the prototypic element in each series (lanthanum, actinium). In the actinides, the $6d$ configuration is also more stable for neutral thorium.

The $6d$ electrons continue to be present in the configurations of the neutral actinide atoms through neptunium.

The configurations considered above are for the neutral gaseous atoms; ionization produces an increase in the relative stability of the f orbitals. This is illustrated for thorium in Figure 2.

For thorium in its normal state of oxidation (4^+) the $5f$ configuration is more stable than the $6d$ by more than 30 kcal.

Element	Cs	Ba	La	Ce	Pr	Nd	Pm	Sm
Excited states, eV (scale 1–4)	−4 −5d	−6s4f −6s5d	−5$d^2$4f −5$d^2$6s					
Ground state	6s	6s^2	5d6s^2	[4f5d6s^2]	4$f^3$6s^2	4$f^4$6s^2	4$f^5$6s^2	4$f^6$6s^2

Element	Eu	Gd	Tb	Dy	Fr	Ra	Ac	Th
Excited states, eV (scale 1–4)						−7s6d		
Ground state	4$f^7$6s^2	4$f^7$5d6s^2	4$f^9$6s^2	4f^{10}6s^2	[7s]	7s^2	6d7s^2	6$d^2$7s^2

Element	Pa	U	Np	Pu	Am	Cm	Bk	Cf
Excited states, eV (scale 1–4)								
Ground state	[5f6$d^2$7s^2]	5$f^3$6d7s^2	5$f^4$6d7s^2	5$f^6$7s^2	5$f^7$7s^2	[5$f^7$5d7s^2]	[5$f^8$6d7s^2]	[5f^{10}7s^2]

Species	Th	Th^+	Th^{2+}	Th^{3+}
Excited states, eV (scale 1–4)		−5f7s^2	−5f6d	−6d
Ground state	6$d^2$7s^2	6d7s^2	6d^2	5f

Fig. 1. Relative energies of d and f configurations for elements in the vicinity of lanthanum and actinum. Configurations based on interpolation or extrapolation are enclosed in brackets.

Conformation of the f^1 configurations for Pa(IV)[43] and U(V)[44] in crystal matrices has been obtained from their paramagnetic resonance spectra; numerous magnetic susceptibility measurements[45] are in agreement with the assignment of f^n configurations to other actinide compounds.

For elements of high atomic number, L and S are relatively poor quantum numbers.

The spectroscopic and magnetic properties of the $5f$ elements must be interpreted on the basis of an intermediate, rather than a pure LS coupling model.[46]

Excited states energy, eV	Th	Th^+	Th^{2+}	Th^{3+}
3				
2				$-6d$
1		$-5f7s^2$		
0			$-5f6d$	
Ground state	$6d^27s^2$	$6d7s^2$	$6d^2$	$5f$

Fig. 2. Stabilization of $5f$ relative to $6d$ configurations with increasing ionic charge for thorium.

Although the electronic configurations are of decisive importance in determining the magnetic and spectroscopic properties of the various ions they provide little quantitative insight into oxidation–reduction behavior or compound stability.

The major features of the chemistry of the actinide elements undoubtedly are imposed by thermodynamic quantities such as the sublimation energies of the elements, their ionization potentials, the crystal energies of their compounds, and the hydration energies of their aqueous ions.

B. Thermodynamic Properties

Except for the elements of technological importance—thorium, uranium, and plutonium—the thermodynamic properties of the actinides have been the subject of but little accurate study. There are no experimental measurements of the heats or free energies of formation of any compounds of actinium, protactinium, or the transcurium elements.

Thermodynamic considerations are of basic importance in the selection of favorable conditions for preparative reactions; where the data needed are lacking attempts should be made to estimate them as accurately as possible.

1. *The Elements*

Stull and Sinke[47] give heat capacity, heat content, entropy, and free energy functions for solid, liquid, and gaseous actinium, thorium, protactinium, and uranium to 3000°K, but the data for protactinium are all estimated while those for actinium are based on indirect estimates of the melting and boiling points derived from a single preparation of the metal. Two recent independent measurements[48,49] of the melting point of protactinium are in reasonably close agreement.

TABLE III
Some Properties of the Light Actinide Metals[a]

Element	Crystal structure[b,c]	$S°_{298°K}$	mp, °K	bp, °K	ΔH_{vap}, kcal/mole
Ac	fcc	(15)	(1470)	(3000)	(95)
Th	fcc	12.76	1968	4500	130
	1673°K				
	bcc				
Pa	bc tetragonal	(12.40)	1870 ± 20	(4300)	(110)
	~1500°K				
	bcc				
U	Orthorhombic	12.03	1406	4200	101
	966°K				
	Tetragonal				
	1072°K				
	bcc				
Np	Orthorhombic	(12.1)	938 ± 5	(4200)	—
	576°K				
	Tetragonal				
	868°K				
	Cubic (?)				
Pu	Monoclinic	(12.1)	938 ± 3	—	83.1
	420°K				
	Orthorhombic				
	504°K				
	fcc				
	617°K				
	bc tetragonal				
	775°K				
	bcc				
Am	dhcp	(15.0)	1292 ± 7	2880	~60
Cm	dhcp	(18.0)	1640 ± 40	—	—

[a] Estimated values are placed in parentheses.

[b] The temperatures interpolated between two structures are the phase transition temperatures.

[c] dhcp represents double hexagonal close packed.

TABLE IV
Thermodynamic Values for Some Actinide Compounds (298°K)[a,b,c]

Compound	ΔH_f°, kcal/mole	ΔF_f°, kcal/mole	S°, cal/mole-degree
$AcCl_3$	(>−312)	—	(40)
ThH_2	−35.2	(26.2)	(14)
ThO_2	−293.2 ± 0.4	−279.6	17.0
ThF_4	−477	−457	(35.9)
$ThCl_4$	−285	−264	(48.3)
$ThBr_4$	−242	−225	(55.9)
ThI_4	−161	−138	(67.9)
ThC	−7 ± 6	(−6.4 ± 6)	(12)
ThC_2	−38	(−32.5)	(19.6)
PaF_4	(>−527)	—	(40)
UH_3	−30.3	−17.7	15.27 (β form)
UD_3	−31.0	—	—
UO_2	−259.2 ± 0.6	−246.9	18.63
$UO_{2.25}$	−270	−256	20.07
$UO_{2.33(\alpha)}$	(−273)	(−258)	19.73
$UO_{2.33(\beta)}$	(−273)	(−258)	19.96
$UO_{2.67}$	−284.5 ± 0.5	−268.5	22.51
$UO_{3(\alpha)}$	−294	−275.8	23.57
UF_3	−357	−339	26
UF_4	−443 ± 2	−421 ± 3	36.13
$UF_{5(\alpha)}$	−483.7 ± 1.3	−458.2 ± 1.4	48.0 ± 0.4
$UF_{5(\beta)}$	−485.2 ± 1.4	−458.7 ± 1.5	43.3 ± 0.5
$UF_{6(g)}$	−511 ± 3	−483.9 ± 3	90.3 ± 1
UCl_3	−212.0 ± 0.6	−196.7	(40.5)
UCl_4	−251.0	−229.6	47.1
UCl_5	−262.1 ± 0.6	−235.7 ± 2	(57)
UCl_6	−272.3 ± 0.7	−241.4 ± 1	68.28
UBr_3	−181.6 ± 0.6	−166.9 ± 1.5	(50.6)
UBr_4	−211.3 ± 0.6	−190.2 ± 1.5	(58.5)
UI_3	−136.9 ± 0.6	−123.2 ± 1.5	(59.5)
UI_4	−156.7 ± 0.6	−136.2 ± 1.5	(68.0)
$UOCl_2$	−261.7	−246.3	(38.1)
$UOBr_2$	−246.9 ± 0.7	−231.3 ± 2	(42.9)
UC	−20.8 ± 0.9	−20.2 ± 1	11.3 ± 0.5
U_2C_3	−49 ± 4	−48 ± 5	25
$UC_{1.86}$	−18 ± 4	−19 ± 5	(19)
UN	−70	−65	15
U_2N_3	−169	−150	29
U_3Si_2	−40.7 ± 0.5	—	—
USi	−19.2 ± 0.3	—	—
USi_2	−31.1 ± 0.3	—	—
USi_3	−31.6 ± 0.1	—	—
NpF_3	(−360)	(−342)	(26)
NpF_4	(−428)	(−406)	(36)

(continued)

TABLE IV (*continued*)

Compound	ΔH_f°, kcal/mole	ΔF_f°, kcal/mole	S°, cal/mole-degree
$NpCl_3$	(−216)	(−200)	(26)
$NpBr_3$	(−185)	(−170)	(49)
$NpBr_4$	(−198)	(−177)	(58)
NpI_3	(−142)	(−128)	(56)
PuH_2	−37.4 ± 1.2	(−28)	(14)
PuD_2	−35.5 ± 0.7	—	—
PuO_2	−252.8	−224	(19.7)
PuF_3	(−357)	(−337)	(26)
PuF_4	(−424)	(−400)	(36)
$PuF_{6(g)}$	(−453)	(−429)	(91)
$PuCl_3$	(−230)	(−214)	(38)
PuOCl	−219.7 ± 1	—	—
$PuBr_3$	(−199)	(−184)	(49)
PuI_3	(−155)	(−141)	(60)
PuC	(−25)	(−25)	(12)
PuN	(−95)	(−89)	(15)
AmF_3	(−394)	(−377)	(27)
$AmCl_3$	−249.2 ± 3	(−232)	(39)
AmOCl	−227.6 ± 3	—	—
$AmBr_3$	(−218)	(−203)	(52)
CmF_3	(−357)	(−339)	(29)
$CmCl_3$	−226.6	(−210)	(41)
$CmBr_3$	(−196)	(−181)	(54)

[a] Estimated values are enclosed in parentheses.
[b] Sources of data are given in references 52–58.
[c] The standard states of bromine and iodine are taken as $Br_2(g)$ and $I_2(g)$.

Hultgren[50] gives thermodynamic functions for plutonium based on careful experimental work.

The melting points of americium and curium have been determined, and the vapor pressure of americium has been measured.[51]

At least some crystal-structure studies have been made of all of the metals through curium.

Crystal structures, solid phase transformation temperatures, melting points, and room temperature entropies for the lighter actinide metals are collected in Table III.

Americium and curium exhibit close packed structures similar to those of the light lanthanide metals; their magnetic properties indicate a metallic valence close to 3.[16,17,26]

2. *Compounds*

Heat, free energy, and entropy data for some typical compounds are summarized in Table IV. Many of the values are estimated.

The estimates are made on the basis of the following approximations: (*1*) the entropies of solid compounds of a given structure type are the same for the different elements, except for variations due to differences in ground-state multiplicities, (*2*) room-temperature heat capacities are the same for compounds of a given structure type, and (*3*) the difference between the heats of formation of two compounds of a given element in a given state of oxidation is the same as the difference between the heats of formation of the analogous compounds of another element in the series, also in the same state of oxidation. Thus the difference between the heats of formation of ThO_2 and ThF_4 is 184 kcal/mole. The difference between the heats of formation of UO_2 and UF_2 is 185 kcal/mole.

This last approximation is usually reliable within a few kilocalories if applied to adjacent elements of the series.

Extensive data are given in Table IV for uranium, since many of the values are known accurately, and they provide a reliable starting point for estimating thermodynamic quantities for the other actinides.

The oxide and carbide data are from the combustion measurements of Holley and co-workers.[59–61]

3. *Aqueous Ions*

Heats of formation of Th^{4+}(aq), U^{4+}(aq), Np^{4+}(aq), Pu^{3+}(aq), Am^{3+}(aq), and Cm^{3+}(aq)[62] have been calculated from solution data on the metals and appropriate compounds. U, Np, and Pu metals exist in different crystalline modifications which differ appreciably in heat content.

The particular crystalline form of the metal used for heat of solution measurements has not always been clearly defined.

Fuger and Cunningham[63] measured the heat of solution of very pure α-plutonium in order to remove this uncertainty from previously published data.

Uranium, neptunium, and plutonium exhibit oxidation numbers of III, IV, V, and VI in aqueous solution; in dilute acid americium exists in the III, V, and VI state, and the IV state can be stabilized in the presence of high concentrations of F^-.

The III–IV and V–VI actinide couples are readily reversible and their potentials accurately measurable. Heat and entropy values for the couples have in some cases been measured from the temperature coefficients of the EMF's.[23,24] The heats of reduction by Fe(II) of Am(V) and Am(VI) to Am(III) have been measured in a calorimeter.[64]

The heats of formation of the aqueous ions are given in Table V and the potentials in Table VI.

TABLE V
H_f(298°K) for the Aqueous Ions of the Actinide Elements

Element	ΔH_f(298°K), kcal/mole			
	M(III)(aq)	M(IV)(aq)	M(V)(aq)	M(VI)(aq)
Th	—	−183	—	—
U	−123.0	−146.7	−247.4	−250.4
Np	−127	−132.5	−231	−208
Pu	−138.6 ± 0.7	−125.9	−210	−193
Am	−163.2 ± 2	−114 ± 4	−207.8 ± 3	−171.0 ± 3
Cm	−141.1 ± 3	—	—	—

TABLE VI
Potentials of the Actinide Couples in Acid Solution
(Measured in Volts at 298°K)

Element	III–IV	IV–V	V–VI
U	0.61	−0.62	−0.05
Np	−0.147	−0.75	−1.15
Pu	−0.97	−1.15	−0.93
Am	−1.7	−1.26	−1.64
Bk	−1.6	—	—

In many cases where only the potentials of the couples have been measured, heats were calculated by using the aqueous-ion entropies estimated by Latimer.[53] Conversely, heat data were converted to free energies by the same method. The aqueous-ion entropies estimated by the method of Powell and Latimer[65] are given in Table VII, but some may be in error by as much as 10 eu.

TABLE VII
Entropies of the Aqueous Actinide Ions (cal/mole-deg. at 298°K)

Element	M^{3+}	M^{4+}	MO_2^+	MO_2^{2+}
Th	—	−75	—	—
U	−30	−78	12	−17
Np	−31	−78	12	−17
Pu	−39	−87	−19	−13
Am	−38	−89	—	—

C. Crystallographic Properties

A considerable number of the compounds of the actinide elements in the III and IV oxidation states appear to be largely ionic in nature.

Obvious evidence of directional covalent bonding appears most prominently in the colinear O—M—O^{+} and O—M—O^{++} oxyions of the V and VI oxidation states.

This grouping is found in some solid compounds as well, such as $NaUO_2(Ac)_3$, UO_2F_2, and U_3O_8. In these structures the U—O distance to the two covalently bonded oxygens lies in the range 1.8 ± 0.1 Å; other nearest-neighbor oxygens are more distant by several tenths of an angstrom.[66]

In the fluorite-type dioxides, on the other hand, the eight nearest oxygen neighbors to the metal cation are all equidistant, lying at the corners of an imaginary cube of which the cation forms the center.

In the hexagonal trichlorides, the cation is surrounded by nine Cl^- ions, for all of which the M—Cl distance is the same within a few hundredths of an angstrom.

Even in the hexagonal sesquioxides, which exhibit the unusual cation coordination number of 7, all seven oxygens lie within ±0.17 Å of the mean distance.

The plutonium tribromide structure type, exhibited by $PuBr_3$, $AmBr_3$, UI_3, NpI_3, PuI_3, and AmI_3, is an example of eightfold halide ion coordination about the central cation; it may be interpreted as a strong distortion of the ninefold symmetrical coordination of Cl^- ions observed in the hexagonal MCl_3 structures, the distortion resulting from increased anion–anion repulsion.

The concept of ionic radius thus has a fairly well-defined meaning for the 3^+ and 4^+ actinide ions and is of considerable value in rationalizing the structures that are observed.

The ions of a given charge exhibit a monotonic decrease in radius with increasing atomic number. This is called the "actinide contraction" and is similar to the "lanthanide contraction" observed in the rare earths.

In a homologous series of compounds the anion-to-cation radius ratio increases along the series. At some critical value of this ratio a change in structure type may occur. Thus the high temperature stable sesquioxides of actinium through americium are hexagonal, while the high temperature curium sesquioxide has the monoclinic Sm_2O_3 structure.[18]

This new type of structure for curium sesquioxide was anticipated before it was observed experimentally, since the ionic radii of Cm^{3+} and Sm^{3+} are nearly the same.

The ionic radii of the actinide and lanthanide ions of a given charge are approximately the same, averaging a few hundredths of an angstrom larger for the 5*f* ions. The radii overlap, thus Pu^{3+} and Ce^{3+}, Am^{3+} and Pr^{3+}, etc. have nearly identical radii.

If a change in structure type occurs at some critical value of the radius ratio in the lanthanide series, a similar change can be anticipated in the analogous actinide compounds at the same radius ratio.

This similarity in the crystallography of the 3^+ and 4^+ lanthanide and actinide ions is useful in predicting the structures of various actinide compounds from existing data on the rare earths.

By contrast, there is [illegible] similarity between the structures of the lanthanide and actinide metals, especially in the early part of the series. The metallic radii in the actinide series show much greater variability than is observed in the lanthanides.

Metallic and ionic radii of the light actinides are given in Table VIII.

TABLE VIII
Metallic and Ionic Radii of the Light Actinides[a]

Element	Metallic form, Å	3^+ ion, Å	4^+ ion, Å
Ac	1.88	1.11	—
Th	1.79	(1.08)	0.99
Pa	1.63	(1.05)	0.96
U	1.56	1.03	0.93
Np	1.55	1.01	0.92
Pu	1.59	1.00	0.90
Am	1.73	0.99	0.89
Cm	1.74	0.98	0.88
Bk	—		0.87

[a] Corrected to coordination number 12 for the metals and 6 for the ions.

III. PREPARATIVE REACTIONS

If one includes all distinguishable phases the number of known compounds of the actinide elements is around five hundred. A comprehensive treatment of preparative methods for all possible systems is beyond the scope of this chapter. Attention has been confined mainly to the binary compounds, and especially to those which are susceptible to at least crude thermodynamic treatment.

The majority of the more important compounds of the actinide elements have been synthesized either by "dry" methods at elevated temperatures, or by comparatively fast ionic reactions in solution.

Kinetic considerations are rarely of major importance. However in diffusion-controlled solid–gas phase reactions, a large solid surface area favors more rapid reaction, and preparation for a synthetic reaction may include a step designed to insure a fine state of subdivision in the starting material. For example (1) finely divided oxides are made by low temperature drying of hydroxides or low temperature oxalate decompositions; (2) finely divided metal is obtained by first making and then decomposing the metal hydride.

However the dominant consideration usually is simply that of selecting conditions that favor formation of the desired product.

In many cases the thermodynamic data required for calculating reaction equilibria are not known; in such cases estimates should be attempted by the methods discussed in the preceding section.

Because the actinide metals vary so widely in their properties, one usually cannot obtain reliable estimates of heats or free energies of formation of compounds by interpolation or extrapolation of the thermodynamic properties of compounds of adjacent elements.

However, if the heat or free energy of formation of a single ionic species or compound of an element is known, heats or free energies of formation may be estimated for a variety of other compounds of the element which are in the same state of oxidation as the species for which the datum exists.

Room-temperature or higher heat capacities may be assumed to be quite similar for analogous compounds; this similarity would not be expected to hold at very low temperatures because of differences in the population of the low-lying energy levels arising from crystal field splittings of the ground states of the ions.

The room-temperature entropies of analogous compounds of adjacent elements would also be expected to be the same within 1–2 entropy units, except for differences in the ground-state multiplicities of the cation; it seems probable that the multiplicities are closely approximated by $2J + 1$, where J is derived from the $L + S$ values given by the Russell-Saunders coupling approximation and the application of Hund's rules for the field-free ions.

The entropies of the aqueous ions may be estimated from the semi-empirical equation of Powell and Latimer[65]; they may then be corrected for differences in ground-state multiplicity.

The methods discussed usually can be relied upon to give ΔF values that are accurate to 5–10 kcal.

The preparative methods described below are applicable to milligram or smaller quantities of material.

A. The Metals

All of the actinide metals have been prepared through the first half of the series.

The preparation of curium metal will serve as a typical example of thermodynamic and other considerations which influence the selection of a particular preparative method.

Room-temperature thermodynamic data, including estimated values from Table IV, suggest several possible reactions for making the metal:

$$2CmF_3 + 3Ca = 2Cm + 3CaF_2 \qquad \Delta F^\circ = -155 \text{ kcal} \qquad (5)$$

$$2CmF_3 + 3Ba = 2Cm + 3BaF_2 \qquad \Delta F^\circ = -140 \text{ kcal} \qquad (6)$$

$$CmF_3 + 3Li = Cm + 3LiF \qquad \Delta F^\circ = -80 \text{ kcal} \qquad (7)$$

$$CmCl_3 + 3K = Cm + 3KCl \qquad \Delta F^\circ = -85 \text{ kcal} \qquad (8)$$

In terms of the free energy change per mole of curium the reactions are roughly equivalent. However reaction (8) involves the preparation and handling of a hygroscopic compound, $CmCl_3$, which makes the reduction scheme technically more difficult. For this reason it would not ordinarily be used.

As a matter of experience it has been found that the recovery of the product metal in the form of a coherent piece requires that the reduction temperature be high enough to insure melting both of the metal and the slag, otherwise the metal will remain in a finely divided state which is difficult to recover in usable form.

The melting point of curium metal is 1340° and that of BaF_2, the highest melting slag formed in any of the above reactions, is 1360°. Since even on a milligram scale the heat of the reduction reaction usually raises the temperature of the reacting mass by 50° or more, a reduction temperature of ca. 1300° would be chosen.

Of the remaining possibilities, eq. (6) is selected for the following practical reasons: (*1*) the at. % sensitivity for the detection of barium impurity in the product metal is better than the sensitivity for Li or Ca, (*2*) the relatively nonvolatile BaF_2 slag forms a protective coating around the metal during the cooling period after reduction, and (*c*) barium is the purest of the reductant metals available.

Actually since the reaction is carried out at 1350° (~1620°K), the free energy should be calculated for this temperature. The reaction becomes:

$$2CmF_3(s) + 3Ba(g) = BaF_2(l) + 2Cm(l) \qquad (9)$$

Estimating ΔH° for eq. (6) at 298°K we obtain −236 kcal/mole; $\Delta F^\circ_{298} = -215$ kcal/mole. A crude estimate gives $\Delta C_p = +2$ cal/degree-mole. Using the relation

$$d(\Delta F/T) = (\Delta H/T^2)dT$$

we calculate $\Delta F^\circ_{1620^\circ K} = -120$ kcal, or $\Delta F^\circ_{1620^\circ K} = -60$ kcal/mole of CmF_3. K_{eq} for $1/(p_{Ba})^{3/2} = \sim 10^4$.

Even if the free energy change were 10 kcal more positive than that estimated, it would still be favorable for the formation of curium metal.

Fluorides used for metal preparation must be free of oxygen; otherwise the metal will be contaminated with oxide.

Although the trifluoride is easily prepared by precipitation from aqueous solution:

$$Cm^{3+}(aq) + 3HF(aq) = CmF_3\cdot{}^1/_2H_2O(s) + 3H^+(aq) \tag{10}$$

the precipitate contains water which is not easily removed.

The dehydration reaction must be carried out in such a way as to prevent hydrolysis:

$$2CmF_3\cdot{}^1/_2H_2O(s) = CmOF(s) + CmF_3(s) + 2HF(g) \tag{11}$$

This requires either very prolonged room-temperature drying or, preferably, treatment with anhydrous HF(g) at 500–600°. Any oxyfluoride formed is converted back to the trifluoride:

$$CmOF(s) + 2HF(g) = CmF_3(s) + H_2O(g) \tag{12}$$

Trifluoride that has been heated to elevated temperatures is nonhygroscopic. It may be that the water held by the aqueous precipitate is physically, rather than chemically, bound to the finely divided solid. Crystal growth, with consequent reduction in surface area, occurs on heating and thus reduces the amount of adsorbed water.

Finally the actual reduction step must be carried out in the absence of oxygen, nitrogen, water, or hydrogen, because curium metal will react with these substances. In practice the reduction is carried out in high vacuum in an all-metal crucible system which is heated inductively.

Chemical contamination of the molten metal must be avoided by proper choice of the supportive material; molten curium does not react appreciably with tungsten.[17] In practice, the piece of curium trifluoride is supported inside a tungsten spiral which projects into a tantalum crucible containing metallic barium.

The system is heated inductively; barium vapor comes in contact with the trifluoride while excess barium effuses through a small hole in the crucible lid. After cooling to room temperature the crucible system is disassembled and the metal is cut free from its tungsten-wire support. After cleaning to remove slag, the metal is stored in vacuum until needed.

The laboratory-scale preparation of other actinide metals may be carried out by the same general process as that described for curium. Reduction temperatures and reductants are given in Table IX.

For those elements that form tetrafluorides—Pa, U, Np, Pu, Am—the tetrafluorides may be preferred for metal preparation, because the larger heat of reaction favors agglomeration of the metal.

TABLE IX
Conditions for the Preparation of the Actinide Metals

Metal	Starting material	Reductant	Reduction temperature, °C	References
Ac	AcF_3	Ba	1200	68
Ac	$AcCl_3$	K	ca. 500	69
Th	ThF_4	Ba	1700	
Pa	PaF_4	Li or Ba	1400	70
U	UF_4	Ba	1200	
Np	NpF_4	Ba	1200	71
Pu	PuF_4	Ba	1200	
Am	AmF_3	Li or Ba	1200	16
Cm	CmF_3	Ba	1300	17

In the case of americium, the most volatile of the light actinide metals, prolonged heating at elevated temperatures must be avoided to prevent loss by vaporization.

Several of the actinide metals exist in more than one crystallographic form (see Table III): the allotrope obtained may depend upon the conditions used in a particular preparation.

The product from any given run should be characterized crystallographically.

B. Binary Compounds

1. Hydrides

The actinide metals form hydrides of moderate stability. (The free energies of formation at room temperature are -20 to -30 kcal/mole.) These black compounds belong to a class of hydrogen–metal systems intermediate between the true hydride salts and the absorptive associations of hydrogen with the platinum metals.

The hydrides are easily prepared by reacting the metals with hydrogen at 200–300°:

$$M(s) + XH_2(g) = MH_2 \tag{13}$$

Once initiated, the reactions proceed rapidly. Hydriding produces powdering of massive metal. Since the reactions are thermally reversible at moderately elevated temperatures, hydride decomposition may be used to obtain finely divided metal which serves as an excellent starting material for the synthesis of a variety of compounds.

Alternatively, the hydrogen obtained by decomposition of the hydrides is a source of extremely pure hydrogen. The thermal decomposition of UH_3 at 300–400° is often employed as a convenient source of hydrogen which is very dry and free of both oxygen and nitrogen. (The partial pressure of hydrogen in equilibrium with UH_3 is about 1 atm at 400°.)

Although uranium forms a single hydride of well-defined composition, UH_3 (which exists in two crystalline modifications) nonstoichiometric hydrides generally are encountered in the actinide metal–hydrogen systems. If pure hydrogen is added in increments to pure metal the typical sequence of events is: (*1*) formation of a very limited single-phase region in which the equilibrium hydrogen pressure increases with increasing hydrogen content of the metal; (*2*) the separation from the metal of a substoichiometric MH_{2-x} phase (biphasic region); (*3*) formation of another monophasic region in which x decreases as the equilibrium pressure of hydrogen increases; (*4*) separation of a second hydride phase.

The hydrides of Th, U, and Pu have been studied in some detail.[52] Thorium forms two hydrides, ThH_2 and Th_4H_{15}. The plutonium–hydrogen system exhibits variable composition in the range from $PuH_{2.0}$ to $PuH_{3.0}$; the hydride structure changes from face centered cubic to hexagonal as the hydrogen–plutonium ratio exceeds 2.7.

Other known actinide hydrides are PaH_3 (isostructural with β-UH_3), AcH_2 (isostructural with LaH_2 and PuH_2), Np_4H_{15}, AmH_2, and $AmH_{2.7\pm0.3}$.

In the preparation of the hydrides extremely pure metal and hydrogen should be used, otherwise surface impurities may inhibit initiation of the hydriding reaction.

2. *Oxides*

Phases which closely approximate the compositions M_2O_3 and MO_2 are found in various actinide–oxygen systems; uranium forms UO_3 and several actinide monoxides have been identified by x-ray diffraction as contaminants on the surfaces of the metals.[67,68] However the monoxides have not been well characterized chemically and in some cases they may be nitrides or mixed oxide–nitride compounds.

The fluorite-type dioxide is the most persistent oxide in the first half of the series. It is observed in Th, Pa, U, Np, Pu, Am, Cm, and Bk.

The increasing stability of the 3^+ state with increasing atomic number is shown by the formation of the well-defined sesquioxides of americium, curium, berkelium, and californium.

Although oxides of simple stoichiometry exist, the oxide systems of the elements which show multiple valency tend to be highly complex.

The uranium–oxygen system is a typical, if somewhat extreme example.

If oxygen is added in increments to pure uranium at 500° and the system brought to equilibrium, there is at first a very limited monophasic region corresponding to the solubility of oxygen in uranium. With the addition of more oxygen a UO_2 phase appears. The system is monophasic from UO_2 to $UO_{2.08}$. Additional oxygen causes a new cubic phase U_4O_9 to appear. When $O/U > 9/4$ an orthorhombic phase, U_3O_{8-x} ($x = 0.4$ at 500°), separates out. The solid phase is then homogeneous from $U_3O_{7.6}$ to U_3O_8. Heating U_3O_8 in 30–40 atm of pressure can lead to the formation of either β-UO_3 or a $UO_{2.9}$ phase. Uranium trioxide itself exists in five different crystalline modifications as well as an amorphous form.[69] The lower temperature isotherms of the U–O systems are even more complex than the 500° isotherm.

The plutonium–oxygen phase diagram[70] is somewhat less complex than the U–O system. The 500° isotherm follows the sequence: (*1*) very slight solubility of O in Pu (*2*) hexagonal Pu_2O_3 + metal (*3*) $PuO_{1.50-1.51}$ (*4*) $PuO_{1.51}$ + cubic $PuO_{1.61}$ (*5*) $PuO_{1.61-1.64}$ (*6*) $PuO_{1.64}$ + second cubic phase to $PuO_{1.98}$ (*7*) $PuO_{1.98-2.00}$.

The neptunium–oxygen and americium–oxygen systems are also known to exhibit complicated behavior but they have not been studied in detail.

The intricacies of the actinide–oxygen systems are paralleled by the lanthanide systems of Ce, Pr, and Tb.[71–74] The low temperature phases of these oxide systems are often difficult to characterize because of the slow approach to equilibrium. Conditions for the preparation of a number of actinide oxides are given in Table X. The ignition in air of almost any actinide compound at ca. 1000° will convert it to the oxide composition given in the first column of the table. The sulfates are an exception, for they must be heated to ca. 1200° for rapid conversion to the oxide.

3. *Fluorides*

The following fluorides have been prepared: AcF_3, ThF_4, PaF_4, PaF_5, UF_3, UF_4, UF_5, UF_6, NpF_3, NpF_4, NpF_6, PuF_3, PuF_4, PuF_6, AmF_3, AmF_4, CmF_3, and CmF_4. The hexafluorides are the most volatile compounds, having vapor pressures of several centimeters of mercury at 25°. Elemental fluorine is generally used to prepare CmF_4,[75] AmF_4, NpF_6, and PuF_6. Hydrofluorinations or other reactions suffice for the preparation of the other compounds. Reactions at elevated temperatures are carried out in equipment made of nickel, copper, or monel. The preparation of UF_3 is difficult because of the low stability of the tripositive state of uranium.[76]

For the reaction:

$$UF_4(s) + {}^1/_2H_2(g) = UF_3(s) + HF(g) \qquad (14)$$

$F \cong 5$ kcal/mole at 1000°K and $\log K_{eq} = -1.1$.

In spite of the unfavorable equilibrium, UF_3 is formed by using a stream of very pure hydrogen and excluding all water and air from the system.

TABLE X
Actinide Oxide Compositions

Element	Oxide obtained by heating in air at 1000°	Oxide obtained by heating in hydrogen at 1000°
Ac	(Ac_2O_3)	(Ac_2O_3)
Th	ThO_2	ThO_2
Pa	Pa_2O_5	PaO_2
U	U_3O_8	UO_2
Np	NpO_2	—
Pu	PuO_2	—
Am	AmO_2	Am_2O_3
Cm	Cm_2O_{3+x}	Cm_2O_3
Bk	BkO_2	Bk_2O_3
Cf	(Cf_2O_3)	Cf_2O_3

A less difficult method of preparation[77] is based on the reaction:

$$UF_4(s) + Al(g) \xrightarrow{900°} AlF(g) + UF_3(s) \qquad (15)$$

A stoichiometric mixture of aluminum and UF_4 is heated at 900° and the AlF is distilled off.

The equilibrium constant for the reaction:

$$NpF_4(s) + {}^1/_2H_2(g) = NpF_3(s) + HF(g) \qquad (16)$$

is considerably more favorable for the production of NpF_3 than is the analogous uranium reaction for UF_3 preparation, and NpF_4 is readily reduced to NpF_3 by hydrogen.

The trifluorides of the remaining actinide elements are best prepared by precipitation from aqueous solution, followed by dehydration at around 500° in an atmosphere of dry HF(g):

$$M^{3+}(aq) + 3HF(aq) = MF_3 \cdot {}^1/_2H_2O(s) + 3H^+(aq) \qquad (17)$$

$$MF_3 \cdot {}^1/_2H_2O(s) \xrightarrow[500°]{HF(g)} MF_3(s) + {}^1/_2H_2(g) \qquad (18)$$

Methods for the preparation of the actinide tetrafluorides vary, depending upon the relative stability of the tetrapositive state, as compared to other oxidation states for a particular element. Thus ThF_4 is easily made by treating Th, ThH_2, or ThO_2 with HF(g) at elevated temperatures:

$$Th(s) + 4HF(g) \rightarrow ThF_4(s) + 2H_2(g) \quad (19)$$

$$ThH_2(s) + 4HF(g) \rightarrow ThF_4(s) + 3H_2(g) \quad (20)$$

$$ThO_2(s) + 4HF(g) \xrightarrow{600°} ThF_4(s) + 2H_2O(g) \quad (21)$$

Difficulty may be experienced in controlling the first two reactions (19) and (20), which are highly exothermic, or a problem may be encountered because of the formation of an inert coating on the metal; Reaction (21) may be extremely slow if the oxide used has been heated to a high temperature. It is preferable to start with very finely divided oxide obtained by drying the hydroxide at temperatures of a few hundred degrees, or else by igniting the oxalate at 500–600°.

Protactinium tetrafluoride may be prepared by the two step process:

$$Pa_2O_5(s) + {}^1/_2H_2(g) \xrightarrow{550°} 2PaO_2(s) + {}^1/_2H_2O(g) \quad (22)$$

$$PaO_2(s) + 4HG(g) \xrightarrow{600°} PaF_4(s) + 2H_2O(g) \quad (23)$$

or by

$$PaF_5(s) + {}^1/_2H_2(g) \xrightarrow{500°} PaF_4(s) + HF(g) \quad (24)$$

In either case it is necessary to use very pure hydrogen and to exclude all traces of air and water from the system in order to avoid the formation of the oxyfluoride, Pa_2OF_8.[78] An intermediate fluoride, Pa_4F_{17}, corresponding to U_4F_{17}, has also been observed as another product of the preparative method indicated by eq. (24).

A hydrated U(IV) fluoride, $UF_4 \cdot H_2O$, can be precipitated by adding HF to acid solutions of U(IV); this compound can be dehydrated to give mainly anhydrous UF_4. The dehydrated product usually contains significant amounts of oxyfluoride.

A more satisfactory method for making UF_4 is the reaction of UO_2 with HF[79]:

$$UO_2(s) + 4HF(g) \xrightarrow{550°} UF_4(s) + 2H_2O(g) \quad (25)$$

Neptunium tetrafluoride is obtained by heating NpF_3 with a mixture of O_2 and HF gas at 500°.[80]:

$$HF(g) + NpF_3(s) + {}^1/_4O_2(g) \xrightarrow{500°} NpF_4(s) + {}^1/_2H_2O(g) \quad (26)$$

while plutonium tetrafluoride is easily prepared by treating finely divided PuO_2 [$Pu(OH)_4$ dried at ca. 150°] with HF(g):

$$PuO_2(s) + 4HF(g) \xrightarrow{550°} PuF_4(s) + 2H_2O(g) \quad (27)$$

Since commercial HF frequently contains H_2, organic compounds, and other reducing agents, oxygen is added to insure the formation of PuF_4 rather than PuF_3. The analogous reaction should be applicable to the preparation of NpF_4.

In principle it should be possible to make AmF_4 from AmO_2 and pure HF; adequate purification of the HF is so troublesome, however that it is customary to use the reaction:

$$AmF_3(s) + {}^1/_2F_2(g) \xrightarrow{500°} AmF_4(s) \quad (28)$$

CmF_4 is made by the analogous reaction:

$$CmF_3(s) + {}^1/_2F_2(g) \xrightarrow{500°} CmF_4(s) \quad (29)$$

The only known actinide pentafluorides are PaF_5 and UF_5. PaF_5 can be prepared in a straightforward manner by hydrofluorination of the pentoxide:

$$Pa_2O_5(s) + 10HF(g) \xrightarrow{550°} 2PaF_5(s) + 5H_2O(g) \quad (30)$$

or by treatment of the tetrafluoride with fluorine:

$$PaF_4(s) + {}^1/_2F_2(g) \xrightarrow{450°} PaF_5(g) \quad (31)$$

The preparation of UF_5 requires careful control of the experimental conditions. It is made by passing $UF_6(g)$ over $UF_4(s)$[81]:

$$UF_4(s) + UF_6(g) \xrightarrow[120\text{–}140\text{ mm}]{100°} 2UF_5(s,\beta) \quad (32)$$

The reaction yields the β form of UF_5. At 200° under the same conditions α-UF_5 is obtained.

Uranium pentafluoride is unstable with respect to disproportionation into UF_6 and the intermediate lower fluorides U_2F_9 and U_4F_{17}. Low partial pressures of UF_6 favor the disproportionation. By controlling the partial pressure of UF_6 and the temperature, either one or the other of the intermediate fluorides can be obtained in relatively pure form[81]:

$$3UF_5(s) \xrightarrow[18\text{ mm}]{200°} U_2F_9(s) + UF_6(g) \quad (33)$$

$$7UF_5(s) \xrightarrow[18\text{ mm}]{320°} U_4F_{17} + 3UF_6(g) \quad (34)$$

Uranium hexafluoride has received an enormous amount of study because it is used for the separation of uranium isotopes by gaseous diffusion. A convenient laboratory-scale method for its preparation which avoids the use of elemental fluorine is:

$$UF_4(s) + 2CoF_3(s) \xrightarrow{250-275^\circ} UF_6(g) + CoF_2(s) \tag{35}$$

Uranium tetrafluoride and cobaltic fluoride are ground together in an inert atmosphere. The mixture is placed in a platinum boat, transferred to a thoroughly dry glass vacuum line and heated to ca. 275°. The UF_6 is collected in a Dry Ice cold trap.

A second method of preparation of UF_6 uses oxygen rather than fluorine as the oxidizing agent[82]:

$$2UF_4(s) + O_2(g) \xrightarrow{800^\circ} UF_6(g) + UO_2F_2(s) \tag{36}$$

The yield of the hexafluoride is only about 30% of the theoretical yield, probably because of reaction of UF_6 with nickel at the high reaction temperature. Plutonium hexafluoride may be made in a similar way, but again the yields are poor.

The preferred method of making PuF_6 is by reaction of PuF_4 with fluorine[83]:

$$PuF_4(s) + F_2(g) \xrightarrow{750^\circ} PuF_6(g) \tag{37}$$

The PuF_6 is condensed on a cold surface adjacent to the nickel boat. An ingeneous arrangement circulates liquid nitrogen through the coils of the induction heater which serves to heat the nickel boat.

The only other known actinide hexafluoride, NpF_6, has been prepared by a method similar to that used for the preparation of PuF_6.

It is worthy of note that the radioactivity of $Pu^{239}F_6(g)$ causes decomposition of the compound at a rate of 1.5% a day.

4. *Chlorides*

The known actinide chlorides are $AcCl_3$, $ThCl_4$, $PaCl_4$, $PaCl_5$, UCl_3, UCl_4, UCl_5, UCl_6, $NpCl_3$, $NpCl_4$, $PuCl_3$, $AmCl_3$, $CmCl_3$, $BkCl_3$, and $CfCl_3$. There are fewer chlorides than fluorides because of the failure of Np, Pu, and Am to form V and VI chlorides. This reflects a general trend of decreasing stability of the higher oxidation states with increasing size and decreasing electronegativity of the anion.

A very convenient and general method for the synthesis of all of the trichlorides, except those of Np and U, consists of heating the oxides with $CCl_4(g)$[84]:

$$2M_2O_3(s) + 3CCl_4(g) \xrightarrow{500^\circ} 3CO_2(g) + 4MCl_3(s) \tag{38}$$

$$MO_2(s) + 2CCl_4(g) \xrightarrow{500^\circ} MCl_3(s) + 2CO_2(g) + {}^1/_2Cl_2(g) \tag{39}$$

The free energies of the reactions are favorable, the chlorinating agent is easily obtained in a state of high purity and only moderate temperatures are required for the synthesis.

In practice the oxide is contained in a glass capillary or small finger attached to a vacuum line. After evacuation, CCl_4 vapor is admitted by opening a stopcock to a reservoir containing degassed liquid CCl_4. The capillary is surrounded by a furnace heated to 500–600°. After exposing the oxide to $CCl_4(g)$ for a few minutes the system is evacuated and fresh CCl_4 readmitted. This process is continued until the oxide is converted completely to chloride. The product may be further purified by raising the temperature to ca. 700° and subliming the trichloride into a cold portion of the tube.

Uranium trichloride is made by reducing UCl_4 with aluminum:

$$3UCl_4(s) + Al \xrightarrow{400°} 3UCl_3(s) + AlCl_3(g) \tag{40}$$

and neptunium trichloride by reduction of $NpCl_4$ with ammonia:

$$6NpCl_4(s) + 2NH_3(g) \xrightarrow{375°} 6NpCl_3(g) + N_2(g) + 6HCl(g) \tag{41}$$

Ammonia rather than hydrogen is used for the reduction because the free energy of the reaction is more favorable and because it proceeds at a lower temperature where there is less danger of losing the rather volatile $NpCl_4$.

Protactinium tetrachloride has been made by reduction of $PaCl_5$ with $H_2(g)$ at 800°.[85] Thorium and neptunium tetrachlorides are obtained if the dioxides are exposed to CCl_4 vapor at about 500°; while $PaCl_5$ results from a similar reaction of the pentoxide with CCl_4.

The thermodynamic data of Table II indicate $\Delta F_{700°K} = -1$ kcal/mole for the reaction:

$$UCl_4(s) + {}^1/_2Cl_2(g) \xrightarrow{400°} UCl_5(s) \tag{42}$$

At somewhat elevated temperature UCl_5 is unstable with respect to decomposition into UCl_4 and Cl_2; it is also unstable with respect to disproportionation.

$$2UCl_5 = UCl_6 + UCl_4$$

Uranium hexachloride may be prepared from the pentachloride by this disproportionation reaction.

Uranium pentachloride prepared by the treatment of UCl_4 with Cl_2 is apt to be contaminated with UCl_6. It is difficult to separate these compounds by volatility methods.

5. *Bromides*

The known bromides are $ThBr_4$, $PaBr_5$, UBr_3, UBr_4, $NpBr_3$, $NpBr_4$, $PuBr_3$, and $AmBr_3$. Actinium tribromide, $PaBr_4$, $CmBr_3$, and the higher actinide tribromides undoubtedly are stable, but they have not been prepared. No higher bromide than $PaBr_5$ is likely to exist for the 5*f* elements.

All of the bromides listed, with the possible exceptions of $PaBr_4$, $PaBr_5$, and the uranium bromides, can be made by reaction of the oxides with $AlBr_3$, prepared *in situ* by mixing the oxides with aluminum and adding bromine[84]:

$$3MO_2(s) + 4AlBr_3 \xrightarrow{350\text{–}400^\circ} 3MBr_4(s) + 2Al_2O_3(s) \qquad (43)$$

Except for thorium the tribromides are obtained if excess aluminum is present. The reactions are carried out in sealed tubes. Subsequently the tubes are opened *in vacuo* and excess Al or $AlBr_3$ are sublimed *in vacuo*. The halides may be separated from Al_2O_3 by sublimation at higher temperatures.

Uranium trihydride reacts smoothly with HBr(g) at 300° to give UBr_3:

$$UH_3(s) + 3HBr(g) \xrightarrow{300^\circ} UBr_3(s) + 3H_2(g) \qquad (44)$$

and with bromine to give UBr_4:

$$2UH_3(s) + 7Br_2(g) \xrightarrow{650^\circ} 2UBr_4(s) + 6HBr(g) \qquad (45)$$

$PaBr_5$ has been prepared by heating a mixture of Pa_2O_5, C, and Br_2 in a sealed silica tube at 600–700°. The pentabromide is collected in a cold finger attached to the reaction tube[86]:

$$2Pa_2O_5(s) + 5Br_2(g) + 5C(s) \xrightarrow{600\text{–}700^\circ} 2PaBr_5(s) + 5CO_2(g) \qquad (46)$$

The oxybromide, $PaOBr_3$, is formed as a by-product in the preparation. Upon heating the oxybromide decomposes:

$$2PaOBr_3(s) \xrightarrow{500^\circ} PaBr_5(s) + PaO_2Br(s) \qquad (47)$$

6. *Iodides*

The known iodides are "ThI_3," ThI_4, UI_3, UI_4, NpI_3, PuI_3, NpI_3, and AmI_3; with the exception of "ThI_3" all may be made from Al and AlI_3 in a manner analogous to that discussed for the preparation of the bromides.

There is evidence for the existence of a thorium iodide having a composition in the vicinity of "ThI_3"[87]; the formula is supported by analytical data. The product has been obtained in various ways. Jantsch et al.[88] obtained $ThI_{2.3-3}$ by thermal decomposition of ThI_4 at 400° and $ThI_{2.96-3.03}$ by reduction of ThI_4 with Al. Watt et al.[89] heated mixtures of Th and I_2 in Vycor for 3 days at 550°, separated excess ThI_4 by sublimation, determined unreacted Th by dissolving portions of the sample in dilute $HClO_4$, and measured hydrogen evolution of the remaining product when it was dissolved in liquid NH_3. The calculated I/Th ratio was 2.98.

7. Refractory Compounds: Borides, Carbides, Nitrides, Silicides, Phosphides, and Sulfides

Interest in the construction of high temperature reactors has prompted an investigation of a number of high melting actinide compounds[56] other than the oxides. These include borides, carbides, nitrides, silicides, phosphides, and sulfides.

In general these substances are prepared by reacting mixtures of the elements at high temperatures; however the nitrides may be produced by reacting the metals or their hydrides with nitrogen or ammonia, and the sulfides by heating the metals or hydrides with H_2S.

Plutonium hydride reacts rapidly with nitrogen, even at 230° [90]:

$$PuH_{2.7}(s) + N_2(g) = PuN(s) + 0.9NH_3(g) \qquad (48)$$

Some of the more important phases are ThB_4, ThB_6, UB_2, UB_4, UB_{12}, ThC, ThC_2, UC, U_2C_3, UC_2, NpC_2, PuC, Pu_2C_3, ThN, PaN_2, UN, U_2N_3, UN_2, NpN, PuN, U_3Si, U_3Si_2, USi, USi_2, $NpSi_2$, PuSi, Pu_2Si_3, $PuSi_2$, Np_3P_4, Th_3P_4, PuP, ThS, Th_2S_3, Th_7S_{12}, U_2S_3, Np_2S_3, PuS, Pu_2S_3, and Pu_3S_4.

The borides are characterized by the presence of boron–boron bonds in chain, sheet, or polyhedral structures and hence the stoichiometries of the compounds do not indicate the valencies of the metals. The carbides contain C_2^{2-} groupings. The nitrides having the NaCl structure may be regarded as compounds of the metals with N^{3-}, and plutonium monophosphide as $Pu^{3+}P^{3-}$.

Like the borides, the stoichiometries of the silicides can not be interpreted in terms of ordinary metal valences, since many of these compounds contain chains or sheets formed by Si—Si bond.

C. Complex Compounds

1. Organo Compounds

A number of organo compounds of the actinide elements have been investigated because they possess useful extraction properties or have sufficiently high volatilities to be of possible technological interest. A few examples may be mentioned by way of illustration.

The actinide ions form stable chelate complexes with a number of 1,3-diketones. The acetyl acetone complex[91] is a representative example:

$$M^{4+} + 4CH_3{-}\overset{\overset{\displaystyle O}{\|}}{C}{-}H_2\overset{\overset{\displaystyle O}{\|}}{C}{-}CH_3 = M(CH_3{-}\overset{\overset{\displaystyle O}{\|}}{C}{-}CH_2{-}\overset{\overset{\displaystyle O^-}{|}}{C}{=}CH_2)_4 + 4H^+ \quad (49)$$

Such complexes are extractable into organic solvents and provide a basis for important separation procedures at controlled hydrogen ion concentrations.[92]

The actinide alkoxides[93,94] possess considerable stability and relatively high volatibility. The uranium alkoxides have received extensive study. Two important methods of preparation are indicated by the reactions:

$$UCl_4 + 4NaOR \rightarrow U(OR)_4 + 4NaCl \quad (50)$$

$$UCl_4 + 4KNH_2 \rightarrow [U(NH_2)_4] \xrightarrow{t\text{-}C_4H_9OH} U(t\text{-}OC_4H_9)_4 + 4NH_3 \quad (51)$$

Cyclopentadienyl compounds[95] have been synthesized by reaction with sodium cyclopentandienide in tetrahydrofuran.

2. *Miscellaneous Compounds*

There are some hundreds of actinide compounds which are both interesting and important but which cannot be discussed here for lack of space. Of special interest are the alkali fluoride–actinide fluoride systems,[96–99] compounds of the actinide oxides with alkaline earth oxides,[100] and the intermetallic compounds.[101]

D. Aqueous Ions

The relative stabilities of the various aqueous oxidation states are drastically different for each of the elements which comprise the first half of the actinide series. Thus the aqueous U^{3+} ion is a strong reducing agent whereas Am^{4+}(aq) is a powerful oxidizing agent. AmO_2^{2+}(aq) is difficult to prepare, while UO_2^{2+}(aq) is the common aqueous oxidation state of uranium.

As shown by the data in Table VI, many of the intermediate oxidation states are unstable with respect to disproportionation into lower and higher states. $UO_2{}^+$(aq), Pu^{4+}(aq), $PuO_2{}^+$(aq), Am^{4+}(aq), and $AmO_2{}^+$(aq) undergo disproportionation in acid solution. Pure, stable solutions of these ions in the uncomplexed state cannot be prepared.

However the potentials of the couples may be greatly altered by adding complexing agents or by adjusting the hydrogen ion concentration.

Thus Am(IV) can be stabilized in concentrated fluoride solutions, and the disproportionation of Pu(IV) is reduced by the addition of sulfate ion which forms a more stable complex ion with Pu^{4+} than with the other plutonium aqueous species.

The disproportionation reaction

$$3MO_2{}^{+}(aq) + 4H^{+}(aq) = 2MO_2^{2+}(aq) + M^{3+}(aq) + 2H_2O \qquad (52)$$

is repressed if the hydrogen ion concentration is decreased, but increases again at high pH because of the slight solubility of $Pu(OH)_3$.

The investigation of a particular oxidation state may require careful preparation of a milieu in which disproportionation is prevented or inhibited.

There are three general methods for obtaining a solution of a desired oxidation state: (*1*) dissolution of a soluble compound of that state; (*2*) electrolytic oxidation or reduction; and (*3*) chemical oxidation or reduction. Method *3* is used most often because of its convenience, but *1* and *2* have the advantage of not adding impurities to the actinide solution.

1. The III State

Solutions of 3^{+} Ac, U, Np, Pu, Am, and Cm may be prepared by dissolving the corresponding trichlorides in dilute HCl.

The aqueous tripositive ion of uranium is unstable with respect to oxidation by H^{+}, although the oxidation is slow. The solution must be protected from oxygen, however, which rapidly oxidizes $U^{3+}(aq)$ to $U^{4+}(aq)$:

$$U^{3+}(aq) + H^{+}(aq) + {}^{1}/_{4}O_2(aq) = U^{4+}(aq) + {}^{1}/_{2}H_2O \qquad (53)$$

Neptunium 3^{+} also is readily oxidized to Np^{4+} by oxygen.

An alternative method of preparing solutions of U^{3+} and U^{4+} is by cathodic reduction using a divided cell. U^{3+} and Np^{3+} may be produced chemically by reduction with zinc in an air-free acid solution:

$$Zn(s) + 2Np^{4+}(aq) = 2Np^{3+}(aq) + Zn^{2+}(aq) \qquad (54)$$

Tetra-, penta-, or hexapositive plutonium or americium ions are strong oxidizing agents, as is $Cm^{4+}(aq)$. The addition of hydroxylamine to solutions of any of these ions gives the 3^{+} aqueous ion.

The tripositive aqueous ions of Th or Pa have not been prepared.

2. *The IV State*

Solutions of the tetrapositive states of Th, Pa, U, and Np can be obtained by dissolving the solid tetrachlorides in acid solution. A hydrogen ion concentration of ca. 0.5*M* is required to prevent the hydrolysis:

$$M^{4+}(aq) + H_2O = M(OH)^{3+}(aq) + H^+(aq) \qquad (55)$$

Alternatively Pa(IV) can be obtained by electrolytic reduction of Pa(V) solutions or by reduction with chromous ions,[102] U^{4+} by air oxidation of U^{3+}, and Np^{4+} by reduction of the higher states with iodide ion in 5*M* HCl:

$$4H^+(aq) + NpO_2{}^{2+}(aq) + 2I^-(aq) = Np^{4+}(aq) + 2H_2O + I_2(aq) \qquad (56)$$

Fluorocomplex ions of Am(IV) and Cm(IV) are obtained by dissolving the tetrafluorides in concentrated fluoride solutions.

3. *The V State*

Aqueous solutions of Pa(V) and U(V) are best prepared by dissolving the pentachlorides in acid solution.

When uranium pentachloride is dissolved in dilute acid, $UO_2{}^+$ is formed by the reaction:

$$UCl_5(s) + 2H_2O = UO_2{}^+(aq) + 5Cl^-(aq) + 4H^+(aq) \qquad (57)$$

Aqueous Pa(V) is stable toward hydrolysis and the eventual precipitation of a polymeric hydroxide only in solutions of hydrofluoric or sulfuric acids.

Neptunium(V) is obtained by heating Np^{3+} with dilute nitric acid, or by the reduction of Np(VI) with hydroxylamine.

Plutonium(V) solutions are easily prepared by dissolving $KPuO_2CO_3(s)$ in dilute acid, but $PuO_2{}^+(aq)$ will then disproportionate.

Potassium plutonium(V) carbonate[103] may be prepared by adding I^- to PuO_2^{2+}:

$$2PuO_2^{2+}(aq) + 2I^-(aq) = 2PuO_2{}^+(aq) + I_2(aq) \qquad (58)$$

then extracting the iodine with CCl_4 and adding sufficient solid K_2CO_3 to the aqueous solution to bring the pH to ~7. Slightly soluble $KPuO_2CO_3$ precipitates from this solution.

The $AmO_2{}^+(aq)$ is obtained by dissolving $KAmO_2CO_3$ in acid solution:

$$KAm_2CO_3(s) + 2H^2(aq) = AmO_2{}^+(aq) + K^+(aq) + H_2CO_3(aq) \qquad (59)$$

Potassium americium(V) carbonate precipitates when a solution of Am(III) in saturated K_2CO_3 is treated with sodium hypochlorite:

$$Am(III)(aq) + OCl^-(aq) + 2OH^-(aq) = AmO_2{}^+(aq) + Cl^-(aq) + H_2O \qquad (60)$$

4. The VI State

U, Np, Pu, and Am form aqueous ions of the type MO_2^{2+}. UO_2^{2+} is obtained by dissolving UCl_6 in dilute acid solution:

$$UCl_6(s) + 2H_2O = UO_2^{2+}(aq) + 6Cl^-(aq) + 4H^+(aq) \quad (61)$$

or by oxidation of the lower states with dilute nitric acid.

The classical method of obtaining solutions of NpO_2^{2+}, PuO_2^{2+}, and AmO_2^{2+} is by oxidation of the lower states with peroxydisulfate in the presence of a trace of silver ion as a catalyst.

$$2M^{3+}(aq) + 3S_2O_8^{2-}(aq) + 4H_2O = 2MO_2^{2+}(aq) + 6(SO_4)^{2-}(aq) + 8H^+(aq) \quad (62)$$

but anodic oxidation in a divided cell is a superior method for obtaining $AmO_2^{2+}(aq)$.[104] Bromate in acid solution will oxidize the lower oxidation states of Pu or Np to $PuO_2^{2+}(aq)$ and $NpO_2^{2+}(aq)$ fairly rapidly at ca. 75°.

Acknowledgments

The writer is indebted to Miss Lilly Goda and Mrs. Patricia Herr for valuable assistance in the preparation of this chapter.

REFERENCES

1. F. T. Hagemann, *J. Am. Chem. Soc.*, **72**, 768 (1950).
2. V. M. Goldschmidt, *Geochemistry (USSR) (English Trans.)*, **1954**, 427.
3. R. M. Kiehn, *The Metal Plutonium*, A. S. Coffinberry and W. N. Miner, Eds., Univ. of Chicago Press, Chicago, 1961, pp. 335.
4. D. F. Peppard, G. W. Mason, P. R. Gray, and J. F. Mech, *J. Am. Chem. Soc.*, **74**, 6081 (1952).
5. D. F. Peppard, M. H. Studier, M. V. Gergel, G. W. Mason, J. C. Sullivan, and J. F. Mech, *J. Am. Chem. Soc.*, **73**, 2529 (1951).
6. J. L. Green, J. T. Haley, and B. B. Cunningham, U.S. At. Energy Comm. Doc. UCRL-16413, March 11, 1965.
7. *Ann. Rep. Congr., At. Energy Comm.*, **1965**, 243.
8. G. T. Seaborg, *The Transuranium Elements*, Yale University Press, New Haven, 1958, pp. 270–277.
9. A. Ghiorso, T. Sikkeland, J. R. Walton, and G. T. Seaborg, *Phys. Rev. Letters*, **1**, 17 (1958).
10. A. Ghiroso, T. Sikkeland, A. E. Larsh, and R. Latimer, *Phys. Rev. Letters*, **6**, 473 (1961).
11. D. A. Collins, J. J. Hillary, J. S. Nairn, and G. M. Phillips, *J. Inorg. Nucl. Chem.*, **24**, 441 (1962).
12. L. B. Asprey, private communication.
13. D. F. Peppard, S. W. Moline, and G. W. Mason, *J. Inorg. Nucl. Chem.*, **4**, 344 (1957).
14. B. B. Cunningham, *Microchem. J.*, **5**, 69 (1961).
15. *Natl. Bur. Std. Handbook*, **69**, 1959.

16. D. B. McWhan, B. B. Cunningham, and J. C. Wallmann, *J. Inorg. Nucl. Chem.*, **24**, 1025 (1962).
17. B. B. Cunningham and J. C. Wallmann, *J. Inorg. Nucl. Chem.*, **26**, 271 (1964).
18. J. L. Green, U.S. At. Energy Comm. Doc. UCRL-16516, 1965, 91 pp.
19. M. G. Inghram, *J. Phys. Chem.*, **57**, 809 (1953).
20. T. A. Sandenau, unpublished data, 1962, referred to by E. Westrum in *Thermodynamics of Nuclear Materials*, I.A.E.A., Vienna, 1962.
21. E. F. Westrum, Jr., J. B. Hatcher, and D. W. Osborne, *J. Chem. Phys.*, **21**, 419 (1953).
22. J. L. Burnett, U.S. At. Energy Comm. Doc. UCRL-11850, 1964, 66 pp.
23. D. Cohen and J. C. Hindman, *J. Am. Chem. Soc.*, **74**, 4682 (1952).
24. E. H. Lowenhaupt, "Microdetermination of Oxygen and Carbon in Lanthanides and Actinides," Master's Thesis, University of California, 1965.
25. C. W. Koch and B. B. Cunningham, *J. Am. Chem. Soc.*, **76**, 1470 (1954).
26. S. A. Marei, U.S. At. Energy Comm. Doc. UCRL-11984, 1965, 99 pp.
27. B. B. Cunningham and T. C. Parsons, unpublished data.
28. W. F. Meggers, M. Fred, and F. S. Tompkins, *J. Res. Natl. Bur. Std.*, **58**, 297 (1957).
29. P. Schuurmans, *Physica*, **11**, 475 (1946).
30. C. C. Kiess, C. J. Humphreys, and D. D. Laun, *J. Res. Natl Bur. Std.*, **37**, 57 (1946).
31. P. Schuurmans, *Physica*, **11**, 419 (1946).
32. M. Fred and F. S. Tompkins, *J. Opt. Soc. Am.*, **44**, 824 (1934).
33. J. C. Hubbs, R. Marrus, and J. Winocur, *Phys. Rev.*, **114**, 586 (1959).
34. J. C. Hubbs, R. Marrus, W. A. Nierenberg, and J. L. Worcester, *Phys. Rev.*, **109**, 390 (1958).
35. R. G. Albridge, J. C. Hubbs, and R. Marrus, *Phys. Rev.*, **111**, 1137 (1958).
36. A. Cabezas, E. Lipworth, R. Marrus, and J. Winocur, *Phys. Rev.*, **118**, 233 (1960).
37. R. Marrus, Biorganic Chemistry Quarterly Report UCRL-8457, 1958, 54 pp.
38. A. Cabezas, I. Lindgren, E. Lipworth, R. Marrus, and M. Rubenstein, *Nucl. Phys.*, **20**, 509 (1960).
39. R. Marrus, W. A. Nierenberg, and J. Winocur, U.S. At. Energy Comm. Doc. UCRL-9207, 1960, 27 pp.
40. A. Cabezas and I. Lindgren, U.S. At. Energy Comm. Doc. UCRL-9163, 1960, 27 pp.
41. J. Winocur, U.S. At. Energy Comm., Doc. UCRL-9174, 1960, 128 pp.
42. *Natl. Bur. Std. (U.S.), Circ.*, **46.7** (May 1958).
43. J. D. Axe, U.S. At. Energy Comm. Doc. UCRL-9293, 1960, 68 pp.
44. M. J. Reisfield and G. A. Crosby, *Inorg. Chem.*, **4**, 65 (1965).
45. G. T. Seaborg, *The Transuranium Elements*, Yale Univ. Press, New Haven, 1958, 328 pp.
46. M. Abraham, B. R. Judd, and H. H. Wickman, *Phys. Rev.*, **130**, 611 (1963).
47. D. R. Stull and G. C. Sinke, *Advan. Chem. Ser.*, **18**, (1956).
48. B. B. Cunningham, *Proc. Intern. Colloq. Phys. Chem. Protactinium*, **154**, 45 (1966).
49. J. A. C. Marples, *Proc. Intern. Colloq. Phys. Chem. Protactinium*, **154**, 40 (1966).
50. R. Hultgren, R. L. Orr, P. D. Anderson, and K. Kelley, *Selected Values of Thermodynamic Properties of Metals and Alloys*, Wiley, New York, 1963.
51. S. C. Carniglia and B. B. Cunningham, *J. Am. Chem. Soc.*, **77**, 1451 (1955).

52. J. J. Katz and G. T. Seaborg, *The Chemistry of the Actinide Elements,* Methuen, London, 1957, 508 pp.
53. W. M. Latimer, *The Oxidation States of the Elements and Their Potentials in Aqueous Solution,* Prentice Hall, New York, 1952.
54. *Noveau Traite de Chemie Minerale,* Vol. XV, published under the direction of Paul Pascal, Masson, Paris, 1962.
55. *Natl. Bur. Std. (U.S.), Circ.,* **500** (February 1952).
56. *Symposium on Thermodynamics of Nuclear Materials,* I.A.E.A., Vienna, 1962.
57. J. J. Katz and E. Rabinowitch, *The Chemistry of Uranium,* NNES VIII-5, McGraw-Hill, New York, 1951.
58. *Proc. Symposium on Thermodynamics,* Vienna, 1965.
59. E. J. Huber, Jr., and C. E. Holley, Jr., *Symposium on Thermodynamics of Nuclear Materials,* I.A.E.A., Vienna, 1962, pp. 581, 601.
60. E. J. Huber, Jr., C. E. Holley, Jr., and E. H. Meierkord, *J. Am. Chem. Soc.,* **74,** 3406 (1952).
61. E. J. Huber, Jr., E. L. Head, and C. E. Holley, Jr., Los Alamos Scientific Laboratory Report LA-2279, 1958.
62. J. C. Wallmann, J. Fuger, H. Haug, S. A. Marei, and B. M. Bansal, *J. Inorg. Nucl. Chem.,* in press.
63. J. Fuger and B. B. Cunningham, *J. Inorg. Nucl. Chem.,* **25,** 1423 (1963).
64. S. R. Gunn and B. B. Cunningham, *J. Am. Chem. Soc.,* **79,** 1563 (1957).
65. R. E. Powell and W. M. Latimer, *J. Chem. Phys.,* **19,** 1139 (1951).
66. A. F. Wells, *Structural Inorganic Chemistry,* 3rd ed., Clarendon Press, Oxford, 1962.
67. R. C. L. Mooney and W. H. Zachariasen, in *The Transuranium Elements,* G. T. Seaborg and J. J. Katz, Eds., NNES IV 14-B, McGraw-Hill, New York, 1949, Paper 20.1.
68. W. H. Zachariasen, in *The Transuranium Elements,* G. T. Seaborg, J. J. Katz, Eds, NNES IV 14-B, McGraw-Hill, New York, 1949, Paper 20.8.
69. H. R. Heckstra and S. Siegel, *J. Inorg. Nucl. Chem.,* **18,** 154 (1961).
70. E. R. Gardner, T. L. Markin, and R. S. Street, *J. Inorg. Nucl. Chem.,* **27,** 541 (1965).
71. G. Braver, *Proc. Rare Earth Res. Conf., 4th,* Session V, April 22–25, 1964.
72. D. S. Chopin, M. C. Finn, and J. M. Honig, *Proc. Rare Earth Res. Conf., 4th,* Session V, April 22–25, 1964.
73. B. G. Hyde and L. Eyring, *Proc. Rare Earth Res. Conf., 4th,* Session V, April 22–25, 1964.
74. M. Hoch and Hyo Sub-Yoon, *Proc. Rare Earth Res. Conf., 4th,* Session V, April 22–25, 1964.
75. L. B. Asprey, F. H. Ellinger, S. Fried, and W. H. Zachariasen, *J. Am. Chem. Soc.,* **77,** 1702 (1955).
76. J. J. Katz and E. Rabinowitch, *The Chemistry of Uranium,* NNES VIII, 351, McGraw-Hill, New York, 1951.
77. O. J. C. Runnalls, *Can. J. Chem.,* **31,** 694 (1953).
78. L. Stein, *Proc. Intern. Colloq. Phys. Chem. Protactinium,* **154,** 101 (July, 1965).
79. J. K. Dawson, R. W. M. D'Eye, and A. E. Truewell, *J. Chem. Soc.,* **1954,** 3922.
80. E. F. Westrum Jr. and L. Eyring, *J. Am. Chem. Soc.,* **73,** 3396 (1951).
81. J. J. Katz and E. Rabinowitch, *The Chemistry of Uranium,* NNES VIII, 384, McGraw-Hill, New York, 1951.
82. J. J. Katz and E. Rabinowitch, *The Chemistry of Uranium,* NNES VIII, 401, McGraw-Hill, New York, 1951.

83. A. E. Florin, I. R. Tannenbaum, and J. F. Lemons, *J. Inorg. Nucl. Chem.*, **2**, 368 (1956).
84. S. Fried and N. Davidson, *The Transuranium Elements*, Seaborg, Katz, and Manning, NNES IV, 14-B, McGraw-Hill, New York, 1949 in, Paper 15.5.
85. P. A. Sellers, S. Fried, R. E. Elson, and W. H. Zachariasen, *J. Am. Chem. Soc.*, **76**, 5935 (1954).
86. D. Brown and P. J. Jones, *J. Chem. Soc., Ser. A*, **1966**, 262.
87. R. J. Clark and J. D. Corbett, *Inorg. Chem.*, **2**, 460 (1963).
88. G. Jantsch, J. Homayr, and R. Zemek, *Monatsh. Chem.*, **82**, 575 (1951).
89. G. W. Watt, D. M. Sowards, and S. C. Malhotra, *J. Am. Chem. Soc.*, **79**, 4908 (1957).
90. F. Brown, H. M. Ockenden, and G. A. Welch, *J. Chem. Soc.*, **1955**, 4196.
91. W. Biltz and J. Clinch, *Z. Anorg. Chem.*, **40**, 218 (1904).
92. J. C. Reid and M. Calvin, *J. Am. Chem. Soc.*, **72**, 2948 (1950).
93. H. I. Schlesinger, H. C. Brown, J. J. Katz, S. Archer, and R. A. Lad, *J. Am. Chem. Soc.*, **75**, 2446 (1953).
94. R. G. Jones, G. Karmas, G. A. Martin, Jr., and H. Gilman, *J. Am. Chem. Soc.*, **78**, 4285 (1956).
95. L. T. Reynolds and G. Wilkinson, *J. Inorg. Nucl. Chem.*, **2**, 246 (1956).
96. R. A. Penneman, G. D. Sturgeon, and L. B. Asprey, *Inorg. Chem.*, **3**, 126 (1964).
97. D. Brown and J. F. Easey, *J. Chem. Soc., Ser. A*, **1966**, 254.
98. K. W. Bagnall, D. Brown, and J. G. H. du Perez, *J. Chem. Soc.*, **1964**, 2603.
99. K. W. Bagnall and D. Brown, *J. Chem. Soc.*, **1964**, 3021.
100. H. R. Hoekstra and J. J. Katz, *J. Am. Chem. Soc.*, **74**, 1683 (1954).
101. O. J. C. Runnalls, *Trans. Metals Soc. AIME*, **197**, 1460 (1953).
102. G. Bouissieres and M. Haissinsky, *Proc. Intern. Congr. Pure Appl. Chem., 11th, London, 1947* (Publ. 1950), p. 17.
103. J. P. Nigon, R. A. Penneman, E. Staritsky, T. K. Keenan, and L. B. Asprey, *J. Phys. Chem.*, **58**, 403 (1954).
104. S. R. Gunn, Thesis, U.S. At. Energy Comm. Doc. UCRL-2541, April 7, 1954.

Boron–Nitrogen Compounds

R. A. GEANANGEL AND S. G. SHORE

Department of Chemistry, The Ohio State University, Columbus, Ohio

CONTENTS

I. INTRODUCTION

The purpose of this chapter is to present a survey of synthetic procedures which can be applied to most of the known boron–nitrogen compounds, with the exception of the boron nitrides, and to include a comprehensive listing of these compounds and their physical properties. No effort has been made to discuss systematically the chemistry, structures, or bonding of these materials. However, the references cited in this chapter should prove to be useful for providing much information of this type, as well as providing specific syntheses for boron–nitrogen compounds. In addition to these specific references, the following general works should prove to be valuable sources of information:

K. Niedenzu and J. W. Dawson, *Boron–Nitrogen Compounds,* Academic Press, New York, 1965.

K. Niedenzu, Chairman, "Boron–Nitrogen Chemistry," *Advan. Chem. Ser.,* **45** (1964).

H. Steinberg and A. L. McCloskey, *Progress in Boron Chemistry,* Macmillan, New York, 1964.

E. K. Mellon, Jr. and J. J. Lagowski, "The Borazines," *Advan. Inorg. Chem. Radiochem.,* **5,** 259–305 (1963).

Classically, boron–nitrogen compounds have been placed in three broad categories: amine–boranes, aminoboranes, and borazines. It has become apparent in recent years, however, that these categories are inadequate for cataloging many of the novel species which have been synthesized. In lieu of a complete and generally accepted systematic nomenclature for boron–nitrogen compounds, it has been necessary to compromise in this chapter, using recommendations of the Boron Nomenclature Committee of the American Chemical Society, the Ring Index, names which have achieved common usage, and names which have been assigned by individuals who have been very active in a particular area of boron–nitrogen chemistry.

We have listed below titles of sections of this chapter and the specific categories of nomenclature which are employed, including examples in each category, in order to simplify the search for syntheses of specific types of boron–nitrogen compounds.

Section I. Introduction.

Section II. Amine-Boranes. Amine-boranes are addition compounds of amines with the borane unit, BH_3, or substituted boranes. Examples are: H_3NBH_3, $F_3BN(CH_3)_3$, and $(CH_3)_3BN(CH_3)_3$.

Section III. Unsymmetrical Cleavage of Diborane by Amines; Analogs of the Diamminedihydridoboron(1+) Cation, $H_2B(NH_3)_2^+$. When diborane reacts with certain amines, ionic products are formed, analogous to $H_2B(NH_3)_2^+BH_4^-$.

Section IV. Aminoboranes, Bis(amino)boranes, Tris(amino)boranes, and Cycloborazanes. Aminoboranes are monomeric, unsaturated species. In the literature this nomenclature has also been applied to chainlike and cyclic materials which have the same empirical composition as the monomer, e.g., $(BH_2NH_2)_n$. In the present chapter the term aminoborane will be exclusively applied to monomeric species such as $H_2BN(C_3H_7)_2$ and $Cl_2BN(C_2H_5)_2$, while the term poly(aminoborane) will refer to chainlike species, and the term cycloborazane will refer to cyclic species. The degree of association is included in the nomenclature of the cycloborazanes. Thus $(BH_2NH_2)_2$ is cyclodiborazane, a four-membered ring (**1**), and $(BH_2NH_2)_3$ is cyclotriborazane, a six-membered ring (**2**).

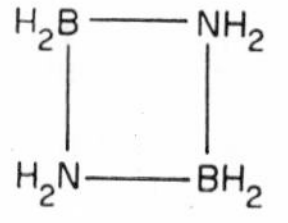

H_2B—NH_2
H_2N—BH_2

(**1**)

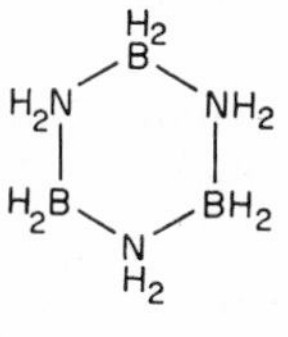

H_2B
H_2N NH_2
H_2B BH_2
NH_2

(**2**)

Bis- and tris(amino)boranes are monomeric, noncyclic species which have two and three nitrogens, respectively, directly bonded to boron. Example of bis- and tris(amino)boranes are $HB[N(CH_3)_2]_2$, bis(dimethylamino)borane, and $B[N(CH_3)_2]_3$, tris(dimethylamino)borane.

Section V. Borazines(4,6,8-Membered Rings and Polycyclic Species). Borazines are unsaturated cyclic compounds containing boron–nitrogen atoms. Structure **3** represents the structure of borazine. The com-

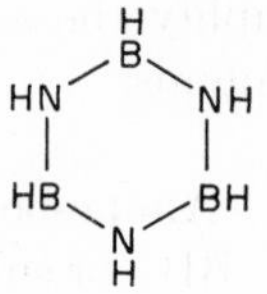

(3)

pound shown in structure **4** is commonly called *B*-trichloroborazine.

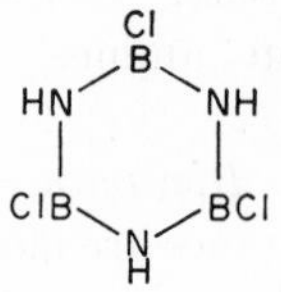

(4)

The four-membered borazine rings and the eight-membered borazine rings are perhaps best named as derivatives of *s*-diazadiborine and *s*-tetrazatetraborine which are shown in structures **5** and **6**, respectively.

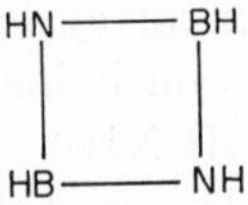

(5)

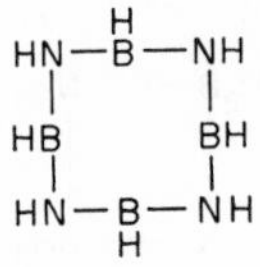

(6)

The eight-membered borazines have also been called tetrameric borazynes.

The polycyclic borazines are named after the parent hydrocarbon. Thus the structure shown in structure **7** is called borazanaphthalene.

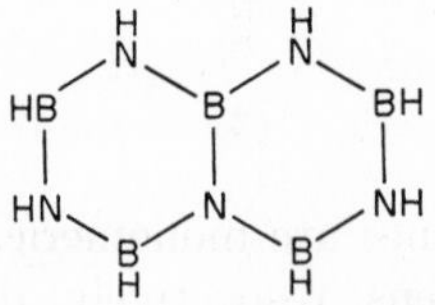

(7)

It is unfortunate that this nomenclature is similar to that used for so-called "heteroaromatic" boron–nitrogen compounds (see Sect. VIII).

Section VI. Cyclic Compounds Containing Either the Amine-Borane Linkage or Aminoborane Linkages (Mono, Bis, and Tris). The compounds in this section are usually prepared by less direct methods than the amine–boranes and aminoboranes. In general, they are best named according to the rules of the Ring Index. Structure **8** represents an

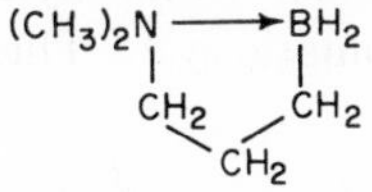

```
(CH3)2N ——→ BH2
   |          |
  CH2        CH2
     \      /
       CH2
```

(**8**)

example of a compound with an amine-borane linkage. It can be named either 1,1-dimethyl-1,2-azaborolidine or cyclo-*N*,*B*-dimethylaminopropylborane. Structure **9** represents an example of a compound

```
  H
  N
   \
    B — C6H5
```

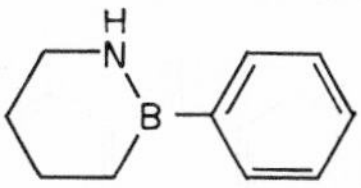

(**9**)

with an aminoborane linkage. It is named 2-phenyl-1,2-azaboracyclohexane. Structure **10** represents an example of a compound with a bis-

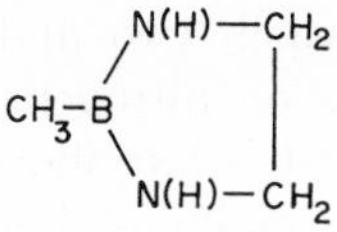

```
       N(H)—CH2
      /       |
CH3—B         |
      \       |
       N(H)—CH2
```

(**10**)

(amino)borane linkage. It is named 2-methyl-1,3,2-diazaboracyclopentane. Structure **11** represents an example of a tris(amino)borane

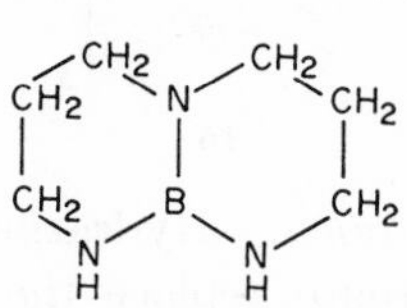

```
   CH2       CH2
CH2    \N/      CH2
 |      |        |
CH2     B       CH2
   \N/    \N/
    H      H
```

(**11**)

linkage. It is named 1,8,10,9-triazaboradecalin.

Section VII. μ-Aminodiboranes. μ-Aminodiboranes are compounds in which an amino group replaces one of the bridge hydrogens in the diborane structure. The structure of μ-dimethylaminodiborane is shown in structure **12**.

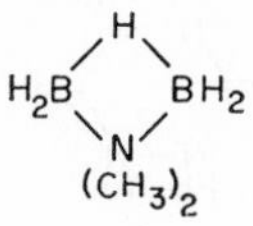

```
      H
    /   \
 H2B     BH2
    \   /
      N
   (CH3)2
```

(**12**)

Section VIII. Heteroaromatic Boron–Nitrogen Compounds. Compounds in this category are derived from aromatic molecules by substitution of boron and nitrogen atoms for carbon atoms. Nomenclature is based upon that of the isoelectronic hydrocarbon analogs using the prefix "aro" to indicate aromaticity.[1] The compound in structure **13**

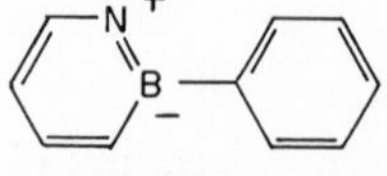

(**13**)

is called 2-phenyl-2,1-borazarobenzene. The compound in structure **14** is called 10,9-borazaroanthracene.

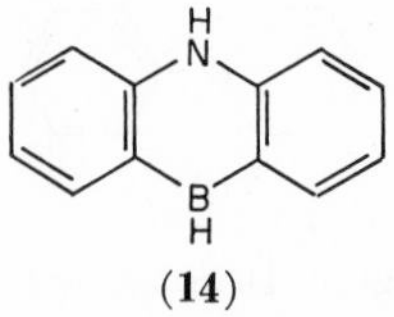

(**14**)

Section IX. Diborylamines and Triborylamines. Di- and triboryl amines are compounds in which two and three boryl groups, R_2B-, respectively, are substituents on nitrogen. An example of a diborylamine is $[(C_4H_9)_2B]_2NH$, bis(di-*n*-butylboryl)amine. The structure of tri(1,3,2-benzodioxaborol-2-yl)amine is shown in structure **15**.

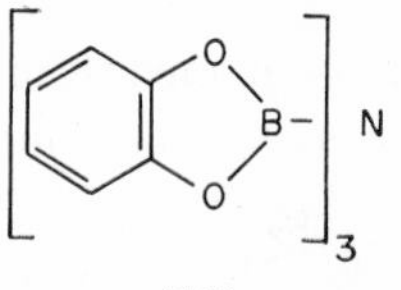

(**15**)

Section X. Hydrazinoboranes. Hydrazinoboranes are species in which one or two boryl groups replace the hydrogens on hydrazine, H_2NNH_2. Acyclic hydrazinoboranes are named as substituted hydrazines. For example, $(C_4H_9)_2BN(H)N(H)B(C_4H_9)_2$ is called bis-(*N*,*N*′-di-*t*-butylboryl)hydrazine. Cyclic hydrazinoboranes are numbered according to the Ring Index. The structure shown in structure **16** is called 1,2,4,5-tetraphenyl-1,2,4,5-tetraza-3,6-diborine.

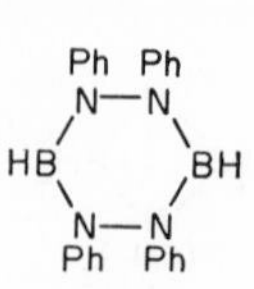

(**16**)

Section XI. Amino-Substituted Diboron Compounds. Although compounds which possess a boron–boron bond have been named as derivatives of the hypothetical molecule diborane(4), $H_2B—BH_2$, they are generally referred to as diboron compounds. Thus, for example, the common name for $[(CH_3)_2N]_2B—B[N(CH_3)_2]_2$ is tetrakis(dimethylamino)diboron, while its name as a derivative of diborane(4) is tetrakis-(dimethylamino)diborane(4).

II. AMINE-BORANES

A. Introduction

Amine-boranes represent the largest number of known boron–nitrogen compounds. The properties of these substances are markedly dependent upon the substituent atoms or groups on boron and nitrogen. Largely through the thermodynamic studies of Brown and co-workers,[2–8] steric effects of substituent alkyl groups on the strength of the B—N bond have been correlated. Thus the sterically hindered ligands $(C_2H_5)_3N$ and t-$C_4H_9NH_2$ form significantly less stable borane complexes, being essentially completely dissociated in the vapor phase, than the unhindered methyl amines. Sterically hindered amine–boranes such as $(C_2H_5)_3NBH_3$ and t-$C_4H_9BH_2N(CH_3)_3$ have proved to be useful hydroborating agents because of the relative instability of the B–N bond.[9–11]

Thermodynamic and qualitative observations reveal that the stability of the B—N bond, with respect to a given nitrogen donor, increases in the following series.[12–15]

$$B(OCH_3)_3 < B(CH_3)_3 < BF_3 < BH_3 \approx BCl_3 < BBr_3$$

(*Note:* The position of BH_3 is determined by recent estimates of the bridge dissociation energy of B_2H_6.[16])

In general, alkoxyboranes form very weak amine complexes which are highly dissociated at ordinary temperatures. A convenient rationale has been given to account for the order of increasing Lewis acid character shown above.[12] It considers the opposing effects of electron-withdrawing ability and pi bonding ability of the atoms on boron. Thus, in the case of trimethoxyborane, the tendency for oxygen to pi bond or back-bond unshared electrons to boron overshadows its electron-withdrawing ability. Back-bonding presumably decreases the ability of boron to accept an electron pair from an external donor ligand. The fact that BF_3 is the weakest of the boron halide Lewis acids is attributed to the greater ability of boron to pi bond with fluorine than the other halogens.

TABLE I
Amine Boranes Prepared by Direct Reaction of the Components

Compound	mp, °C	bp (mm), °C	Remarks	References
$H_3BNH_2CH_3$	56			40,42–44
$H_3BNH(CH_3)_2$	36	49 (.01)		40,42–44
$H_3BN(CH_3)_3$	93.5	171		40,45
$H_3BN(C_2H_5)_3$	−2	42 (.0001)		40,46–48
$H_3BNC_5H_5$	9–10			43,49
$H_3BN\equiv CCH_3$			Undergoes chemical change at 40° to liquid	50
$[H_3BNH_2CH_2]_2$	89 (decomp.)			51–53
$H_3BNH[C(CH_3)_3]_2$	111–112			54
$H_3B\cdot$quinoline	95–96			49
$H_3B\cdot$ethyleneimine			Unstable at room temp.	55
$H_3B\cdot$azetidine			Liquid at room temp.	55
$H_3B\cdot$pyrrolidine			Not characterized	55
$H_3B\cdot$piperidine			Not characterized evolves H_2 at room temp.	55
F_3BNH_3	163			56–59,242
$F_3BNH_2(CH_3)$	70–71			60
$F_3BNH_2(C_4H_9)$	75			61
F_3BNH_2Ph	158–160			62
$F_3B\cdot$ethylenediamine	70–74		Impure	63
$(F_3B)_2\cdot$ethylenediamine	169–170		n_D^{25} 1.390 d_{25} 1.530	52,63
$[F_3BNH_2(CH_2)_3]_2$	179–180.5		n_D^{25} 1.397 d_{25} 1.234	63
$F_3BNH(CH_3)_2$			Not isolated	56
$F_3BN(CH_3)_3$	145–146		Sublimes *in vacuo* at 125–130	64–66,67
$F_3BN(C_2H_5)_3$	29.5			58,68
$F_3BN(CH_3)_2C_6H_5$	90–92			66
$F_3BNC_5H_5$	45±1			69
$F_3BN(C_2H_5)_2CH_2Ph$	99–102			70
$(F_3B)_2$phenylenediamine			Decomposes on heating	71
$(F_3B)_2$dimethylaminoaniline			Decomposes on heating	71
$(F_3B)_2$diethylaminoaniline			Decomposes on heating	71
$(F_3B)_2$hexamethylenediamine			Decomposes on heating	71
$(F_3B)_2$benzidine			Decomposes on heating	71
$F_3BNH_2NH_2$	87			72
$(F_3BNH_2)_2$	266			72
$F_3BN(CH_3)_2CHO$	58–59	100 (0.1)		73
F_3BNH_2CHO			Oil, unstable at room temp.	73
$F_3BNH_2C(CH_3)O$			Decomposes at 90°	73
$F_3BN(CH_3)_2Cl$	82–85			74
$F_3BNH(C_2H_5)_2$	160			58
$F_3BNH_2(C_2H_5)$	89			58
$F_3BN\equiv CCH_3$	135.5 ± 0.5			75
$Cl_3BNH_2C(O)CH_3$	75.5–76.5			76
$Cl_3BNH_2C(O)C_2H_5$			Liquid	76
$Cl_3BNH_2C(O)Ph$	95			76

(*continued*)

TABLE I (*continued*)

Compound	mp, °C	bp (mm), °C	Remarks	References
$Cl_3BNH(CH_3)CHO$			Viscous liquid	76
$Cl_3BNH(CH_3)C(O)CH_3$	88–90			76
$Cl_3BNH(Ph)C(O)CH_3$	130			76
$Cl_3BNH(p\text{-}CH_3OC_6H_4)C(O)CH_3$	103–104			76
Cl_3BNHF_2			Stable at −130°	77
$Cl_3BN(CH_3)_3$	243			65,78
$Cl_3BN(C_2H_5)_3$	92–93.5			79,80
$Cl_3BN(Ph)_3$			Unstable at room temp. *in vacuo*	82
$Cl_3BNC_5H_5$	113–114 (decomp.)			81,82
$Cl_3BN \equiv CCH_3$	195–200 (decomp.)			75,83
$Cl_3BN(p\text{-}CH_3C_6H_4)_3$				82
$Cl_3BN \equiv CC_2H_5$	142			83,84
$Cl_3BN \equiv CC_3H_7$	92			83,84
$Cl_3BN \equiv CC_4H_9$	34–38	61 (12)		83,84
$Cl_3BN \equiv CC_6H_5$	167			84
$Cl_3BN \equiv CCH{=}CH_2$	135–141			83,84
$Cl_3BN(CH_3)_2C(O)H$	119–122			76
$Cl_3BN(CH_3)_2C(O)CH_3$	99–101			76
$Cl_3BN \equiv CCH_2Ph$	131–134			83
$Cl_3BN \equiv C(p\text{-}CH_3C_6H_4)$	136–142			83
$Cl_3BN \equiv C(p\text{-}ClC_6H_4)$	127–133			83
$Cl_3BN \equiv C(p\text{-}CH_3OC_6H_4)$	107–113			83
$Br_3BNH_2COCH_3$	98–99			76
$Br_3BNH(CH_3)COCH_3$	104–106			76
$Br_3BN(CH_3)_3$	238–240			85
$Br_3BN(Ph)_3$			No mp given	82
$Br_3BN(p\text{-}CH_3C_6H_4)_3$			No mp given	82
$Br_3BNC_5H_5$	128–129			86
$Br_3B \cdot$quinoline			No mp given	87
$Br_3B \cdot$4-picoline			No mp given	87
$Br_3BN(CH_3)_2CO(CH_3)$	110–114			76
$Br_3BN \equiv CH$	70			88
$(Br_3B)_2N(p\text{-}CH_3C_6H_4)_3$			No mp given	82
$H_2ClBN(C_2H_5)_3$	43	120(1)		40,47,89
$H_2ClBNH_2(CH_3)$	47			90
$H_2ClBNH(CH_3)_2$	18			90
$H_2ClBNC_5H_5$	45			90
$HCl_2BN(CH_3)_3$	85			90,91
$HCl_2BN(C_2H_5)_3$	5	132(1)		89
Ph_2ClBNH_3			Softens at 175–180° but does not completely melt up to 250°	92
$Ph_2ClBNC_5H_5$	135–138			92
$Ph_2ClBN(C_2H_5)_3$	125–133			93
$Ph_2ClB \cdot$piperidine		165–175		94
$Ph_2ClB \cdot 2NH_3$			Softens at 175–180° but does not melt even at 250°	93
$Ph_2ClB \cdot 2NH_2C_2H_5$	125–126			95
$(C_6H_4CH_2)_3BNH_3$	194–196			102
$(p\text{-Xylyl})_3BNH_3$	181–182 (decomp.)			102

(*continued*)

TABLE I (*continued*)

Compound	mp, °C	References
(α-Naphthyl)$_3$BNH$_3$	193–194	102
(PhCH=CH)$_3$BNC$_5$H$_5$	138–140 (decomp.)	103
Ph$_3$BNH$_3$	213–217	93,104–106
Ph$_3$B · quinoline	166–172	105,106
(C$_6$H$_4$CH$_2$)$_3$BNC$_5$H$_5$	129–131	102
(p-Xylyl)$_3$BNH$_2$CH$_3$	155–156 (decomp.)	102
(p-Xylyl)$_3$BNC$_5$H$_5$	146–148 (decomp.)	102
Ph$_3$BNH$_2$CH$_3$	208–209 (decomp.)	106
Ph$_3$BNH$_2$C$_3$H$_7$	101–102	106
Ph$_3$BNH$_2$C$_6$H$_5$	138–140	106
Ph$_3$BNH(CH$_3$)$_2$	186–187	106
Ph$_3$BN(CH$_3$)$_3$	135–137 (decomp.)	106
Ph$_3$BNC$_5$H$_5$	214 (decomp.)	106
Ph$_3$B · quinalidine	110–112	106
Ph$_3$B · piperidine	213–214	106
Ph$_3$B · phenylhydrazine	138–140	106

The effects of strongly electron-withdrawing atoms and atoms which can, in principle, pi bond with nitrogen are exemplified in the ligands NF_3 and $N(SiH_3)_3$. Nitrogen trifluoride does not form an addition compound with BF_3. The strong electron-withdrawing tendency of fluorine atoms apparently causes the nitrogen to have insignificant donor ability. On the other hand, the ammonia adduct of BF_3 can be sublimed at 180° without apparent decomposition.[17] The violent detonation of B_2H_6–NF_3 mixtures precludes the determination of the existence of the entity NF_3BH_3.[18] Trisilylamine is a weak Lewis base; $(SiH_3)_3N \cdot BH_3$[19] and $(SiH_3)_3N \cdot BF_3$[20–23] are unstable at room temperature. It is assumed that the lone pair on the nitrogen can pi bond with silicon through vacant *d* orbitals, thereby minimizing the ability of nitrogen to behave as an electron-pair donor toward boron.

Sterically unhindered amine complexes of BH_3 and BF_3 are generally solids at room temperature; they are little affected by moisture and oxygen in the atmosphere. Quaternization of the boron through adduct formation stabilizes markedly the BH_3 and BF_3 boranes. Although most of the amine-boranes have not been thoroughly characterized in the solid state, it is usually assumed that they are simple, unambiguous substances. X-ray crystallographic studies have confirmed the molecular formulas H_3NBH_3[24–26] $(CH_3)_3NBH_3$,[27] H_3NBF_3,[28] $CH_3H_2NBF_3$,[28] and $(CH_3)_3NBF_3$.[28] Molecular weights in liquid ammonia are consistent with the monomeric formulas for H_3NBH_3,[29] H_3BNF_3,[30] $CH_3H_2BNH_3$,[30] $(CH_3)_2HNBH_3$,[30] and $(CH_3)_3NBF_3$.[31] Significant association has been observed in benzene solutions and has been attributed to the low dielectric constant of the solvent.

B. Principles of Syntheses

1. Preparation of Amine-Boranes through Direct Combination of Reactants

Many amine-boranes have been prepared through the direct combination of components. Table I lists the properties of compounds which have been prepared in this way. However, pure, stable amine-borane adducts containing the BH_3 group can not be prepared through the direct reaction of diborane with amine containing N—H bonds. They are generally prepared through other synthetic routes. The only reported exception is the reaction of diborane with ethylenediamine to give $H_3BNH_2CH_2CH_2NH_2BH_3$.[32,33] The reaction of diborane with amines containing N—H bonds can lead to ionic species, e.g., $H_2B(NH_3)_2^+BH_4^-$, or mixtures of ionic species and simple amine-borane adducts. Reactions of diborane with amines containing N—H bonds are discussed in Section III.

Amine-boranes which contain BH_2R or BHR_2 groups are more conveniently prepared through indirect methods of synthesis rather than direct combination of reactants because of difficulties in preparing and handling organodiboranes.

With the exception of boron trifluoride and organoderivatives of boron trifluoride (BF_2R and BFR_2), stable boron halide adducts with amines containing N—H, bonds, in general, have not been prepared. However, compounds prepared through combination with acetamides have been claimed. Protolysis of the boron-halogen bond occurs, resulting in the elimination of hydrogen halide and the formation of mixtures of ill-defined amino- and iminoboranes when a boron halide reacts with amines containing N—H bonds.[34]

$$2BI_3 + 9NH_3 \rightarrow B_2(NH)_3 + 6NH_4I$$

2. Preparations of Amine-Boranes by Indirect Methods

Amine-boranes containing N–H bonds and the BH_3 unit are best prepared through indirect reactions which do not involve cleavage of the hydrogen bridges of diborane by a nitrogen base. Table II is a list of the properties of compounds which have been prepared in this way. Indirect methods of synthesis fall into three classes and are discussed below.

TABLE II
Amine Boranes Prepared by Indirect Reactions

Compound	mp, °C	bp (mm), °C	Remarks	References
H_3BNH_3			Slowly evolves H at room temp.	19,107,108 108
$H_3BNH_2CH_3$	56			40,43
$H_3BNH_2C_2H_5$	19		Unstable at 20°	40,43
$H_3BNH_2(n\text{-}C_3H_7)$	45			40,43
$H_3BNH_2(\text{iso-}C_3H_7)$	65			40,43
$H_3BNH_2(n\text{-}C_4H_9)$	73			40,43
$H_3BNH_2(\text{iso-}C_4H_9)$	20			109
$H_3BNH_2C_{12}H_{25}$	38			109
$H_3BNH(CH_3)_2$	37	49 (0.01)		40,43,110, 111
$H_3BNH(C_2H_5)_2$	−18	84 (4)		40,109
$H_3BNH(n\text{-}C_3H_7)_2$	30			40,109
$H_3BNH(\text{iso-}C_3H_7)_2$	23	88 (1)		40,109
$H_3BNH(n\text{-}C_4H_9)_2$	15			40,113
$H_3BNH(\text{iso-}C_4H_9)_2$	19			40
$H_3BNH(\text{iso-Am})_2$	54–56			111
$H_3BNH(CH_2)_4CH_2$ (ring)	80–82			111
$H_3BN(CH_3)_3$	94–94.5	171 (est.)		40,114,115
$H_3BN(C_2H_5)_3$	−2	42 (10^{-4})		40,113,116
$H_3BN(C_3H_7)_3$	18			40,116
$H_3BN(C_4H_9)_3$	−28	80 (10^{-5})		40,116
$H_3BNC_5H_5$	10–12			43,113
$H_3B\cdot$acridine	225 (decomp.)			109
$H_3B\cdot$isoquinoline			Liquid, decomp. at 50°	109
$H_3B\cdot$quinalidine	112			109
$(H_3B)_2\cdot$piperazine			Decomp. at 250°	109
$H_3B\cdot(CH_2)_6N_4$			Decomp. at 300°	109
$H_3BNH_2NH_2$	61			117,118
$H_3B\cdot$picoline(2)	40			119
$H_3B\cdot$picoline(4)	72–73			119
$H_3BNH_2OCH_3$	53–58			117
F_3BNH_3	161–163			112,188
$F_3BNH_2C_2H_5$	89			112
F_3BNH_2OH			Decomp. at 180°	120
$F_3BN(C_2H_5)_3$	29.5			121
$F_3BN(C_4H_9)_3$	59–61			112
$Cl_3BNH_2CH_3$	126–128			122
$Cl_3BN(C_2H_5)_3$	92–93			113
$Cl_3BNC_5H_5$	115			123
Ph_3BNH_3			Decomp. at 226–230°	124
$(\text{iso-}C_3H_7)H_2BNC_5H_5$			Oil	125
$(n\text{-}C_4H_9)H_2BNC_5H_5$			Oil	125
$PhH_2BNC_5H_5$	80–83			125,126
$(p\text{-}ClC_6H_4)H_2BNC_5H_5$	61–62			125,126
$(p\text{-}CH_3C_6H_4)H_2BNC_5H_5$	63–65			125,126
$(C_6H_5CH_2)H_2BNC_5H_5$	105–106			125
$(p\text{-}CH_3OC_6H_4)H_2BNC_5H_5$	78–79			125,126
$(o\text{-}CH_3OC_6H_4)H_2BNC_5H_5$	55–56			126
$(\text{mesityl})H_2BNC_5H_5$	116–118			127
$Cl_2HBN(CH_3)_3$	151			128
$Ph_2HBNC_5H_5$	108–109			125,129
$CH_3F_2BN(CH_3)_3$	35			67

(continued)

TABLE II (*continued*)

Compound	mp, °C	bp (mm), °C	Remarks	References
$C_2H_5F_2BN(CH_3)_3$	23.9–25.3			96
$(C_6F_5)Cl_2BNC_5H_5$			No mp given	97
$H_2BrBNH_2CH_3$	10			90
$H_2BrBNH(CH_3)_2$	5–6			90
$H_2BrBN(CH_3)_3$	67			90
$H_2BrBNH_2[C(CH_3)_3]$	98			90
$H_2IBNH_2(CH_3)$	8–9			90
$H_2IBNH(CH_3)_2$	25			90
$H_2IBN(CH_3)_3$	73–74			90
$H_2IBNH_2[C(CH_3)_3]$	99			90
$(C_4H_9)_2BrB \cdot 2NC_5H_5$	125–132			98
$Ph_2(C\equiv CH)BNC_5H_5$	150			99
$Ph_2(C\equiv CCH_3)BNC_5H_5$	170			99
$Ph_2(C\equiv CC_6H_5)BNC_5H_5$	158			99
$Ph_2[C\equiv C(p\text{-}BrC_6H_4)]BNC_5H_5$	165			99
$(CH_3)H_2BN(CH_3)_3$	0.8	176.4 (760)		100
$(CH_3)_2HBN(CH_3)_3$	−18.0	171.4 (760)		100,134
$(n\text{-}C_4H_9)H_2BN(CH_3)_3$		72 (3.0)		36
$(sec\text{-}C_4H_9)H_2BN(CH_3)_3$		60 (2.5)		36
$(t\text{-}C_4H_9)H_2BN(CH_3)_3$		60 (3.5)		36
$(C_6H_{11})H_2BN(CH_3)_3$	40–41			36
$(C_6H_4CH_2)H_2BN(CH_3)_3$	58–60			36
$(CH_3)_3BNH_3$	56	110		101
$(CH_3)_3BN(CH_3)_3$	120			100
$(p\text{-}ClC_6H_4)_2HBNC_5H_5$	103–104			125
$(p\text{-}CH_3C_6H_4)_2HBNC_5H_5$	110–113			125
$(p\text{-}CH_3OC_6H_4)_2HBNC_5H_5$	109–110			125
$(p\text{-}CH_3C_6H_4)Ph_2BNH_3$			Decomp. at 189–191°	130
$(p\text{-}CH_3C_6H_4)Ph_2BNC_5H_5$	156–158			130
$(o\text{-}CH_3C_6H_4)Ph_2BNC_5H_5$	177–179			130
$(p\text{-}ClC_6H_4)_2PhBNH_3$	213–215			130
$(1\text{-}C_{10}H_7)Ph_2BNC_5H_5$			Decomp. at 175–180°	130
$(1\text{-}C_{10}H_7)_2PhBNC_5H_5$			Decomp. at 215–217°	130
$(1\text{-}C_{10}H_7)_2(o\text{-}CH_3C_6H_4)BNC_5H_5$	203–205			130
$(p\text{-}BrC_6H_4)_2(o\text{-}CH_3C_6H_4)BNC_5H_5$				130

a. Elimination Reactions

$$NR_3HCl + LiBH_4 \rightarrow R_3NBH_3 + H_2 + LiCl$$

$$NH_4Cl + LiBH_4 \rightarrow H_3NBH_3 + H_2 + LiCl$$

This type of reaction is based upon the fact that the N—H hydrogen in a quaternary nitrogen salt can be sufficiently protonic to react with an hydridic hydrogen in a borohydride salt. Such reactions are generally carried out in anhydrous diethyl ether, tetrahydrofuran, or glyme. Lithium borohydride is used because it is more soluble than the other alkali metal borohydrides which react very slowly in these solvents. A typical synthetic procedure for preparing an alkylamine-borane is given in Section II. C.2.a.

b. Displacement Reactions

$$B_2H_6 + 2\ \mathrm{O}\!\square \longrightarrow 2\ H_3BO\!\square$$

$$H_3BO\!\square + \begin{cases} NH_3 \longrightarrow H_3NBH_3 + \mathrm{O}\!\square \\ NHR_2 \longrightarrow HR_2NBH_3 + \mathrm{O}\!\square \end{cases}$$

Displacement reactions involve initial symmetrical cleavage of the hydrogen bridged bonds in diborane by an oxygen base such as tetrahydrofuran or tetrahydropyran, followed by the addition of ammonia or an amine which displaces the oxygen base to form the desired amine-borane. Diethyl ether is too weak an oxygen base to be used to cleave the bridge system of diborane.

There are two ways in which the $THFBH_3$ complex can be produced. The first procedure essentially requires the condensation of a given amount of diborane into a tube containing an excess of THF and warming the system to $-78°$ in order to form the complex. This procedure is potentially hazardous if relatively large quantities of diborane are to be used (20 mmoles of B_2H_6 or more). The second procedure is much safer. It involves generating diborane and passing it, as it is formed, on a stream of nitrogen, into the tetrahydrofuran. The advantage of this procedure is that at any given instant the concentration of free diborane is small, so that hazards due to sudden entrance of air to the system are minimized. This second procedure is described in the section which deals with detailed preparations.

c. Reduction of Alkoxy- and Aryloxy-Boron Compounds. Amine-alkyl- and arylboranes which contain at least one B—H bond have been prepared by reducing the appropriate oxyboron compound with lithium aluminum hydride in the presence of amine [35,36].

$$2\ (RBO)_3 + 3LiAlH_4 + 6NR_3' \rightarrow 6R_3'NBH_2R + 3LiAlO_2$$

$$2PhB(OEt)_2 + LiAlH_4 + 2NR_3' \rightarrow 2R_3'NBH_2Ph + LiAl(OEt)_4$$

$$4Ph_2BOH + LiAlH_4 + 4NR_3' \rightarrow 4R_3'NBHPh_2 + LiAl(OH)_4$$

The reactions outlined above are perhaps the most convenient methods for preparing such compounds. To start with the appropriate organo-diborane and treat it with an amine, presents a more difficult synthetic method. Preparative procedures are described in Sections II.C.2.c and II.C.2.d.

C. Preparative Procedures

1. Amine-Boranes by Direct Reaction

$$BR_3 + NR_3' \rightarrow R_3BNR_3'$$

a. Bench Equipment.[37] Many amine-boranes may be prepared by simply reacting the borane (e.g. B_2H_6, BF_3, $B(CH_3)_3$, etc.) with an amine in a suitable solvent. Some examples of amine-boranes which may be obtained in this manner are F_3BNH_3, $H_3BN(CH_3)_3$, and $(CH_3)_3BN(CH_3)_3$. A typical procedure is presented as follows.

Each side neck of a three-necked 1-liter flask is fitted with a one-hole stopper carrying a piece of 9-mm glass tubing which extends nearly to the bottom of the flask. The center neck is closed with another one-

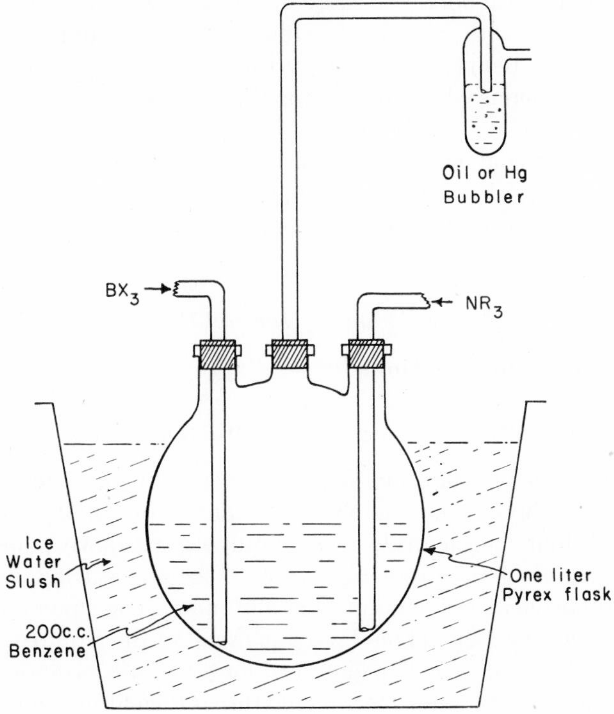

Fig. 1. Apparatus for preparation of amine-boranes by direct combination of reactants.

hole stopper bearing a short length of glass tubing which does not extend below the stopper and which is connected by means of Tygon tubing to a mercury or oil bubbler as shown in Figure 1. About 200 ml of a thoroughly dried inert solvent, such as benzene, is placed in the flask and the gas delivery tubes are adjusted to project slightly below the surface of the liquid. The flask is immersed in a large ice bath and the whole apparatus transferred to a hood.

Ammonia or the appropriate volatile amine is admitted to one of the side arms at a rate sufficient to cause bubbling in the blowout. Then the required amount of borane is admitted with its rate of flow adjusted so that there is no escape of gas through the bubbler. Most amine-boranes are solids which ordinarily separate from nonpolar organic solvents so that they can be filtered and purified by recrystallization or vacuum sublimation. If the product is found to be soluble in a particular solvent, the amine-borane is obtained by stripping off the solvent and purifying the residue by recrystallization or vacuum sublimation.

b. Vacuum Line Method.[38] A slight excess of amine is condensed with the appropriate borane, usually in the absence of a solvent, into a reaction chamber with stir-bar at −196°. The mixture is then slowly warmed to room temperature with stirring. The reaction tube should be opened to a mercury blow-out during this time as a precaution against a buildup of pressure. If the product is appreciably volatile, it may be purified by fractional condensation of the impure product into consecutive traps cooled with slush baths at appropriate temperatures. Vacuum sublimation may also prove to be a useful purification method as mentioned previously.

2. *Amine-Boranes by Indirect Reactions*

a. Elimination Reactions[39,40]

$$R_3NHCl + LiBH_4 \xrightarrow{Et_2O} R_3NBH_3 + LiCl + H_2$$

A flask equipped as shown in Figure 2 is charged with a slurry of dried and powdered alkylammonium chloride in anhydrous diethyl ether. A solution of lithium borohydride in anhydrous ether is slowly added to the slurry by means of the dropping funnel. Vigorous stirring and a dry nitrogen atmosphere are maintained at all times. The amount of alkylammonium salt used should be slightly in excess of the required stoichiometric quantity. Stirring is maintained for 3 hr after evolution of hydrogen ceases, and the crude reaction mixture is then filtered under nitrogen. The ether is removed from the filtrate under reduced pressure, and the amine-borane residue is further purified by vacuum sublimation.

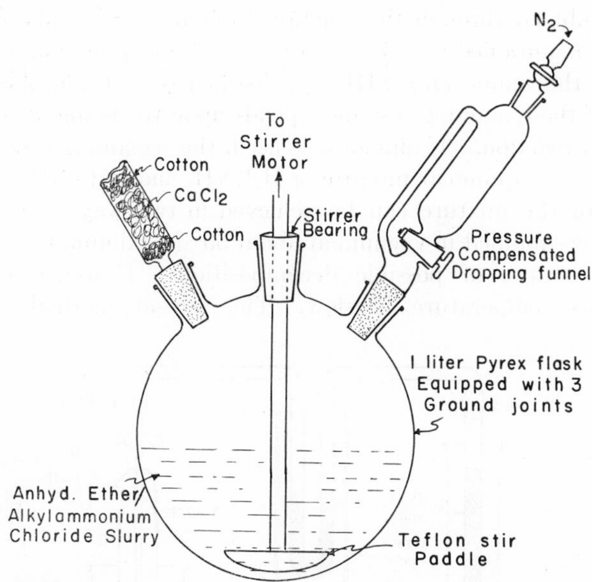

Fig. 2. Apparatus for preparation of amine-boranes by elimination reactions.

b. Displacement Reactions[41, 42]

$$\text{THF}\cdot BH_3 + NH_3 \longrightarrow H_3NBH_3 + \text{THF}$$

Ammonia-borane, methylamine-borane, and dimethylamine-borane have been prepared by this procedure. The apparatus used is shown below in Figure 3. It consists of a B_2H_6 generator (*A*) and a reaction tube *B*. About 20 ml of anhydrous THF, dried over $LiAlH_4$, is distilled into the evacuated reaction tube which is then connected to the U-trap of the B_2H_6 generator. This system is then thoroughly flushed with dry nitrogen and the cooling jacket, U-trap, and the reaction tube are maintained at −78° with a Dry Ice–isopropanol slush. About 2 g of powdered $LiAlH_4$ and 100 ml of anhydrous ether (reagent grade) are introduced to the round-bottomed section of *A*, and a 10-ml quantity of $BF_3O(C_2H_5)_2$ is poured into the dropping funnel. While a stream of nitrogen is continually flowing through the system, $BF_3O(C_2H_5)_2$ is allowed to drop slowly into the stirred suspension of $LiAlH_4$ in ether. Half an hour after the last drop of etherate has been added to the diborane generator, the reaction vessel, with stopcocks closed, is removed from the apparatus and connected to a vacuum line. About 10 ml of anhydrous amine (NH_3, CH_3NH_2, or $(CH_3)_2NH$) is distilled onto the THF solution at

−196° or bubbled through the reaction tube at −78°. The reaction tube is then maintained at −78° and is stirred for approximately 1 hr, after which the amine and THF are distilled off. From this point, treatment of the remaining residue depends upon the amine used in the displacement reaction. If ammonia is used, the remaining residue consists of about an equimolar mixture of H_3BNH_3 and $BH_2(NH_3)_2{}^+BH_4{}^-$. Separation of the mixture can be achieved in two ways. Ammonia-borane can be sublimed in vacuum at about 50° (maximum temperature to be used because of possible decomposition). However, sublimation at this temperature is slow. The second method involves

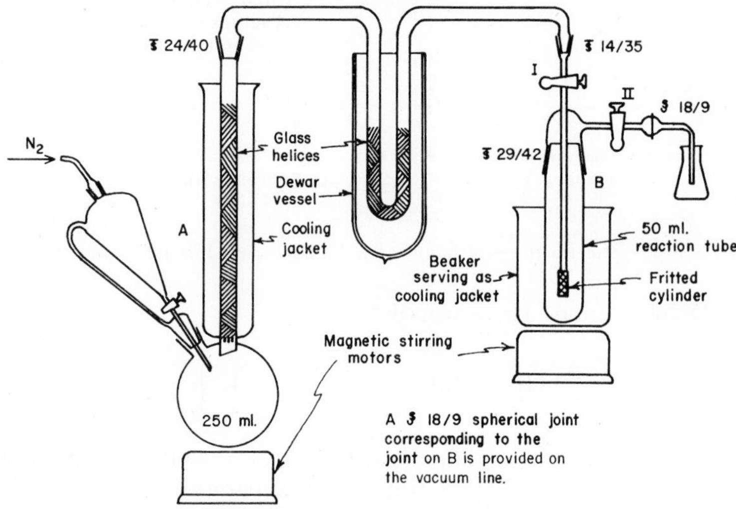

Fig. 3. Diborane generator and reaction tube.

extraction from the residue, using diethyl ether as a solvent. It is inadvisable to use THF or glyme as a solvent because of the solubility of $BH_2(NH_3)_2{}^+BH_4{}^-$. The ether should be previously dried over $LiAlH_4$, and the extraction should be carried out under anhydrous conditions, preferably using a vacuum line extractor such as the one shown in Figure 4. The reaction mixture is placed on the frit and the system is evacuated. Anhydrous ether is distilled onto the frit by filling the jacket of the extractor with Dry Ice–isopropanol. By immersing the tube in a −78° slush, ether flows through the frit. Repeated extractions are carried out by simply recondensing the ether from the bottom tube onto the frit. Ammonia-borane is isolated by distilling away the ether at −65°.

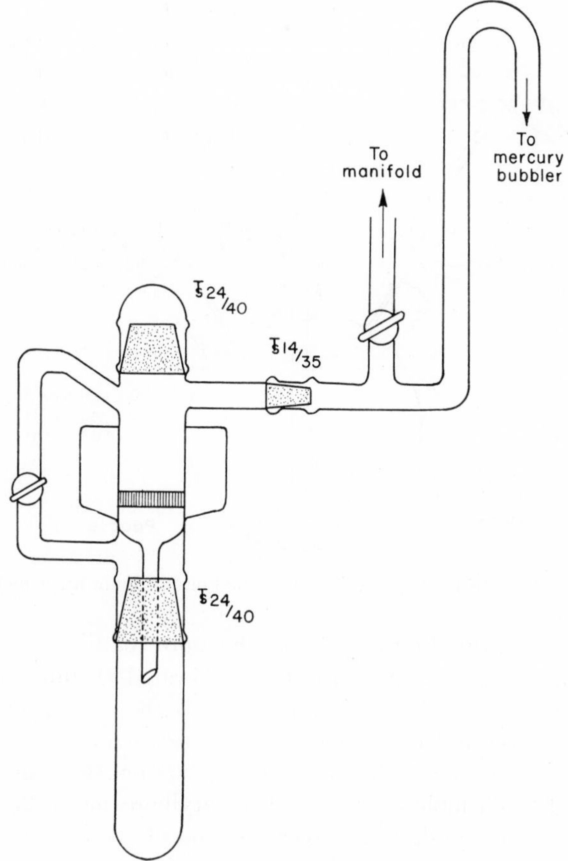

Fig. 4. Vacuum line extractor.

Methylamine-borane and dimethylamine-borane are formed in essentially quantitative yields in the procedure outlined above and may be purified by vacuum sublimation at about 50°. They are not highly sensitive to moisture and can be handled in the open if the humidity is not high.

c. Reduction of Alkyl- and Arylboroxines[36]

$$2(RBO)_3 + 3LiAlH_4 + 6NR_3' \xrightarrow[35°]{(C_2H_5)_2O} 6R_3'NBH_2R + 3LiAlO_2$$

Lithium aluminum hydride (0.10 mole) is dissolved in 100 ml anhydrous diethyl ether by stirring and refluxing under nitrogen. The solution is transferred under nitrogen to a dry, three-necked, flask of about 500-ml capacity equipped as shown in Figure 5. A tertiary amine

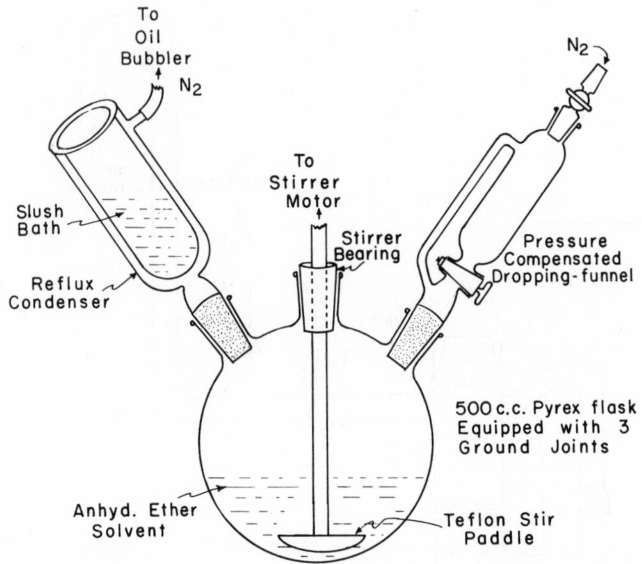

Fig. 5. Apparatus for preparation of amine-boranes by indirect methods.

(0.17 mole) is measured into the flask (the more volatile amines, such as trimethylamine are best measured in a calibrated vacuum system and then distilled into the flask), and a cooling bath (usually Dry Ice–isopropanol) is placed in the condenser trap to retain all the reaction components. The solution is then heated to reflux under a slow stream of nitrogen and 0.033 mole of the alkyl- or arylboroxine in 25 ml of dry diethyl ether is added dropwise over a period of about 1 hr. Vigorous stirring and a slow passage of nitrogen are maintained during this addition, and the reaction mixture is refluxed for one additional hour, then cooled in an ice bath. Excess hydride is destroyed by slow addition of 6.5 ml of water. The mixture is filtered and the ether removed from the filtrate under reduced pressure. The product may be obtained in pure form by recrystallization or vacuum sublimation of the residue.

d. Reduction of Dialkyl- and Diarylboric Esters[35]

$$4R_2BOR'' + LiAlH_4 + 4NR_3' \xrightarrow{(C_2H_5)_2O} 4R_3'NBHR_2 + LiAl(OR'')_4$$

A solution of lithium aluminum hydride (5 g) in 500 ml of anhydrous diethyl ether is prepared by stirring and refluxing under nitrogen. The solution is transferred under nitrogen to a three-necked flask equipped as shown in Figure 5. A solution of 0.12 mole of dialkyl- or diarylborinate in 100 ml of anhydrous diethyl ether is added slowly with stirring to the flask which is maintained at about −70°. After the addition has been completed the contents of the flask are allowed to warm to 0° with stirring, and then a solution of 0.12 mole of tertiary amine in 25 ml of ice water is added. The mixture is immediately filtered and the precipitate washed with ether. The combined ether solution is shaken three times with portions of ice water, separated, dried over magnesium sulfate and evaporated under reduced pressure at −10°. Generally the product may be purified by recrystallization from benzene or another suitable organic solvent.

III. UNSYMMETRICAL CLEAVAGE OF DIBORANE BY AMINES; ANALOGS OF THE DIAMMINEDIHYDRIDOBORON(1+) CATION, $H_2B(NH_3)_2^+$

A. Introduction

Diborane reacts with a variety of electron pair donors to yield adducts of empirical composition LBH_3, where L represents the donor species. These reactions are intimately associated with the bridge system of diborane. In principle, one can imagine that the bridge system is cleaved in one of two possible ways. If a simple borane adduct is produced, the reaction is called a "symmetrical cleavage" reaction implying, though not necessarily demonstrating, that hydrogens in the bridge system are displaced in the following way:

```
H   ¦ H     H
 \  ¦/ \   /
  B ¦    B        +  2L  →  2BH2L2+BH4−
 /  ¦\ /   \
H   ¦ H     H
```

Typical ligands which produce "symmetrical" cleavage are THF,[131] $O(CH_3)_2$,[132] $NH(CH_3)_2$,[44] $N(CH_3)_3$,[19] $S(CH_3)_2$,[133] and $P(CH_3)_3$.[136]

If an ionic product $BH_2L_2^+BH_4^-$ is produced, the reaction is called an "unsymmetrical cleavage" reaction, implying the following scheme:

```
H  .  H     H
 \  `/ \   /
  B   `.  B       +  2L  →  2LBH3
 /  \  /`.  \
H    H   `  H
```

In addition to the amine bases cited below, $OS(CH_3)_2$ is the only other well-documented example of a base which produces "unsymmetrical" cleavage upon reaction with diborane.[135]

The controlled addition of diborane to ammonia leads to apparent "unsymmetrical" cleavage of the hydrogen-bridged bonds, resulting in the formation of the "diammoniate of diborane" [diamminedihydridoboron(1+)hydroborate].[41,136–144] Direct reaction of diborane with an organoamine containing an N–H bond has been shown in the cases of NH_2CH_3 and $HN(CH_3)_2$ to produce mixtures of "symmetrical" and "unsymmetrical" cleavage products of diborane.[44] Earlier literature suggested that simple borane adducts are formed in these reactions.[30,145,146] Factors which determine whether a Lewis base will cleave diborane "symmetrically" or "unsymmetrically" are still not understood. However, it appears that in the case of the methylamines that "symmetrical" cleavage is more likely to occur with increasing methyl substitution of the nitrogen.[44]

There is evidence which indicates that cleavage of the bridge system of diborane takes place in stepwise fashion. It has been suggested that the first step involves the rupture of one hydrogen-bridge bond,

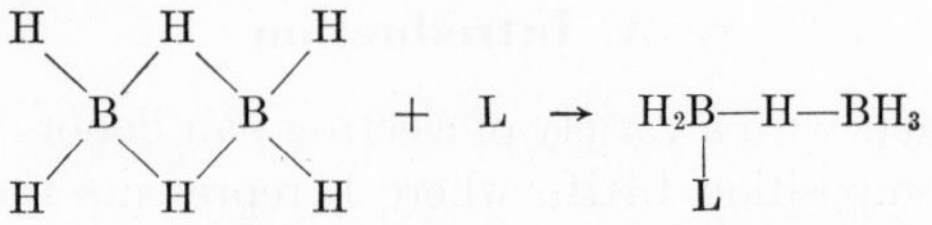

$$B_2H_6 \text{ (H}_2\text{B(}\mu\text{-H)}_2\text{BH}_2\text{)} + L \rightarrow H_2B(L)\text{—H—}BH_3$$

while the second step involves rupture of the second bridge bond, with the point of attack determining whether the cleavage is "symmetrical" or "unsymmetrical."[142,144]

$$H_2B(L)\text{—H—}BH_3 + L \rightarrow H_2BL_2{}^+BH_4{}^- \quad \text{"unsymmetrical" cleavage}$$

$$H_2B(L)\text{—H—}BH_3 + L \rightarrow 2\ LBH_3 \quad \text{"symmetrical" cleavage}$$

The postulated intermediates in the reaction of diborane with trimethylamine and ammonia have been prepared[147].

$$B_2H_6 + N(CH_3)_3 \xrightarrow{CH_2Cl_2} H_2B(N(CH_3)_3)\text{—H—}BH_3$$

$$B_2H_6 + NH_3 \xrightarrow{CH_2Cl_2} H_2B(NH_3)\text{—H—}BH_3$$

These intermediates react with a second mole of base in the following way,

$$H_2B(N(CH_3)_3)\text{—H—}BH_3 + N(CH_3)_3 \rightarrow 2\ (CH_3)_3NBH_3$$

$$H_2B(NH_3)\text{—H—}BH_3 + NH_3 \rightarrow H_2B(NH_3)_2{}^+BH_4{}^-$$

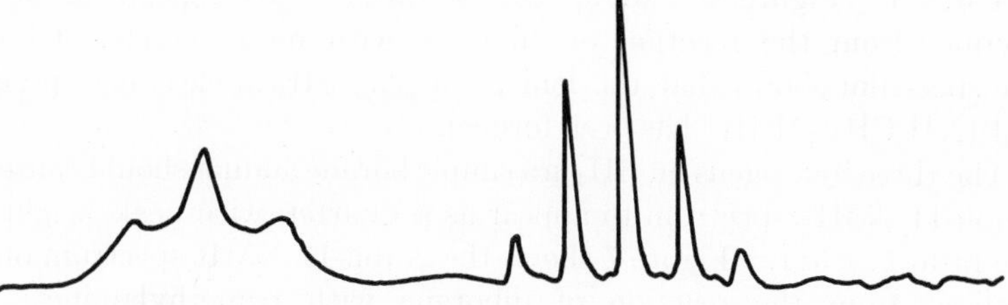

Fig. 6. Boron-11 NMR spectrum of $BH_2(NH_2CH_3)_2^+ BH_4^-$.

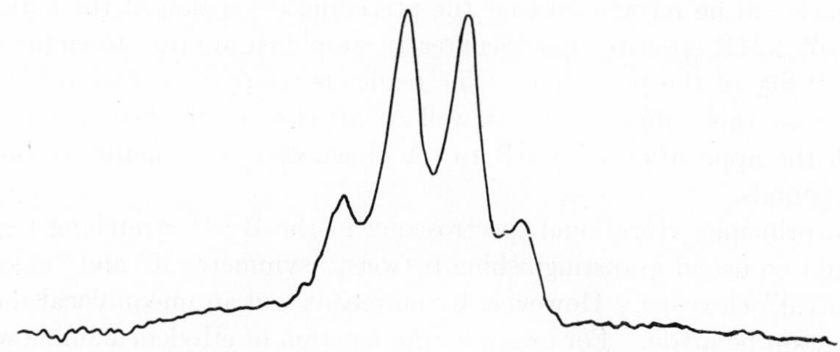

Fig. 7. Boron-11 NMR spectrum of $(CH_3)_3NBH_3$.

giving the same product observed from the direct reaction of diborane with ammonia and with trimethylamine.

Although the examples cited above are the only demonstrated cases of "unsymmetrical" cleavage of diborane by an amine base, it is not unlikely that other examples will be found. The higher boron hydrides, notably B_4H_{10},[149–151] undergo reactions with electron-pair donors which also can be classified as "symmetrical" and "unsymmetrical" cleavage.

Since "symmetrical" and "unsymmetrical" cleavage products have the same empirical composition, the type of cleavage cannot be determined through chemical analysis. The best method for distinguishing between the ionic product, $H_2BL_2^+BH_4^-$, and the simple borane adduct involves the application of boron-11 NMR spectroscopy. In general, the number of protons which are directly bonded to boron determines the multiplet character of the boron-11 NMR spectrum, providing other atoms which are bonded to boron have nuclei which do not spin-couple with the boron nucleus.

The two hydrogens on the cation $BH_2L_2^+$ should cause the boron-11 NMR spectrum to appear as a triplet, with peak heights in the ratio 1:2:1, while the four hydrogens in BH_4^- cause the boron-11 NMR spectrum of this ion to appear as a quintet with peak heights in the ratio

1:4:6:4:1. Figure 6[44] shows the boron-11 NMR spectrum of the product from the reaction of diborane with methylamine. Clearly, the spectrum shows that the ionic, "unsymmetrical-cleavage" product $H_2B(NH_2CH_3)_2{}^+BH_4{}^-$ has been formed.

The three hydrogens on BH_3 in a simple borane adduct should cause the boron-11 NMR spectrum to appear as a quartet, with peak heights in the ratio 1:3:3:1. Figure 7 shows the boron-11 NMR spectrum of the product from the reaction of diborane with trimethylamine. The spectrum shows that the "symmetrical-cleavage" product $(CH_3)_3NBH_3$ was formed in the reaction.

It should be recognized that the preceding discussion of the application of NMR spectroscopy was greatly simplified in order to emphasize the utility of the technique. The reader is referred to standard references on this subject[152–154] as well as articles which deal specifically with the application of NMR to the elucidation of structure of boron compounds.

In principle, vibrational spectroscopy in the B—H stretching region should be useful in distinguishing between "symmetrical" and "unsymmetrical" cleavage. However, by no means can an unequivocal interpretation be made. For example, the reaction of ethylenediamine with diborane produces "symmetrical" cleavage, as shown by boron-11 NMR. On the other hand, infrared spectra suggest an "unsymmetrical-cleavage" product.[51,52]

A chemical test for "unsymmetrical" and "symmetrical" cleavage has been described by Schultz and Ring.[155] It is based upon the observation that ammonium borohydride decomposes at temperatures above −20° to yield one mole of hydrogen per mole of ammonium borohydride.[143]

The test involves addition of ammonium chloride to the unknown compound. The mixture is then dissolved in liquid ammonia and the solvent is removed at low temperature. If borohydride ion is present in the unknown sample, some NH_4BH_4 will form through metathesis, and hydrogen will be liberated as the solid reaction product is warmed to room temperature. In the absence of borohydride, no hydrogen is produced since the ammonium ion is not sufficiently protonic to attack the BH_3 group in an amine-borane at room temperature. The evolution of hydrogen in this test indicates the presence of borohydride ion and that "unsymmetrical" cleavage of diborane occurred in the reaction with the amine. The absence of evolved hydrogen indicates "symmetrical" cleavage of diborane. An estimate of the amount of borohydride present is determined by measuring the amount of hydrogen evolved. This procedure was used as the first chemical test to indicate the borohydride structure of $H_2B(NH_3)_2{}^+BH_4{}^-$.[143]

Although relatively few bases are known which will produce the cation $BH_2L_2^+$ upon reaction with diborane, it is still possible to make, through indirect methods, a great variety of salts containing different ligands on boron.[156–159] Some of these ions in combination with appropriate anions are extremely resistant to hydrolytic and oxidative attack. Table III lists most of the known bis(amine)dihydridoboron (1$^+$)salts.

B. Principles of Syntheses

"Unsymmetrical" cleavage products such as $H_2B(NH_3)_2^+BH_4^-$ and $H_2B(NH_2CH_3)_2^+BH_4^-$ are most easily prepared by the direct reaction of the components at low temperature. While the preparations are straightforward in principle, in practice they require a great deal of care in order to prevent side reactions. Detailed synthetic procedures are described in Section III.C.

The preparation of salts containing the $BH_2(NH_3)_2^+$ ion can be achieved in several ways. The most straightforward method for preparing halide salts is outlined below.[143,160]

$$H_2B(NH_3)_2^+BH_4^- + HX \xrightarrow{\text{glyme}} H_2B(NH_3)_2^+X^- + {}^1/_2B_2H_6 + H_2$$

where X = Cl, Br, or I

Presumably any strong protonic acid can be used to prepare salts containing the conjugate base of that acid as the anion.

Another useful synthetic route to bis(amine)dihydridoboron(1$^+$) salts involves the action of ammonium halides on amine-boranes containing the BH_3 group.[156]

$$R_3NBH_3 + R_3'NH^+X^- \xrightarrow{100\text{–}180°} H_2B(NR_3)(NR_3')^+X^- + H_2$$

where X = I$^-$, and R and R′ are alkyl groups such as those shown in Table III.

Less direct synthetic procedures have also proved to be useful for preparing cations which contain ligands other than ammonia.[157–159]

$$NaBH_4 + R_{3-n}H_nNHCl \rightarrow NaCl + R_{3-n}H_nNBH_3 + H_2$$

$$R_{3-n}H_nNBH_3 + HCl \xrightarrow{Et_2O} H_2 + R_{3-n}H_nNBH_2Cl$$

$$R_3NBH_2X + \begin{cases} RNH_2 \rightarrow H_2B(NR_3)(NH_2R)^+X^- \\ R_2NH \rightarrow H_2B(NR_3)(NHR_2)^+X^- \end{cases}$$

where X = Cl, Br, or I, and R represents alkyl groups such as those shown in Table III.

Even though bis(amine)dihydridoboron(1$^+$) cations are very stable toward hydrolysis, the B—H hydrogens are readily substituted by reagents which are known to produce free radicals.[156] Thus the bis-

TABLE III
Bis(amine)dihydridoboron(1+) Salts

Compound	mp, °C	bp (mm), °C	Remarks	References
$H_2B(NH_3)_2{}^+Cl^-$				143,160–162
$H_2B(NH_3)_2{}^+Br^-$				160,161
$H_2B(NH_3)_2{}^+I^-$				160,163
$H_2B(NH_3)_2{}^+BF_4{}^-$				160,164
$H_2B(NH_3)_2{}^+B_3H_8{}^-$				151,160
$H_2B(CH_3NH_2)_2{}^+Cl^-$	76–78			157
$H_2B[(CH_3)_2NH]_2{}^+Cl^-$	78			157
$H_2B[(C_2H_5)_3N][CH_3NH_2]{}^+Cl^-$	73			157
$H_2B[NC_5H_5]_2{}^+Cl^-$	93			157
$H_2B[t\text{-}C_4H_9NH_2]_2{}^+Cl^-$	182 (decomp.)			157
$H_2B[(NC_5H_5)(t\text{-}C_4H_9NH_2)]{}^+Cl^-$	168–171 (decomp.)			157
$H_2B[(NH_3)(t\text{-}C_4H_9NH_2)]{}^+Cl^-$	164			157
$H_2B[(C_2H_5)_3N][t\text{-}C_4H_9NH_2]{}^+Cl^-$	183			157
$H_2B(C_3H_7NH_2)_2{}^+Cl^-$	115			157
$H_2B(t\text{-}C_4H_9NH_2)_2{}^+Br^-$	186			157
$H_2B(t\text{-}C_4H_9NH_2)_2{}^+I^-$	202			157
$H_2B(t\text{-}C_4H_9NH_2)_2{}^+AlCl_4{}^-$	>300			157
$H_2B(t\text{-}C_4H_9NH_2)_2{}^+FeCl_4{}^-$	135 (decomp.)			157
$H_2B(t\text{-}C_4H_9NH_2)_2{}^+B(Ph)_4{}^-$				157
$(H_2B[N(CH_3)_3]_2{}^+)_2B_{12}H_{12}{}^{=}$	260–270 (decomp.)			156
$H_2B[N(CH_3)_3]_2{}^+PF_6{}^-$	200–205 (decomp.)			156
$H_2B[N(CH_3)_3]_2{}^+ICl_2{}^-$	150			156
$H_2B[N(CH_3)_3]_2{}^+AuCl_4{}^-$				156
$H_2B[N(CH_3)_2C_2H_5]_2{}^+PF_6{}^-$	65			156
$H_2B[N(CH_3)(C_2H_5)_2]_2{}^+PF_6{}^-$	135–136			156

$H_2B(CH_3\overline{NCH_2(CH_2)_3C}H_2)_3{}^+PF_6{}^-$	108–109		156
$[H_2B(TMED)^+]_2B_{12}H_{12}{}^{=}$	340–350 (decomp.)	TMED = tetramethyl-ethylenediamine	156
$H_2B(TMED)^+Cl^-$			156
$H_2B(TMED)^+PF_6{}^-$	240–244 (decomp.)		156
$H_2B\left[\begin{matrix}CH_3N\\CH_3N\end{matrix}\right]^+PF_6{}^-$	240–250 (decomp.)		156
$H_2B\left[\begin{matrix}(CH_3)_2N \quad N(CH_3)_2\\ \quad CH_3\end{matrix}\right]^+$			156
$[(NC)_2CC(H)C(CN)_2]^-$	95–96		156
$H_2B(bipy)^+PF_6{}^-$	170 (decomp.)	bipy = bipyridyl	156
$H_2B[N(CH_3)_3][N(C_2H_5)(CH_3)_2]^+PF_6{}^-$	160–165		156

(trimethylamine)dichloroboron(1+) cation, $Cl_2B[N(CH_3)_3]_2^+$, is produced through the action of ICl on the parent cation. In similar fashion, cations of composition $HXB(NR_2)_2^+$ (X = Cl or Br), $X_2B(NR_3)_2^+$ (X = F, Cl, or Br), and $Cl(F)B(NR_3)_2^+$ have been produced.

C. Preparative Procedures

1. Diamminedihydridoboron(1+) Hydroborate

$$B_2H_6 + 2NH_3 \rightarrow H_2B(NH_3)_2^+BH_4^-$$

There are two basic procedures by which $H_2B(NH_3)_2^+BH_4^-$ can be prepared: One method is used for the preparation of small quantities (2–4 mmoles) of this compound,[142] while the other method has been scaled up to 0.5 mole yields.[41]

The small-scale method involves condensing a thin film of ammonia along the walls and bottom of a cylindrical reaction tube, 25 mm in diameter. Diborane, 2–4 mmoles, is then condensed from one to several inches above the ammonia and the entire reactor is warmed slowly from −140° to about −80° in a period of about 8 hr. During this time the diborane vaporizes and adds to the surface of the solid ammonia. Addition is evidenced by a marked decrease in pressure of diborane in the system. Since the addition depends upon the surface available, the ammonia is in excess by at least a 4:1 mole ratio. When the temperature of the system reaches −80°, the tube is thermostated in a Dry Ice–isopropanol bath at −78° and all the excess ammonia is sublimed, leaving behind solid $H_2B(NH_3)_2^+BH_4^-$.

The large-scale procedure involves passing a stream of diborane, diluted in a stream of N_2, into liquid ammonia at −78°. It employs the apparatus shown in Figure 3 and is similar to the procedure described in Section II.C.2.b for the preparation of H_3BNH_3, using comparable amounts of starting material, except that the diborane is bubbled through liquid ammonia in reaction tube *B* rather than through THF. The solution of $H_2B(NH_3)_2^+BH_4^-$ is frozen in liquid N_2, and NH_3 is sublimed at −78°. $H_2B(NH_3)_2^+BH_4^-$ is obtained in almost quantitative yield by this procedure; it is a white, microcrystalline, free-flowing solid which is stable in vacuum up to 80°.

Using the same procedures, $BH_2(NH_2CH_3)_2^+BH_4^-$ and $BH_2(NH(CH_3)_2)_2^+BH_4^-$ can be prepared. However, in these reactions symmetrical cleavage products $H_3BNH_2CH_3$ and $H_3BNH(CH_3)_2$ are also formed. The unsymmetrical cleavage products $H_2B(NH_2CH_3)_2^+BH_4^-$ and $H_2B(NH(CH_3)_2)_2^+BH_4^-$ are liquids at room temperature, readily splitting out hydrogen in vacuum. They have not been well characterized.

2. *Bis(trimethylamine)dihydridoboron(1+) Iodine*[156]

$$H_3BN(CH_3)_3 + (CH_3)_3NH^+I^- \xrightarrow{100\text{–}175^\circ} H_2B[N(CH_3)_3]_2^+ I^- + H_2$$

A 100-ml heavy-walled glass tube is charged with 2.34 g (32 mmoles) of $H_3BN(CH_3)_3$ and 6.0 g (32 mmoles) of $(CH_3)_3NH^+I^-$ (prepared from $(CH_3)_3N$ and aqueous KI; recrystallized from methanol) and heated for 10–12 hr at 100° and then for 8 hr at 175°. The reaction tube is then connected to a vacuum line, cooled to −196°, and opened. At this point, if it is desired, the quantity of hydrogen produced in the reaction may be measured in the vacuum system. After removal of the hydrogen, the tube is warmed to about 80° and all volatile materials are pumped off leaving 7–8 g of white residue. The solid can be recrystallized from ethanol giving the product, bis(trimethylamine)dihydridoboron(1+) iodide, as white needles.

IV. AMINOBORANES, BIS(AMINO)BORANES, TRIS(AMINO)-BORANES, AND CYCLOBORAZANES

A. Introduction

Monomeric aminoboranes are characterized by a structure in which boron and nitrogen are coordinately unsaturated $>$B—N$<$. Formally they are analogous to ethylene and its derivatives. The creation of a pi system by back donation of the lone pair of electrons on nitrogen to the p_z orbital of boron gives a system which is, in principle, analogous to the carbon–carbon double bond. In point of fact, however, this formal picture is misleading. While there is some evidence for back donation, the properties of the monomers suggest that the lone pair is essentially localized on the nitrogen. Evidence for some double-bond character is offered in the form of NMR spectroscopy which indicates the presence of *cis–trans* isomers of compounds such as $(CH_3)(C_6H_5)\cdot BN(C_6H_5)(CH_3)$. However, isomers have not been isolated from solution. NMR spectra also indicate a significant barrier to rotation about the boron–nitrogen bond (10 kcal/mole) for the compound $(CH_3)(C_6H_5)BN(CH_3)_2$,[165] but this rotational barrier is somewhat smaller than that in ethylene (80 kcal/mole). Extended Hückel-type molecular orbital calculations[166] indicate back donation between the lone pair on nitrogen and the vacant p_z orbital on boron. However, they also show that, due to the greater electron-withdrawing ability of nitrogen a greater amount of change is transferred from boron to nitrogen through the sigma bond than from nitrogen to boron through the pi bond, resulting in a larger net negative charge on nitrogen than on boron.

In view of this situation, it is perhaps best to represent the charge distribution in the following way:

$$>{}^{+\delta}\text{B—N}^{\delta-}<$$

With the exception of sterically hindered aminoboranes such as 2,6-dimethylpiperidino-dichloroborane (**17**), almost all of the monomeric

CH_3

$N-BCl_2$

CH_3

(**17**)

aminoboranes show some tendency to associate. The lone pair on nitrogen forms a sigma bond with the vacant boron orbital through intermolecular association, $-(\overset{|}{\underset{|}{\text{B}}}-\overset{|}{\underset{|}{\text{N}}})_n-$. Two types of associated aminoboranes are known. One type, the poly(aminoboranes), consist of ill-defined polymers which appear to be chainlike and of indefinite chain length. The second type, the cycloborazanes, consist of well-defined crystalline species which are rings that are structural analogs of the cyclic hydrocarbons. The cycloborazanes show significantly greater thermal and hydrolytic stability than the less well-defined poly(aminoboranes).

Aminoborane chains poly(aminoboranes) have been reported in the case of BH_2NH_2 in which chain lengths of 3–4 units have been observed.[167,168] In the case of $(CH_3)_2NBH_2$ a chain length of 10 units has been reported.[428] This latter material exists only at low temperature, breaking down into monomeric and dimeric species at room temperature.

The common ring sizes observed for the cycloborazanes are the four- and six-membered rings. The eight- and ten-membered rings $(BH_2NH_2)_4$ and $(BH_2NH_2)_5$ are the only reported examples of saturated B—N rings larger than six.[170]

The unsubstituted aminoborane species BH_2NH_2 shows the greatest tendency to associate. It has been trapped at low temperature and identified by mass spectroscopy.[170] With increasing substitution the tendency to associate decreases. Thus, for example $(CH_3)_2BN(CH_3)_2$ exists as a monomer.[171–173] Equilibria, such as illustrated by the following equation,[174]

$$2Cl_2BNMe_2 \rightleftharpoons Cl_2B\begin{matrix} Me_2 \\ N \\ / \quad \backslash \\ \\ \backslash \quad / \\ N \\ Me_2 \end{matrix}BCl_2$$

have been observed for a variety of aminoboranes. Because the boron in the monomer is not quaternized, the monomer is invariably more reactive with respect to hydrolytic instability than the dimer. Table IV summarizes available data with respect to equilibria between monomer and dimer for the methyl, phenyl, and halo derivatives of the aminoboranes.

TABLE IV
Aminoboranes

Compound[a]	State of association
Methyl derivatives	
CH_3HNBH_2	Trimeric in the solid state
$(CH_3)_2NBH_2$	Exists chiefly as a dimer
$H_2NB(CH_3)_2$	Exists in a monomer–dimer equilibrium
$(CH_3)_2NBHCH_3$	Almost totally monomeric in the vapor but exists in monomer–dimer equilibrium in liquid state which strongly favors dimer but is slow moving
$CH_3HNB(CH_3)_2$	Monomer–dimer equilibrium
$(CH_3)_2NB(CH_3)_2$	Does not polymerize
Phenyl derivatives	
$H_2NB(Ph)_2$	Dimeric in benzene solution
$CH_3HNB(Ph)_2$	Slowly dimerizes at room temperature
$(CH_3)_2NB(Ph)_2$	Monomeric but slightly associated in benzene
Halogen derivatives	
Me_2NBF_2	Dimer as solid at 25°, but mass spectrum indicates complete dissociation in gas phase in vacuum, decomposes in ether solution and slowly in dry air
Me_2NBCl_2	Monomer when formed (mp −43°), when allowed to stand several days at R.T. a crystalline solid dimer form results, mp 142.4 (sealed tube), stable
Me_2NBBr_2	Dimerizes on standing but much more slowly than the chloro compound.

[a] References for these compounds can be found in Table V.

It is of interest to note that cyclodiborazane, which exits as a stable crystalline solid, isomerizes completely to cyclotriborazane in solution

TABLE V
Monoaminoboranes and Cycloborazanes

Compound	mp, °C	bp (mm), °C	Remarks	References
H_2BNH_2			Mass spectral evidence	170
$(H_2BNH_2)_2$			Sublimes *in vacuo* at 30° B^{11} NMR, t (+29.2 ppm)[a]	170
$(H_2BNH_2)_3$			Sublimes at 100° but does not melt up to 150° where it decomposes B^{11} NMR, t (+29.2 ppm)[a]	170,175 176,177
$(H_2BNH_2)_4$			Does not sublime	170
$(H_2BNH_2)_5$			Does not sublime	170
$[H_2BN(CH_3)_2]_2$	73.5			145,178–180
$[H_2BN(C_2H_5)_2]_2$	47		In equilibrium with monomer at room temp. and above	145,181–183
$[H_2BN(H)CH_3]_3$			Two geometric isomers isolated	184,185
$[H_2BN(CH_3)_2]_3$	97.0–97.8			254
$C_4H_9(H)BN(CH_3)_2$		114	B^{11} NMR, d (+12.1 ppm)[a]	186
sec-$C_4H_9(H)BN(CH_3)_2$		49 (91)	B^{11} NMR, two d's (+12.3 and −25.5 ppm)[a]	186
t-$C_4H_9(H)BN(CH_3)_2$		40 (81)	B^{11} NMR, two d's (+13.7 and −25.5 ppm)[a]	186
t-$C_4H_9(H)BN(\text{iso-}C_3H_7)_2$		88–91 (1)	N_D^{20} 1.4616	187
F_2BNH_2			Not well characterized, may be polymeric	171,188
$(CH_3)_2BNH_2$				171
$(C_2H_5)_2BNH_2$		72–73	n_D^{20} 1.4210	189
$(C_3H_7)_2BNH_2$		64–65 (96)	n_D^{20} 1.4170	189,191
$(C_4H_9)_2BNH_2$		64–66 (17)	n_D^{20} 1.4277	189–192
(iso-Am)$_2BNH_2$		74–75 (10)	n_D^{20} 1.4298	189,190
$(CH_2{=}CHCH_2)_2BNH_2$		58–60 (23)	n_D^{20} 1.4902	193
$[(Ph)_2BNH_2]_2$	129–130			194
$(1\text{-}C_{10}H_7)_2BNH_2$	113–134			93
(*o*-tolyl)$_2BNH_2$		86–88 ($<10^{-3}$)		195
(mesityl)$_2BNH_2$	118–120			195
$(CH_3)_2BN(H)CH_3$		70.9		197
$(CH_3)_2BN(H)C_4H_9$		114 (722)		197

$[(CH_3)_2BN(H)CH_2]_2$		25–27 (22)		197
$(CH_3)_2BN(H)Ph$		77 (12)		196,197
				198
$(CH_3)_2BN(H)CH{=}C(CH_3)Ph$		71–78 (3)		199
$Cl_2BN(H)$cyclohexyl	142–143			200
$Cl_2BN(H)CH_2C_6H_5$				200
$Cl_2BN(H)$2-biphenyl				201
$(CH_3)_2BN(H)CH_2CH_2NH_2$		28–30 (20)		197
$(C_3H_7)_2BN(H)$iso-C_4H_9		72.5 (11)	n_D^{20} 1.4250	202
$(C_3H_7)_2BN(H)Ph$		117.5 (11)	n_D^{20} 1.5050 (1.5041)	202,203
$(C_3H_7)_2BN(H)$*p*-ClC_6H_4		107–108 (2)	n_D^{20} 1.5178	203
$(CH_3)_2BN(H)N(H)B(CH_3)_2$		95–97		204
$(C_2H_5)BN(H)N(H)B(C_2H_5)_2$		77 (15)		204
$(C_3H_7)_2BN(H)N(H)B(C_3H_7)_2$		122 (12)		204,205
$(C_4H_9)_2BN(H)N(H)B(C_4H_9)_2$		118 (0.5)	n_D^{20} 1.4495	204,206
$(CH_3)_2BN(H)N(H)CH_3$		53–55		204
$(CH_3)_2BN(H)N(H)Ph$		101 (11)		204
$(C_3H_7)_2BN(H)N(H)Ph$		135 (6)		204,205
$(C_4H_9)_2BN(H)N(H)Ph$		144 (1)	n_D^{20} 1.5132	204–206
$(C_3H_7)_2BNHCH_2CH(CH_3)_2$		65.7–66.3 (7)	n_D^{20} 1.4282	206
$(C_4H_9)_2BN(H)C_2H_5$		73–74 (8)	n_D^{20} 1.4279	189,191
$(C_4H_9)_2BN(H)C_4H_9$		92–93 (8)	n_D^{20} 1.4302	191.202
$(C_4H_9)_2BN(H)Ph$		138–139 (7)	n_D^{20} 1.5001	206–208
(cyclohexyl)$_2BN(H)Ph$		127–130 (1)		203
$[(CH_2)_3N(H)B(C_4H_9)_2]_2$		155–156 (0.04)	n_D^{20} 1.4568	206
$Ph_2BN(H)CH_3$		140–141 (5)	Dimerizes on standing. Dimer mp 61–63, n_D^{20} 1.5952	95
$Ph_2BN(H)C_2H_5$		84–85 (0.08–.06)	n_D^{20} 1.5780	95
$Ph_2BN(H)Ph$	56–58	202–206 (1)		93,208
$Ph_2BN(H)NH_2$	147			204
$Ph_2BN(H)CH_2CH(CH_3)_2$		146–150 (3)	n_D^{20} 1.5606	95
$(CH_2{=}CHCH_2)_2BN(H)C_2H_5$		63–64.5	n_D^{20} 1.4686	193
$(CH_2{=}CHCH_2)_2BN(H)C_4H_9$		85.5–86.5 (17)	n_D^{20} 1.4697	209
$(CH_2{=}CHCH_2)_2BN(H)Ph$		77–78 (2)	n_D^{20} 1.5342	193
$(l\text{-}C_{10}H_7)_2BN(H)CH_3$	104–106			93
$(l\text{-}C_{10}H_7)_2BN(H)$iso-$C_4H_9$		240–245		93
$(l\text{-}C_{10}H_7)_2BN(H)Ph$	125–127			93
$\overline{CH_2(CH_2)_3N}BCl_2$		70–74 (17)		80

(continued)

TABLE V (*continued*)

Compound	mp, °C	bp (mm), °C	Remarks	References
$CH_2(CH_2)_4NBCl_2$		82–83 (20)		80
$CH_2CH_2OCH_2CH_2NBCl_2$		88–90 (25)		80
$CH_3CHCH_2(CH_2)_2CH(CH_3)NBCl_2$				80
$CH_2(CH_2)_3NBBr_2$		97–100 (15)		80
$CH_2(CH_2)_4NBBr_2$		105–106 (14)		80
$(CH_2(CH_2)_3NBCl_2)_2$	131–132			80
$(CH_2(CH_2)_4NBCl_2)_2$	105			80
$(CH_2CH_2OCH_2CH_2NBCl_2)_2$	103			80
$(CH_2(CH_2)_3NBBr_2)_2$	157–158			80
$(CH_2(CH_2)_4NBBr_2)_2$	130.5–131.5			80
$F_2BN(CH_3)_2$	165–168		Sublimes *in vacuo* at 50°, dimer as solid, monomer in vapor	171,173,210,211
$Cl_2BN(CH_3)_2$		51–53 (90)	Converts to cyclic dimer on standing 1–2 days at room temperature	174,178,210,212, 213
$Cl_2BN(CH_3)Ph$		100 (20)	n_D^{20} 1.5288	187,214
$Br_2BN(CH_3)_2$		49–51 (1)		178,213
$F_2BN(C_2H_5)_2$	65.5			215
$F_2BN(t\text{-}C_4H_9)_2$			Syrupy liquid	54
$Cl_2BN(C_2H_5)_2$		144		216,217
$Cl_2BN(\text{iso-}C_3H_7)_2$		83 (30)		218
$Cl_2BN(sec\text{-}C_4H_9)_2$		62 (6)		214
$Cl_2BN(\text{cyclohexyl})_2$		114–116 (4)		214
$Cl_2BN(Ph)_2$	78			195,219
$Cl_2BN(CH_3)CH_2Ph$		68 (2)		218
$Cl_2BN(CH_3)C_{10}H_7$		124 (4)		214

$Cl_2BN(C_2H_5)Ph$		67 (3)		214,217
$Cl_2BN(C_5H_{11})_2$				222
$Cl(Ph)BN(CH_3)CH_2Ph$		123–127 (3)		218
$Cl(Ph)BN(iso\text{-}C_3H_7)_2$		94 (4)		218
$Cl(Ph)BN(CH_3)$-cyclohexyl		108 (3)		218
$Br(H)BN(CH_3)_2$	122–125		Sublimes *in vacuo* at 70°	47
$(CH_3)_2BN(CH_3)_2$		63–65		171–173
$(CH_3)_2BN(CH_3)_2 \cdot BF_3$			Unstable above −78°, loses BF_3 *in vacuo*	211
$[(CH_3)_2BN(CH_3)_2][Cl_2BN(CH_3)_2]$	65			173
$[(CH_3)_2BN(CH_3)Cl][Cl_2BN(CH_3)_2]$	108			173
$(CH_3)_2BN(CH_3)Ph$		51 (4)		214
$(CH_3)_2BN(CH_3)CH_2Ph$		64–65 (5)		218
$(CH_3)_2BN(CH_3)$cyclohexyl		70 (11)		218
$(CH_3)_2BN(CH_3)C_{10}H_7$		89 (3)		214
$(CH_3)_2BN(C_2H_5)_2$		90–92 (712)		197
$(CH_3)_2BN(C_4H_9)_2$		68 (10)		197
$(CH_3)_2BN$(cyclohexyl)$_2$		259		214
$CH_3(Cl)BN(CH_3)_2$		90	Slowly forms dimer, mp 102°	47,173
$CH_3(CH_2{=}CH)BN(CH_3)_2$		90–91		199
$(C_2H_5)_2BN(C_2H_5)_2$		152 (739)	n_D^{20} 1.4262	203,217
$(C_2H_5)_2BN(sec\text{-}C_4H_9)_2$		212–214		214
$(C_2H_5)_2BN(C_2H_5)Ph$		68 (6)		214
$C_2H_5(Cl)BN(CH_3)_2$				223
$(CH_2{=}CH)_2BN(C_2H_5)_2$		85 (90)		224
$(CH_3CH{=}CH)_2BN(C_2H_5)_2$		75 (20)		224
$[CH_2{=}C(CH_3)]_2BN(C_2H_5)_2$		56–60 (16)		224
$CH_2{=}CH(Br)BN(CH_3)_2$		39 (11)		225
$(C_3H_7)_2BN(CH_3)_2$		57–59 (12)		178
$(C_3H_7)_2BN(CH_3)Ph$		64 (3)	n_D^{20} 1.4910	203
$(C_3H_7)BN(H)p$-(cyclohexyl)C_6H_4		152 (1)	n_D^{20} 1.5190	203
$(C_4H_9)_2BN(CH_3)_2$		77 (9)	B^{11} NMR s (−27.2 ppm)[a]	178,186
$(C_4H_9)_2BN(C_2H_5)_2$		52–55 (1.5)	n_D^{20} 1.4377	181
$(C_2H_5)_2BN(CH_2)_3CH_2$ (ring)		53 (3)		218
$(CH_3)_2BNCH(CH_3)(CH_2)_2CH_2$ (ring)		38 (3)		218

(continued)

TABLE V (*continued*)

Compound	mp, °C	bp (mm), °C	Remarks	References
$(C_5H_{11})_2B\overline{N(CH_2)_4CH_2}$		93–94 (2)		218
$(C_5H_{11})_2B\overline{NCH(CH_3)(CH_2)_3CH_2}$		95 (2)		218
$Cl_2BN(C_5H_{11})_2$		121 (10)		222
$(C_5H_{11})_2BN(C_2H_5)_2$		82 (3)		218
$(C_5H_{11})_2BN(C_5H_{11})_2$		124 (8)		222
$Ph(C_6H_{13})BN(CH_3)$cyclohexyl		102–124 (3)		218
p-$BrC_6H_4(Ph)BN(iso\text{-}C_3H_7)_2$	64–66	152–154 (3)		218
(*p*-$BrC_6H_4)_2BN(iso\text{-}C_3H_7)_2$	132–134	195–196 (3)		218
$(C_8H_{17})_2BN(C_2H_5)_2$		150–152 (2)		181
(*p*-tolyl)$_2BN(C_2H_5)Ph$	169			214
(*l*-$C_{10}H_7)_2BN(C_2H_5)_2$	178–179			93
p-anisyl(Cl)$BN(C_2H_5)_2$				223
$(Ph)_2BN(CH_3)_2$		104 (2), 96–98 (10^{-3})		186,194,226,227
$(Ph)_2BN(C_2H_5)_2$	38–39.5	128–132 (2.5)		181
$(Ph)_2BN(iso\text{-}C_3H_7)_2$		124 (4)		218
$(Ph)_2BN(C_2H_5)Ph$		158–165 (5–6)		214
$(Ph)_2BN(Ph)_2$	148–150			194,227
Ph_2BNHNH_2	145–147			227
$Ph_2BN(H)N(CH_3)_2$		123 (3)		227
$(Ph)_2BNH_2$	129–130			194
$(Ph)_2BN(C_6H_4CH_3\text{-}p)_2$	130–132			194
$Ph(Cl)BN(CH_3)_2$				223
$Ph(Br)BN(Ph)_2$				223
$Ph(CH_2{=}CH)BN(CH_3)_2$		60 (2)		199
$Ph(CH_2{=}CH)BN(CH_3)C_4H_9$		74–75 (0.5)		199
$Ph(CH_2{=}CH)BN(CH_3)Ph$		108–111 (1)		199
$Ph(PhCH_2)BN(CH_3)CH_2Ph$		170–180 (3)		218
(*p*-$BrC_6H_4)_2BN(CH_3)_2$	39–40			194
(*p*-$CH_3C_6H_4)_2BN(CH_3)_2$		110–112 (0.04–0.05)		194
(*p*-$CH_3C_6H_4)_2BN(Ph)_2$	72–73			194

[a] Chemical shift with respect to trimethylborate, $B(OCH_3)_3$. d = doublet, t = triplet in B^{11} NMR.

$[(CH_3)OH$, $(C_2H_5)_2O$, and $NH_3]$.[170] Such isomerization from dimer to trimer has not yet been reported for the substituted cycloborazanes.

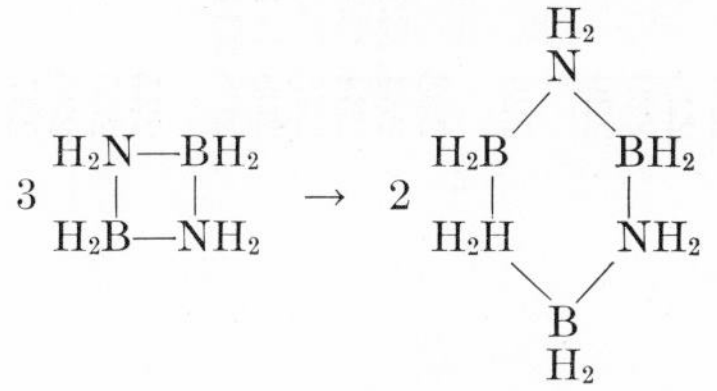

```
                                H2
                                N
                               / \
   H2N—BH2                  H2B   BH2
3   |   |        →     2     |     |
   H2B—NH2                  H2H   NH2
                               \ /
                                B
                                H2
```

Table V lists the properties of most of known monomeric aminoboranes and cycloborazanes.

Bis(amino)boranes and tris(amino)boranes are monomeric species which have two and three nitrogens, respectively, that are directly bonded to boron, e.g., $HB[N(CH_3)_2]_2$ and $B[N(CH_3)_2]_3$. In general these compounds are liquids which are less reactive towards moisture than monomeric aminoboranes, but more reactive than the cycloborazanes. No apparent Lewis-acid character has been reported for the bis- and tris(amino)boranes. This is not unexpected in view of the fact that many of these compounds are sterically hindered. Even if steric effects were minimized, the increased number of nitrogens around boron in these compounds compared to the monomeric aminoboranes would, in principle, reduce the acceptor character of boron through internal pi bonding of the boron with nitrogen. Chemical shifts in the boron-11 NMR spectra are consistent with such expectations.

Properties of the bis(amino)boranes and tris(amino)boranes are listed in Tables VI and VII.

B. Principles of Syntheses

1. Aminoboranes

Aminoboranes can be prepared by several general synthetic procedures.

a. Elimination Reactions. The elimination of hydrogen halide or hydrogen from an appropriately substituted amine-borane, through pyrolysis, represents one of the most common methods for preparing aminoboranes.

$$R_2HNBX_3 \rightarrow R_2NBX_2 + HX$$

$$RH_2NBX_3 \rightarrow RHNBX_2 + HX$$

$$R_2HNBXR_2' \rightarrow R_2NBR_2' + HX$$

$$R_2HNBX_2R' \rightarrow R_2NBXR' + HX$$

where $X = H$, Cl, or Br; and R and R′ are alkyl or phenyl groups.

TABLE VI
Bis(amino)boranes

Compound	mp, °C	bp (mm), °C	Remarks	References
$HB[N(H)CH_2CH{=}CH_2]_2$		62–67 (30)	n_D^{20} 1.4520	228,229
$HB[N(H)C_4H_9]_2$		46–48 (2)	n_D^{20} 1.4306	228,229
$HB[N(H)iso\text{-}C_4H_9]_2$		59–61 (9)	n_D^{20} 1.4263	228
$HB[N(H)Ph]_2$				230
$HB[N(CH_3)_2]_2$		106–108 (720)	n_D^{20} 1.4232	178,180,231,232
$HB[N(C_2H_5)_2]_2$		53–57 (2)	n_D^{20} 1.4348	232
$HB[N(C_3H_7)_2]_2$		84–86 (4)	n_D^{20} 1.4428	232
$HB[N(C_4H_9)_2]_2$		125–126 (3.5)	n_D^{20} 1.4481	232
$HB[N(iso\text{-}C_4H_9)_2]_2$		59–61 (9)	n_D^{20} 1.4263	229
$HB[N(CH_3)Ph]_2$		123–127 (1.5)	n_D^{20} 1.6037	229
$HB[N(iso\text{-}Am)_2]_2$		122–125 (1.5)	n_D^{20} 1.4505	229
$HB[N(CH_2CH{=}CH_2)_2]_2$		77–81 (4)	n_D^{20} 1.4739	229
$HB[\overline{N(CH_2)_4CH_2}]_2$		70–71 (1.5)	n_D^{20} 1.4968	229
$FB[\overline{N(CH_2)_3CH_2}]_2$		110–115 (11)	Impure	233
$C_3H_7B[N(H)C_2H_5]_2$		50–51 (7)	n_D^{20} 1.4230	234,235
$C_4H_9B(N(H)C_2H_5]_2$		55–56 (4)	n_D^{20} 1.4283	234,235
$C_3H_7B[N(H)C_4H_9]_2$		110–111 (11)	n_D^{20} 1.4381	235
$C_3H_7B[N(H)Ph]_2$		133–134 (0.35)	n_D^{20} 1.5820	208,234,235
$C_4H_9B[N(H)Ph]_2$		169 -171 136–138 (0.2)	n_D^{20} 1.5750	208,234
$iso\text{-}AmB[N(H)C_2H_5]_2$		53–54 (3)	n_D^{20} 1.4332	235
$iso\text{-}AmB[N(H)C_4H_9]_2$		93.5–94.0 (2)	n_D^{20} 1.4422	235
$iso\text{-}AmB[N(H)Ph]_2$		173–173.5 (2)	n_D^{20} 1.5700	235
$PhB[N(H)C_2H_5]_2$		97–98 (3)		237
$PhB[N(H)Ph]_2$	84–86			208,237
$PhB[N(H)p\text{-}CH_3C_6H_4]$	85–87			208
$CH_3B<\begin{matrix}N(H)CH_2\\ \vert \\ N(H)CH_2\end{matrix}$		102 (0.72)		197
$ClB[N(CH_3)_2]_2$		38 (10)		178,232,253
$ClB[N(C_2H_5)_2]_2$		74–76 (9)		215,229,232
$ClB[N(iso\text{-}C_3H_7)_2]_2$		55 (0.08)		187,239
$ClB[N(sec\text{-}C_4H_9)_2]_2$		121 (0.15)		239

$ClB[N(cyclohexyl)_2]_2$	116			239
$ClB[N(Ph)_2]_2$		192 (0.03)		187,239
$CH_3B[N(CH_3)_2]_2$		36–38 (13)	n_D^{20} 1.4360–1.4361	197,240
$C_2H_5B[N(CH_3)_2]_2$		33–35 (10)	n_D^{20} 1.4388	240
$C_3H_7B[N(CH_3)_2]_2$		45–48 (8)	n_D^{20} 1.4397	240
$CH_2{=}CHB[N(CH_3)_2]_2$		29 (9)		225
$C_4H_9B[N(CH_3)_2]_2$		50–51 (5)	B^{11} NMR (−16.0 ppm)[a]	186,240
$C_4H_9B[N(C_2H_5)_2]_2$		77 (0.3)	B^{11} NMR s (−21.2 ppm)[a]	236
$CH_2{=}CHB$ $\langle$ $N(CH_3)—CH_2$ / $N(CH_3)—CH_2$ $\rangle$		35–36 (11)		225
$CH_2{=}CHB$ $\langle$ $N(H)$ / $N(H)$ $\rangle$ C_6H_4	119–21			225
sec-$C_4H_9B[N(CH_3)_2]_2$		51 (7)	B^{11} NMR s (−17.3 ppm)[a]	186
t-$C_4H_9B[N(CH_3)_2]_2$		66 (20)	B^{11} NMR s (−17.7 pym)[a]	186
$PhB[N(CH_3)_2]_2$		61 (2.5)	B^{11} NMR s (−14.3 ppm)[a]	186,226,227
$PhB[N(C_2H_5)_2]_2$		70 (2)		227
$PhB[N(Ph)_2]_2$				226
$PhB[N(H)N(CH_3)_2]_2$		80 (2)		227
PhB $\langle$ $N(CH_3)—CH_2$ / $N(CH_3)—CH_2$ $\rangle$		73 (3)		227
PhB $\langle$ $N(C_2H_5)—CH_2$ / $N(C_2H_5)—CH_2$ $\rangle$		95 (8)		227
PhB $\langle$ $N(H)—N(H)$ / $N(H)—N(H)$ $\rangle$ BPh	156			227

[a] Chemical shift with respect to trimethylborate, $B(OCH_3)_3$. s = singlet in B^{11} NMR.

TABLE VII
Trisaminoboranes

Compound	mp, °C	bp (mm), °C	Remarks	References
$B(NH_2)_3$				241
$B[N(H)CH_3]_3$		41 (12)	n_D^{20} 1.4465	187,243,244
$B[N(H)C_2H_5]_3$				245
$B[N(H)C_4H_9]_3$		84 (0.005)	n_D^{20} 1.4460	187,243
$B[N(H)\mathit{sec}\text{-}C_4H_9]_3$		134–136 (4)	n_D^{20} 1.4324	243
$B[N(H)\mathit{n}\text{-}C_6H_{13}]_3$			Decomposes above 150° (0.1 mm)	243,244
$B[N(H)Ph]_3$	170			233,243, 244,246
$B[N(H)\mathit{p}\text{-}CH_3C_6H_4]_3$	157–160			208
$B[N(H)\mathit{p}\text{-}ClC_6H_4]_3$	210			233
$B[N(H)2,4,6\text{-}Br_3C_6H_2]_3$	225			233,246
$B[N(H)1\text{-}C_{10}H_7]_3$	160–190, decomp.			233,246
$B[N(H)2\text{-}C_{10}H_7]_3$	257, decomp.			233
$B[N(CH_3)_2]_3$		146–147 39 (10)	B^{11} NMR s (−9.0 ppm)[a] n_D^{20} 1.4462	174,178,186, 187,232,233, 246,247
$B[N(C_2H_5)_2]_3$		95 (11), 52 (0.2)	n_D^{20} 1.4460	187,215,217,232, 233,239,246,248
$B[N(C_3H_7)_2]_3$		101 (0.15)	n_D^{20} 1.4576	239
$B[N(C_4H_9)_2]_3$	11	139 (0.2)	n_D^{20} 1.4584	215,233,239,246
$B[N(\text{iso-}C_4H_9)]_3$	129–129.5	141 (0.2)		239
$B[N(Ph)_2]_3$	247–248			244
$B[N(CH_2Ph)_2]_3$	266–268			239
$B[N(CH_3)Ph]_3$	211–212			187,233,244, 246,248

$B[N(CH_3)C_{18}H_{37}]_3$	155			233
$B[N(C_2H_5)Ph]_3$	164–165			233,246
$B[N(CH_2)_4]_3$	49	164 (13)		233,246
$B[N(CH_2)_5]_3$	70.5	132–149 (1)		187,243,244
B[carbazyl]$_3$	348			233
B[1,2,3,4-tetrahydrocarbazyl]$_3$	338			233
B[1,2,3,4,5,6,7,8-octahydrocarbazyl]$_3$	325			233
$CH_3(H)NB[N(iso\text{-}C_3H_7)_2]_2$		83 (2.3)	n_D^{25} 1.4562	239
$C_2H_5(H)NB[N(iso\text{-}C_3H_7)_2]_2$		62 (0.05)	n_D^{20} 1.4566	239
$C_3H_7(H)NB[N(iso\text{-}C_3H_7)_2]_2$		92 (0.9)	n_D^{25} 1.4554	239
$iso\text{-}C_3H_7(H)NB[N(iso\text{-}C_3H_7)_2]_2$		62 (0.2)	n_D^{20} 1.4565	239
$C_4H_9(H)NB[N(iso\text{-}C_3H_7)_2]_2$		108 (0.5)	n_D^{25} 1.4562	239
$Ph(H)NB[N(CH_3)_2]_2$		72–75 (0.1)	$n_D^{24.5}$ 1.5353	249
$(CH_3)_2NB[N(C_3H_7)_2]_2$		73 (0.2)	n_D^{22} 1.4530	249
$(CH_3)_2NB[N(iso\text{-}C_3H_7)_2]_2$		73 (0.7)	n_D^{20} 1.4589	239
$(C_2H_5)_2NB[N(iso\text{-}C_3H_7)_2]_2$	76–78	110 (4.5)		239
$(C_3H_7)_2NB[N(CH_3)_2]_2$		32 (0.05)	$n_D^{24.5}$ 1.4485	249
$Ph(CH_3)NB[N(CH_3)_2]_2$		68–69 (0.1)	$n_D^{24.5}$ 1.5338	249
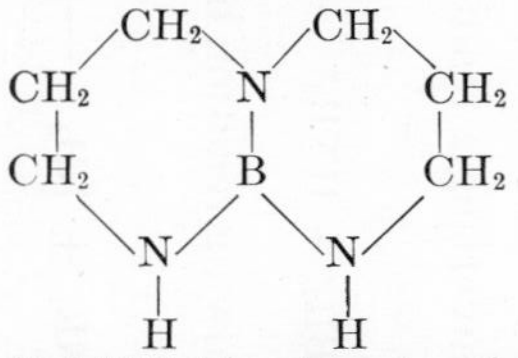 (1,8,10,9-triazaboradecalin)	38–41	62 (1)		250

[a] Chemical shift with respect to trimethylborate, $B(OCH_3)_3$. s = singlet in B^{11} NMR.

The amine-boranes in the above reaction schemes can be generated according to the procedures given in Section II.B.

In many cases where halogen-substituted aminoboranes are to be prepared, the direct reaction of the boron halide with excess amine will provide driving force for the formation of the aminoborane by forming solid ammonium halide. For example, consider the following reaction:

$$BCl_3 + 2(CH_3)_2NH \rightarrow (CH_3)_2NBCl_2 + (CH_3)_2H_2NCl$$

For the preparation of aminoboranes which contain a BH_2 unit, the most convenient procedure probably involves the synthesis of the amine borane *in situ*, using $LiBH_4$ and an ammonium halide as the starting materials.[39]

$$\begin{array}{lcl} NR_2H_2Cl + LiBH_4 & \rightarrow & R_2HNBH_3 + H_2 + LiCl \\ & & \downarrow \\ & & R_2NBH_2 + H_2 \\ NRH_3Cl + LiBH_4 & \rightarrow & RH_2NBH_3 + H_2 + LiCl \\ & & \downarrow \\ & & RHNBH_2 + H_2 \end{array}$$

An analogous elimination reaction, starting with H_3NBH_3 and eliminating hydrogen, does not result in the formation of well-defined BH_2NH_2 species. Instead, an amorphous, ill-defined, polymeric material is produced.[251]

b. Grignard Reactions. A convenient way to prepare an aminoborane which contains a boron–carbon bond is to treat a halogen-substituted aminoborane with the appropriate Grignard reagent.[217]

$$R_2NBX_2 + 2R'MgX \rightarrow R_2NBR_2' + 2MgX_2$$

The principal advantage of this procedure is that it does not require the preparation of a mixed borane, BR_2X.

c. Other Methods. In principle, several other procedures are available for preparing aminoboranes. They have not yet achieved the status of the general reactions cited above and are probably useful only in rather special cases. Of these special methods, transamination might be a useful way of converting a readily available aminoborane to another one.

$$R_2NBR_2' + HNR_2'' \rightarrow R_2''NBR_2' + R_2NH$$

For example, the following reaction has been observed.[252]

$$\left[\begin{smallmatrix}O\\O\end{smallmatrix}\right\rangle BNR_2 + NH_3 \longrightarrow \left[\begin{smallmatrix}O\\O\end{smallmatrix}\right\rangle BNH_2 + NR_2H$$

The particular reaction cited above represents the best way of preparing 2-amino-1,3,2-dioxaborolane. Amminolysis such as

$$\left[\begin{matrix} O \\ O \end{matrix}\right\rangle BCl + 2NH_3 \longrightarrow \left[\begin{matrix} O \\ O \end{matrix}\right\rangle BNH_2 + NH_4Cl$$

leads to the formation of products which are not easily separated from each other.

The reaction of a tris(amino)borane with an organoborane is also a potentially useful route to the preparation of selected aminoboranes.[218,253]

$$B(NR_2)_3 + 2BR_3' \rightarrow 3R_2'BNR_2$$

2. *Cycloborazanes*

Many of the sterically unhindered aminoboranes undergo association to form cyclodiborazanes. The extent of association to form substituted cyclodiborazanes depends upon the substituents on boron and nitrogen (see Table IV). In general, association is observed if the aminoborane has either hydrogen, halogen, or a combination of these elements as substituents. In several cases equilibria between monomer and dimer can be observed and the degree of association can be readily altered.

There has been only one report of a cyclotriborazane which is formed from the usual aminoborane synthesis.

$$LiBH_4 + CH_3H_3NCl \rightarrow CH_3H_2NBH_3 + H_2 + LiCl$$
$$\downarrow$$
$${}^1/_3(CH_3HNBH_2)_3 + H_2$$

The six-membered ring structure formed in this reaction is apparently sufficiently stable so that no apparent equilibrium involving other species (i.e., monomer or dimer) is observed at ordinary temperatures.[184,185] On the other hand, only the cyclodiborazane, $[(CH_3)_2NBH_2]_2$, has been reported to be prepared from a reaction similar to the one cited above.[145,178–180] The synthesis of the cyclotriborazane $[(CH_3)_2NBH_2]_3$ has been observed, but by an unusual method which involves the reaction of the dimer, $[(CH_3)_2NBH_2]_2$, with B_5H_9 at elevated temperature.[254]

Cyclotriborazane, $(BH_2NH_2)_3$, can be prepared by specific reactions which are markedly different from the schemes cited previously. This compound is synthesized by the addition of hydrogen chloride to borazine, followed by treatment with sodium borohydride according to the following equation:

$$2B_3N_3H_6\cdot 3HCl + 6NaBH_4 \xrightarrow{\text{diglyme}} 2(H_2BNH_2)_3 + 3B_2H_6 + 6NaCl$$

By treating the diammoniate of diborane with strong bases in liquid ammonia, all known cycloborazanes are produced in varying proportions.[167,170]

$$NaX + BH_2(NH_3)_2{}^+BH_4{}^- \xrightarrow{NH_3(l)} {}^1/_n(BH_2NH_2)_n + NaBH_4 + HX$$
$$(X = NH_2{}^- \text{ or } HC{\equiv}C^-)$$

$$Na + BH_2(NH_3)_2{}^+BH_4{}^- \xrightarrow{NH_3(l)} {}^1/_n(BH_2NH_2)_n + {}^1/_2H_2 + NH_3 + NaBH_4$$

In general the principal cyclic product from these reactions is $(BH_2NH_2)_5$, with the other cyclic species $(BH_2NH_2)_3$, $(BH_2NH_2)_2$, and $(BH_2NH_2)_4$ occurring in much smaller yields. The cyclic trimer is much more conveniently prepared from the borazine–hydrogen chloride adduct, while $(BH_2NH_2)_2$ is more conveniently obtained from the pyrolysis of $(BH_2NH_2)_5$.

3. *Bis(amino)boranes and Tris(amino)boranes*

Several of the procedures for preparing bis(amino)boranes and tris(amino)boranes are sufficiently similar so that they can be listed together as type reactions.

a. Elimination Reactions. Aminolysis reactions will produce the desired number of amino groups on boron when the molar ratio of reactants is carefully chosen.[79,174,255]

$$BX_3 + 4R_2NH \rightarrow XB(NR_2)_2 + 2R_2NH_2X$$
$$BX_3 + 6R_2NH \rightarrow B(NR_2)_3 + 3R_2NH_2X$$

where X = Cl or Br, and R = alkyl or phenyl group. When secondary amines (branched in the α-position) are used (e.g., isopropylamine), it should be noted that due to steric crowding only the bis(amino)-haloboranes are formed.

b. Exchange Reactions. Reactions of trialkylsilylamines with boron halides have produced bis(amino)boranes and tris(amino)-boranes in 80–90% yields.[178]

$$2(CH_3)_3SiNR_2 + BX_3 \rightarrow XB(NR_2)_2 + 2(CH_3)_3SiX$$
$$3(CH_3)_3SiNR_2 + BX_3 \rightarrow B(NR_2)_3 + 3(CH_3)_3SiX$$

When a bis(dimethylamino)borane or tris(dimethylamino)borane is readily available, it is sometimes easier to convert it into another bis(amino)borane or tris(amino)borane by transamination rather than use other synthetic procedures.

$$RB[N(CH_3)_2]_2 + 2R_2'NH \rightarrow RB(NR_2')_2 + 2(CH_3)_2NH$$
$$B[N(CH_3)_2]_3 + 3R_2'NH \rightarrow B(NR_2')_3 + 3(CH_3)_2NH$$

Generally, transaminations are carried out by simply mixing the starting materials in an appropriate solvent and refluxing the mixture, allowing the simpler amine to escape through the reflux condenser,[197]

$$CH_3B[N(CH_3)_2]_2 + H_2NCH_2CH_2NH_2 \rightarrow CH_3B\begin{matrix} \diagup N(H)CH_2 \\ \diagdown N(H)CH_2 \end{matrix} + 2(CH_3)_2NH$$

Tris(amino)boranes can be converted into bis(amino)haloboranes by reaction with boron halides.[253]

$$BX_3 + 2B(NR_2)_3 \rightarrow 3XB(NR_2)_2$$

where X = Cl or Br.

The halogen in bis(amino)haloboranes can be readily replaced by hydride, alkoxy groups, or organic groups.[232,238]

$$XB(NR_2)_2 + LiH \rightarrow HB(NR_2)_2 + LiX$$

$$XB(NR_2)_2 + R'OH \rightarrow R'OB(NR_2)_2 + HX$$

$$XB(NR_2)_2 + LiR' \rightarrow R'B(NH_2)_2 + LiX$$

where X = Cl or Br; and R and R′ = alkyl or phenyl groups.

C. Preparative Procedures

1. Dialkyl- or Diarylaminodichloroboranes[217]

$$R_2NH + BCl_3 \rightarrow Cl_3BNHR_2$$

$$Cl_3BNHR_2 + (C_2H_5)_3N \xrightarrow[C_6H_6]{\text{reflux}} Cl_2BNR_2 + (C_2H_5)_3NHCl$$

This procedure is generally applicable for syntheses of dialkyl- and diarylaminoboranes. A solution of the secondary amine in dry benzene is slowly added to a stirred benzene solution of boron trichloride. When equivalent amounts of the reactants have been mixed and allowed to react, the resulting 1:1 adduct is mixed with an equimolar quantity of triethylamine and dehydrochlorination is brought about by refluxing the benzene solution for several hours. The triethylammonium chloride which forms is filtered off and the solvent is removed from the filtrate by evaporation at reduced pressure. The product is obtained from the residue by vacuum distillation.

2. Tetraorganosubstituted Aminoboranes[217]

$$R_2NBCl_2 + 2R'MgX \rightarrow R_2NBR_2' + 2ClMgX \qquad (X = Cl \text{ or } Br)$$

The ready availability of aminodichloroboranes provides a convenient starting point for the synthesis of compounds of the type,

R_2NBR_2'. Treatment of dialkyl or diarylaminodichloroboranes with a Grignard reagent produces tetraorgano-substituted aminoboranes readily.

A solution of the Grignard reagent in anhydrous diethyl ether is added dropwise, with stirring, to a benzene solution containing the correct amount of a dialkyl- or diarylaminodichloroborane, and the mixture is refluxed several hours under a nitrogen atmosphere. The magnesium salt is removed by filtration, and the filtrate is fractionally distilled to remove the solvent and purify the product.

3. *Dialkyl- or Diarylaminoboranes*[217]

$$R_2NBCl_2 + 2NaBH_4 \rightarrow R_2NBH_2 + 2NaCl + B_2H_6$$

Compounds corresponding to the formula R_2NBCl_2 may be conveniently reduced with sodium borohydride to produce the corresponding dialkyl- or diarylaminoborane.

A solution of dialkyl- or diarylaminodichloroborane in triglyme (triethyleneglycoldimethyl ether) is added dropwise to a solution of the required amount of sodium borohydride in the same solvent at room temperature. A dry nitrogen atmosphere and vigorous stirring are maintained at all times, and the stirring is continued for several hours after the addition has been completed. The reaction mixture is then filtered under nitrogen, and the filtrate is fractionally distilled at reduced pressure to obtain the product in pure form.

4. *Bromobis(dimethylamino)borane*[253]

$$BBr_3 + 2B[N(CH_3)_2]_3 \rightarrow 3BrB[N(CH_3)_2]_2$$

A solution of boron tribromide in dry pentane (about 2 g BBr_3 per milliliter C_5H_{12}) is added slowly to a vigorously stirred solution of the stoichiometric amount of tris(dimethylamino)borane, also in pentane, (2 ml C_5H_{12} per gram $B[N(CH_3)_2]_3$) maintained near −45°. After the addition is complete, the pentane is removed by rapid distillation at 1.5 mm pressure, and the residue is vacuum distilled to give a nearly 85% yield of bromobis(dimethylamino)borane, bp 20–28° (0.8 mm).

5. *Bis(dimethylamino)phenylborane*[227]

$$Cl_2BPh + 4HN(CH_3)_2 \rightarrow PhB[N(CH_3)]_2 + 2(CH_3)_2NH_2Cl$$

A solution of phenyldichloroborane in dry hexane (4 ml C_6H_{14} per gram $PhBCl_2$) is slowly added to a stirred solution of a 4:1 excess of dimethylamine in hexane [10 ml C_6H_{14} per gram $HN(CH_3)_2$] which has been cooled to −78° in a Dry Ice–methanol bath. After the addition is complete, the cooling bath is removed and stirring is continued until the reaction mixture reaches room temperature. The solid precipitate (dimethylammonium chloride) is filtered off and the solvent evaporated. Distillation of the residue gives pure bis(dimethylamino)phenylborane, bp 59° (3 mm), in about 90% yield.

6. *Tris(diethylamino)borane*[238]

$$BCl_3 + 6HN(C_2H_5)_2 \rightarrow B[N(C_2H_5)_2]_3 + 3(C_2H_5)_2NH_2Cl$$

A quantity of boron trichloride is dissolved in pentane (5 ml C_5H_{12} per gram BCl_3) and cooled to −40° in a jacketed dropping funnel. The solution is then added dropwise to a stirred solution of a 6:1 excess of diethylamine, also in pentane (5 ml C_5H_{12} per gram $HN(CH_3)_2$), which is maintained at about −80°. After the addition is complete, the reaction mixture is allowed to warm to room temperature with continuous stirring and the white precipitate, consisting mainly of diethylammonium chloride, is filtered off and washed with pentane. The combined filtrate and washings are freed from solvent at low pressure, and distillation of the residue gives colorless tris(diethylamino)borane, bp 50–53° (0.4 mm), in about 40% yield.

7. *Cyclotriborazane*, $(BH_2NH_2)_3$

The most convenient starting material for this preparation is *B*-trichloroborazine, $B_3Cl_3N_3H_3$, which may be prepared by heating ammonium chloride and boron trichloride to 200°.[220] *B*-Trichloroborazine may be converted to borazine by reduction with sodium borohydride.[221]

$$B_3Cl_3N_3H_3 + 3NaBH_4 \xrightarrow{\text{diglyme}} B_3H_3N_3H_3 + 3NaCl + {}^3/_2B_2H_6$$

A three-necked flask of appropriate capacity, equipped with a mechanical stirrer, reflux condenser, and dropping funnel, is charged with a solution of sodium borohydride in diglyme (about 8 ml solvent per gram solute). The flask is chilled to 0° and a 25% excess of tri-*n*-butylamine is added with vigorous stirring. The reaction flask is flushed with a slow stream of dry nitrogen and a solution of *B*-trichloroborazine in diglyme (2.5 ml solvent per gram solute) is added dropwise over a 1-hr period. Stirring is maintained for 30 min after the addition is complete.

A spiral reflux condenser, cooled with a salt–ice bath, is attached to the reaction flask, and the reaction mixture distilled under high vacuum, first at room temperature and later with gentle heating to 40–50°. Borazine and some ether collect in a Dry Ice cooled trap. The crude borazine is then fractionally distilled at atmospheric pressure with a distillation head cooled by circulating brine and a receiving flask immersed in an ice bath. The yield of borazine (bp 54.5°) is about 46%.

Borazine may be converted to cyclotriborazane as follows.[175] A quantity (about 1 ml per millimole of borazine) of dry diethyl ether is condensed, using liquid nitrogen, into a dry flask of appropriate capacity equipped with a magnetic stirring bar. A measured amount of pure borazine, $(BHNH)_3$, is then condensed on top of the ether and the mixture is warmed to −80°. The solution is then allowed to absorb an excess (about 4:1) of anhydrous HCl with constant stirring. Within a few minutes, a white precipitate of $(BHNH)_3 \cdot 3HCl$ appears. The reaction is allowed to go to apparent completion, and then the mixture is permitted to warm slowly to room temperature. Ether and excess HCl are pumped off and the solid residue is heated to 60° while being pumped with a mercury diffusion pump, protected by a trap, to remove all possible volatile components.

Enough dry diglyme (diethyleneglycol dimethyl ether) to dissolve the solid is distilled into the flask and warmed to room temperature to effect solution. The flask is then chilled with liquid nitrogen and a quantity of $NaBH_4$ corresponding to a 3:1 excess is dropped into the flask under cover of a dry helium stream. The flask is then reevacuated and warmed slowly to room temperature with continuous stirring. Diborane evolution may be measured, and after a few hours about 75% of the theoretical quantity should have been obtained according to the following equation of reaction:

$$B_3H_3Cl_3N_3H_6 + 3NaBH_4 \xrightarrow{\text{diglyme}} B_3N_3H_{12} + {}^3/_2B_2H_6 + 3NaCl$$

Decantation of the supernatant liquid from the precipitate followed by removal of the diglyme from the decantate leaves a white solid. On slow warming with continuous pumping the white solid sublimes between 90 and 100°.

8. Cycloborazanes[170]

Preparations are carried out on a 1-mole scale with respect to sodium amide, with an excess of diammoniate of diborane in liquid ammonia. The diammoniate of diborane is prepared by passing diborane into liquid ammonia as described in Section III.C.1.

For the preparation of a solution in excess of one mole of diborane as described, the generator is charged with 70 g of lithium aluminum hydride and 2 lb of anhydrous ether; a quantity of 350 ml of boron trifluoride etherate is added in the course of about 15 hr. The reaction

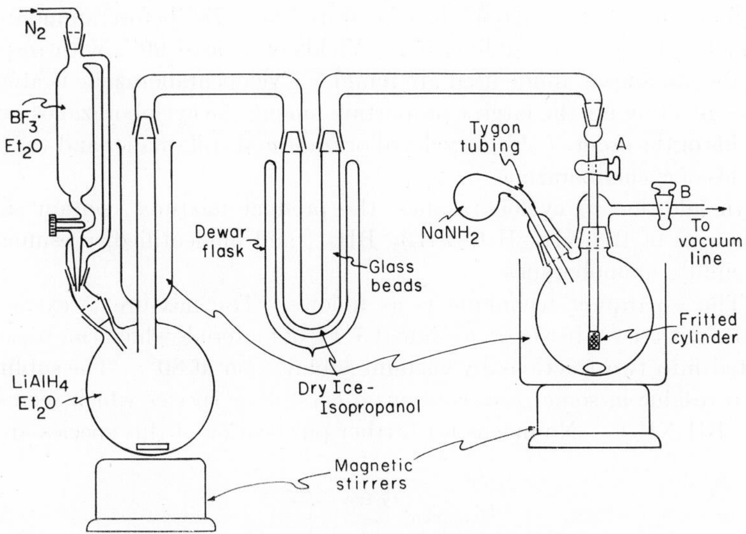

Fig. 8. Apparatus for preparation of cycloborazanes.

is carried out in an apparatus such as that shown in Figure 8. Approximately 700 ml of liquid ammonia is used as the reaction medium, into which the diborane–nitrogen gas mixture is introduced through an extra coarse gas dispersion frit. At high rates of generation of diborane (governed by the rate of addition of $BF_3 \cdot Et_2O$) it becomes difficult to control the pressure in the reaction system due to clogging of the frit by deposits of diammoniate of diborane. A simple gas-flow meter of the "floating ball" type (0–2 ft^3 of gas per hour), situated in the nitrogen line leading to the apparatus, serves both as a qualitative indicator for the rate of nitrogen flow and as a pressure gauge, guiding the adjustment of the rate of diborane generation. A vessel containing sodium amide (see Fig. 8) is connected to the outer end of the glass tube on the side neck of the reaction flask via a short length of heavy-walled Tygon tubing, which is kept closed by means of a pinch clamp. When the reaction flask has been connected to the vacuum line through the side arm and the pressure in the flask has subsequently been lowered to that of the ammonia solution, the pinch clamp is opened. Sodium amide is then added in small portions to the magnetically stirred solution of diammoniate of diborane in liquid ammonia. During this operation the reaction flask and vacuum line remain closed to the pump except for occasional removal of hydrogen gas produced in the reaction.

A total of about two liters of hydrogen is produced in a 1-mole scale reaction. The clear solution (indicating that the ammonia-insoluble sodium amide has reacted) may be stored at −78° before ammonia is removed by vacuum sublimation. Yields of at least 90% with respect to the amount of amide used are found. Cyclopentaborazane is always present in by far the largest proportion among the cycloborazanes, with yields of the order of 5% of cyclotriborazane and still smaller and varying yields of cyclodiborazane.

In addition to cycloborazanes, the product mixtures contain small amounts of BH_3NH_3, $H_2B(NH_3)_2{}^+BH_4{}^-$, and unidentified, presumably chainlike, aminoboranes.

The separation technique is as follows. The mixture is extracted twice with dry ether to yield from 0.5–1 g of materials which can be separated into two fractions by vacuum sublimation at 80°. The sublimation residue in some cases contains a crystalline species which seems to be $(BH_2NH_2)_4$. No means for further purification of this species are as

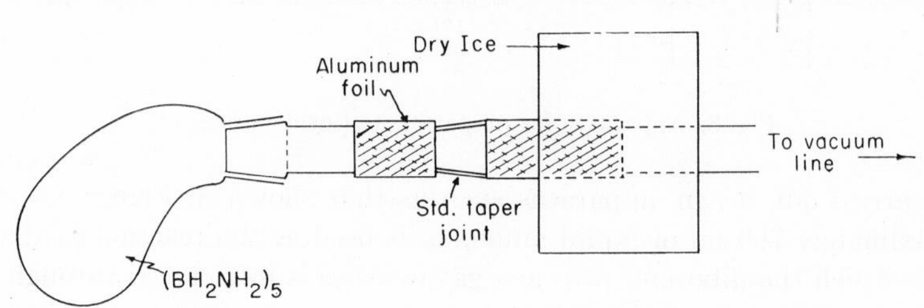

Fig. 9. Apparatus for pyrolysis of cyclopentaborazane, $(BH_2NH_2)_5$.

yet available. The sublimate, consisting of $(BH_2NH_2)_3$, $(BH_2NH_2)_2$, and BH_3NH_3, can be further separated by vacuum sublimation at 45°, at which temperature $(BH_2NH_2)_3$ remains behind.

The separation of cyclodiborazane from ammonia–borane is difficult because both substances sublime *in vacuo* at almost the same temperature in the range of 30–35°C. By means of repeated fractional microsublimation cyclodiborazane can be gradually enriched; however, relatively larger amounts of higher purity cyclodiborazane can be obtained through thermal decomposition of easily accessible $(BH_2NH_2)_5$.

Cyclopentaborazane, which is the major boron–nitrogen product of the reaction, may be broken down into lower cycloborazanes and other materials by pyrolysis. The procedure simply involves heating the substance to 120° followed by a very slow increase of temperature through the decomposition range while pumping through a series of cooled traps. The temperature is increased to 145° over a period of about 24 hr which results in the deposition of three fractions of material along the cooled zones of the apparatus shown in Figure 9.

The liquid nitrogen-cooled section contains volatile and nonvolatile materials which will not be considered here. A transparent brittle material is deposited in the zone cooled with Dry Ice. The nature of this "glass" is not yet understood.

In the region of the tube immediately preceeding the Dry Ice a deposit forms which contains cyclodiborazane. The tube is covered with aluminum foil so that only the center portion of the standard taper joint is exposed. In this manner a fraction rich in cyclodiborazane is deposited in the joint. The enriched fraction (at least 85% purity) may be separated from the other fraction by carefully scraping the substance out of the glass joint. Cyclodiborazane adheres loosely to the glass wall while ammonia–borane adheres much more tenaciously. The yield of $(BH_2NH_2)_2$ is about 5 mg per gram of cyclopentaborazane pyrolyzed.

The residue of the ether extractions is carefully freed of residual ether by subjecting it to high vacuum for a day at 50°. Cyclopentaborazane may be recovered by introducing the mixture in small portions to ice water, in which the compound is only sparingly soluble, while sodium hydroborate is soluble and the other components are hydrolytically destroyed. The precipitate is filtered and dried on the vacuum line to yield lumps of material which are powdered and pumped on again. About 1 liter of ice water is required in order to completely remove $NaBH_4$ from the product. Purity may be checked by observing the characteristic band of $NaBH_4$ at 2240 cm^{-1} in the infrared spectrum.

Caution: The use of contaminated (presumably oxidized) sodium amide may lead to explosion. Furthermore, product mixtures of incomplete reactions which contain sizable fractions of unreacted sodium amide should be abandoned.

V. BORAZINES (FOUR-, SIX-, AND EIGHT-MEMBERED RINGS AND POLYCYCLIC SPECIES)

A. Introduction

Borazines are the analogs of benzene and its derivatives. The remarkably similar physical properties of benzene and borazine are worth noting[256] since they undoubtedly stimulated much of the early research on the preparation, chemistry, and properties of compounds in this class.

Structurally, borazine is a planar ring of D_{3h} symmetry, containing B—N bonds of equal length (**3**). Electronic spectra of borazine and substituted borazines show features which are similar to those of benzene and benzene derivatives.[257,258] Shifts in the electronic spectra as a function of substitution on boron and nitrogen have been interpreted with respect to the effect of substituents on the aromatic character of the ring.[259] A recent self-consistent field molecular orbital calculation[260] suggests that there is some delocalization, through a pi system, of the electronic charge of the nitrogen lone pairs. However, the intrinsically higher electronegativity of nitrogen causes sufficient transfer of charge from boron to nitrogen through the sigma system so that the net charge on nitrogen and boron is practically zero.

While spectra,[256] diamagnetic anisotropy measurements,[261] and molecular orbital calculations[262] suggest some aromatic character for borazine and its derivatives, the chemistry of such systems cannot be conveniently considered as typical of aromatic systems. From the standpoint of systematizing the chemistry of the borazines, the rings behave as if lone pairs are localized on nitrogen, and the groups on boron and nitrogen bear net negative and positive charges, respectively. Such features are suggested by the following typical reactions of borazines.

```
        H                               H2
        N                               N
      / .. \                          /   \
   HB       BH                   H   B     B   H
   |        |    + 3HCl  →      Cl       |     Cl        (1)
   HN:     :NH                     H2N     NH2
      \    /                          \   /
        B                               B
        H                             H   Cl
```

```
        R                               R
        N                               N
      /   \                           /   \
   RB       BR                     RB       BR
   |        |    + LiCH3  →        |        |      + CH4      (2)
   RN       NH                     RN       N⁻Li⁺
      \    /                          \   /
        B                               B
        R                               R
```

```
        R                               R
        N                               N
      /   \                           /   \
   HB       BH                     DB       BD
   |        |    + 3NaBD4  →  4    |        |      + 3NaBH4   (3)
   RN       NR                     RN       NR
      \    /                          \   /
        B                               B
        H                               D
```

In eq. (1)[263,264] above, the nitrogen can formally be considered a Lewis base donating an electron pair to a proton, while the boron can be considered a Lewis acid, accepting an electron pair from chlorine.

In eq. (2)[265,266] the hydrogen on nitrogen is sufficiently protonic in character to react with CH_3^-. In eq. (3)[175] the hydrogen on boron is sufficiently hydridic in character to exchange with D^-. It is well recognized that borohydride hydrogen will exchange with hydridic hydrogen only.

In recent years new unsaturated-ring systems containing alternating boron–nitrogen bonds have been prepared. Polycyclic borazines which are analogs of fused and bicyclic aromatic ring systems are now known.[266–272] However, they have received only cursory attention with respect to their properties, compared to the monocyclic systems.

Only one example of a four-membered ring, an analog of cyclobutadiene, is known,[273] 1,3-di-*t*-butyl-2,4-*t*-butylamino-1,3-diaza-2,4-diborine (**18**).

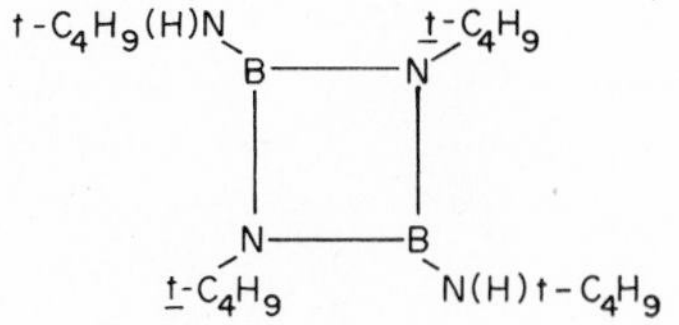

t-C_4H_9(H)N—B—N—*t*-C_4H_9
t-C_4H_9—N—B—N(H)t-C_4H_9

(**18**)

The stability of this structure is attributed to significant pi bonding between boron and the exocyclic nitrogens of the *t*-butylamino groups.

Several analogs of the cyclooctatetraene ring system have been prepared.[274,275] Structure **19** shows the structure of 1,3,5,7-tetra-*t*-butyl-

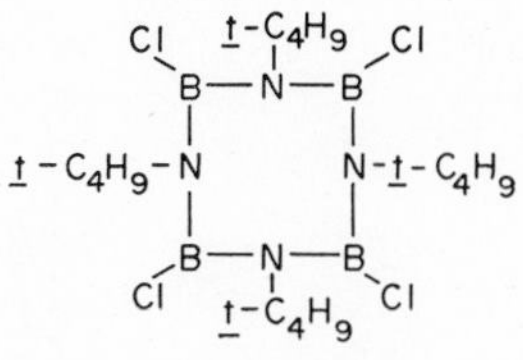

Cl, *t*-C_4H_9, Cl
B—N—B
t-C_4H_9-N   N-*t*-C_4H_9
B—N—B
Cl, *t*-C_4H_9, Cl

(**19**)

2,4,6,8-tetrachloro-1,3,5,7-tetraza-2,4,6,8-tetraborine, (t-$C_4H_9NBCl)_4$. Such compounds have been given the common name of "tetrameric borazynes." They are unusually stable, being unaffected by boiling water, Grignard reagents, and organolithium compounds. Stability is attributed to the *t*-butyl amino groups which sterically protect the boron–nitrogen framework from attack.

Tables VIII and IX list most of the known borazines, polycyclic borazines, and "tetrameric borazynes."

TABLE VIII
Borazines

Compound	mp, °C	bp (mm), °C	Remarks	References
$H_3B_3N_3H_3$	−58	55	$^1/_2B_2H_6 + NH_3 \xrightarrow[2\text{–}3\ hr]{190°}$	276–280
			$B_2H_6 \cdot 2NH_3 \xrightarrow[\text{several hours}]{200°}$	281
			$B_2H_6 + 2NH_3 \xrightarrow[<1\ atm]{200°}$	282
			$LiBH_4 + 3NH_4Cl \xrightarrow[\text{solids}]{\text{dry}}$	283–285
			$X_3B_3N_3H_3 + LiBH_4$ (or $LiAlH_4$) →	175,345
			$Cl_3B_3N_3H_3 + NaBH_4 \xrightarrow[(t\text{-Bu})_3N]{\text{diglyme}}$	221
			Hydrazine hydrochloride + $LiBH_4$	286
$F_3B_3N_3H_3$	122		Prepared by fluorinating $Cl_3B_3N_3H_3$	287–289
$Cl_3B_3N_3H_3$	84			220,286,290, 291
$Br_3B_3N_3H_3$	131			286,290
$I_3B_3N_3H_3$	134			290,292
$F_2ClB_3N_3H_3$			Vapor press. 7 mm, 31°	289
$FCl_2B_3N_3H_3$	49–51			289
$(CH_3)_3B_3N_3H_3$	31.4	118–120 (720)		290,294,295, 310,311

$(C_2H_5)_3B_3N_3H_3$	−46.4	192–193, 66–67 (7–8)		294,296, 297
$(C_3H_7)_3B_3N_3H_3$		117–118 (15)		290,297
$(C_4H_9)_3B_3N_3H_3$		124–126 (5)		192,290, 298
$(CH_3C{\equiv}C)_3B_3N_3H_3$	100–102			293
tris(*B*-chlorovinyl)borazine				298
$(t\text{-}C_4H_9)_3B_3N_3H_3$	32	90–91 (1)		290
$(\text{iso-Am})_3B_3N_3H_3$		114–115.5 (0.1)		299
$(Ph)_3B_3N_3H_3$	181–183			290,294, 300–302
$(p\text{-}ClC_6H_4)_3B_3N_3H_3$	269–270			303,304
$(p\text{-}BrC_6H_4)_3B_3N_3H_3$	292–293			305
$(p\text{-tolyl})_3B_3N_3H_3$	189–190			305
$(PhC{\equiv}C)_3B_3N_3H_3$	139–140			293
$(H_2N)_3B_3N_3H_3$				306,307
$[CH_3(H)N]_3B_3N_3H_3$				306
$[(CH_3)_2N]_3B_3N_3H_3$	112–115			306,308,309
$[(C_2H_5)_2N]_3B_3N_3H_3$		120 (0.1)		306,308,309
$[(\text{iso-}C_3H_7)_2N]_3B_3N_3H_3$	138–143			308
$[(C_4H_9)_2N]_3B_3N_3H_3$		200 (0.05)		308
$[(\text{iso-}C_4H_9)_2N]_3B_3N_3H_3$	47–52	167 (0.3)		308
$[Ph(CH_3)N]_3B_3N_3H_3$	123–132			308
$[Ph_2N]_3B_3N_3H_3$	>325 (decomp.)			308,309
$H_3B_3N_3(CH_3)_3$	−7.5	132	n_D^{20} 1.4375	39,295,310–312
$H_3B_3N_3(C_2H_5)_3$		72.4 (25)	n_D^{20} 1.4380	297,311, 312,314
$H_3B_3N_3(CH_2CF_3)_3$	40–41	106–111 (92)		315

(*continued*)

TABLE VIII (*continued*)

Compound	mp, °C	bp (mm), °C	Remarks	References
$H_3B_3N_3(CH_2CCl_3)_3$	202–203			315
$H_3B_3N_3(C_3H_7)_3$		225	Glassy solid	311,316
$H_3B_3N_3(\text{iso-}C_3H_7)_3$	−6.5	203		311,317
$H_3B_3N_3(CH_2{-}CH{=}CH_2)_3$				228
$H_3B_3N_3(C_4H_9)_3$		109–111 (3.5)	n_D^{20} 1.4524	228,312
$H_3B_3N_3(\text{iso-}C_4H_9)_3$		92–94 (3)	n_D^{23} 1.4466	228,312
$H_3B_3N_3(C_6H_{11})_3$	98			316
$H_3B_3N_3(Ph)_3$	158			316
$H_3B_3N_3(C_6H_4Cl\text{-}2)_3$	118–119			316
$H_3B_3N_3(C_6H_4Cl\text{-}3)_3$	107			316
$H_3B_3N_3(C_6H_4Cl\text{-}4)_3$	207			316
$H_3B_3N_3(C_6H_4Br\text{-}m)_3$	125–125.4			318
$H_3B_3N_3(C_6H_4Br\text{-}p)_3$	234–235			318
$H_3B_3N_3(CH_2C_6H_5)_3$	180–182 (0.005)			319
$H_3B_3N_3(C_6H_4CH_3\text{-}m)_3$	165.5–166.5			318
$H_3B_3N_3(C_6H_4CH_3\text{-}p)_3$	150–152			318
$H_3B_3N_3(\text{dodecyl})_3$				316
$H_3B_3N_3(p\text{-anisyl})_3$	139–140			318
$H_3B_3N_3(H)_2CH_3$		84		295
$H_3B_3N_3(CH_3)_2H$		108		295
$H_3B_3N_3(CH_3)_2C_6H_{11}$	49			297
$H_3B_3N_3(CH_3)_2Ph$	35	64–65 (0.2)		297
$Cl(H)_2B_3N_3H_3$	−34.6	109.5		284
$Br(H)_2B_3N_3H_3$	−34.8			284
$(C_2H_5(H)N)[(C_2H_5)_2N]_2B_3N_3H_3$		122.3		320
$CH_3(H)_2B_3N_3H_3$	−59	87		295
$Cl_2HB_3N_3H_3$	33.0–33.5			284
$Br_2HB_3N_3H_3$	49.5–50.0			284

$(CH_3)_2HB_3N_3H_3$	−48	107	295
$(C_2H_5)_2HB_3N_3H_3$	5–6	72–73	297
$(C_3H_7)_2HB_3N_3H_3$		119.5–124.5	297
$Ph(H)_2B_3N_3H_3$	73.5–75.0		302
$(Ph)_2HB_3N_3H_3$	120–122		302
$CH_3(H)_2B_3N_3(H)_2CH_3$		124	295
$(CH_3)_2HB_3N_3(H)_2CH_3$		139	295
$(C_2H_5)_2HB_3N_3H(C_2H_5)_2$		156–158 (752)	322
$CH_3(H)_2B_3N_3(C_2H_5)_3$			323
$C_3H_7(H)_2B_3N_3(C_3H_7)_3$			323
$(Cl)_2HB_3N_3[C_6H_3(CH_3)_26,2]_3$			324
$CH_3(H)_2B_3N_3(Ph)_3$	138–141		318
$(CH_3)_2HB_3N_3(Ph)_3$	205–207		318
$CH_3(H)_2B_3N_3(C_6H_4Cl\text{-}p)_3$			318
$CH_3(H)_2B_3N_3(C_6H_4CH_3\text{-}m)_3$	137–138		318
$CH_3(H)_2B_3N_3(p\text{-tolyl})_3$	150–151		318
$CH_3(H)_2B_3N_3(p\text{-anisyl})_3$			318
$(CH_3)_2HB_3N_3(p\text{-}C_6H_4Cl)_3$			318
$(CH_3)_2HB_3N_3[C_6H_3(OBu)_2\text{-}3,4]_3$			318
$(CH_3)_2HB_3N_3(p\text{-}C_6H_4Br)_3$	211–213		318
$(CH_3)_2HB_3N_3(\beta\text{-naphthyl})_3$			318
$(H_2N)_2CH_3B_3N_3(CH_3)_3$	90		304
$(CH_3(H)N)_2CH_3B_3N_3(CH_3)_3$		72 (0.17)	304
$[(CH_3)_2N]_2CH_3B_3N_3(CH_3)_3$		102 (1.3)	304
$H_2N(CH_3)_2B_3N_3(CH_3)_3$	87		304
$CH_3(H)N(CH_3)_2B_3N_3(CH_3)_3$		48 (0.15)	304
$(CH_3)_2N(CH_3)_2B_3N_3(CH_3)_3$		72 (1.0)	304
$(CH_3)_3B_3N_3(H)_2CH_3$		158	295
$(H_2N)_3B_3N_3(H)_2C_2H_5$	54	138–140 (5)	325
$F_3B_3N_3(CH_3)_3$	90.5		23,326,327

(continued)

TABLE VIII (*continued*)

Compound	mp, °C	bp (mm), °C	Remarks	References
$F_3B_3N_3(C_2H_5)_3$		26 (3)		327
$F_3B_3N_3(C_3H_7)_3$		59 (3)		327
$F_3B_3N_3(C_4H_9)_3$		89 (3)		327
$F_3B_3N_3(Ph)_3$	154	200 (0.5)		328
$F_3B_3N_3(CH_2C_6H_5)_3$	107	215 (0.4)		328
$F_3B_3N_3(SiH_3)_3$		24 (2.5)		23
$Cl_3B_3N_3(CH_3)_3$	162–4			122,278,286, 309,329, 330,361
$Cl_3B_3N_3(C_2H_5)_3$	57–9			122,329
$Cl_3B_3N_3(C_3H_7)_3$	79–80	110 (10^{-2})		330
$Cl_3B_3N_3(C_4H_9)_3$	30	115–120 (0.5)		122
$Cl_3B_3N_3(sec\text{-}C_4H_9)_3$		102 (5×10^{-3})		330
$Cl_3B_3N_3(C_6H_{11})_3$	217–219			329
$Cl_3B_3N_3(Ph)_3$	273–275			329
$Cl_3B_3N_3(p\text{-}C_6H_4CH_3)_3$	308–309			329,331, 333
$Cl_3B_3N_3(m\text{-}C_6H_4CH_3)_3$	269–271			329,333
$Cl_3B_3N_3(p\text{-}C_6H_4OCH_3)_3$	233–238			329,331
$Cl_3B_3N_3(o\text{-}C_6H_4OCH_3)_3$	198–202			333
$Br_3B_3N_3(CH_3)_3$			Sublimes at 120° under vacuum	286
$Br_3B_3N_3(C_2H_5)_3$	78–82			329
$I_3B_3N_3(CH_3)_3$	118–122			335
$I_3B_3N_3(C_4H_9)_3$	148–150			328
$I_3B_3N_3(Ph)_3$	118			328
$(NC)_3B_3N_3H_3$	200 (decomp.)			291
$(ONC)_3B_3N_3H_3$	166			330

$(SNC)_3B_3N_3H_3$	154 (decomp.)			330
$(H_2N)_3B_3N_3(CH_3)_3$	89			304
$[CH_3(H)N]_3B_3N_3(CH_3)_3$		131 (1.7)		304
$[(CH_3)_2N]_3B_3N_3(CH_3)_3$	64		n_D^{20} 1.5082	304
$[(CH_3)_2N]_3B_3N_3(C_2H_5)_3$	61	102–104 (3)		325
$[(C_2H_5)_2N]_3B_3N_3(CH_3)_3$		138 (5)		325
$[(C_2H_5)_2N]_3B_3N_3(C_2H_5)_3$		133–135 (5)		325
$[C_2H_5(H)N]_3B_3N_3(C_2H_5)_3$		145 (0.1)	n_D^{20} 1.4826	336
$[(CH_3)_2N(H)N]_3B_3N_3(CH_3)_3$	55–59	134 (3)		325
$[(CH_3)_2N(H)N]_3B_3N_3(C_2H_5)_3$		140 (3)		325
$[iso\text{-}C_3H_7(H)N]_3B_3N_3(iso\text{-}C_3H_7)_3$		106 (0.03)	n_D^{20} 1.4628	336
$[C_4H_9(H)N]_3B_3N_3(C_4H_9)_3$		158 (0.005)	n_D^{20} 1.4730	336
$[sec\text{-}C_4H_9(H)N]_3B_3N_3(sec\text{-}C_4H_9)_3$		135 (0.01)	n_D^{20} 1.4695	336
$[t\text{-}C_4H_9(H)N]_3B_3N_3(t\text{-}C_4H_9)_3$		103 (0.04)	n_D^{20} 1.4631	336
$[C_6H_{11}(H)N]_3B_3N_3(C_6H_{11})_3$	52–55			336
$[Ph(H)N]_3B_3N_3(Ph)_3$	152–155			336
$(CH_3)_3B_3N_3(CH_3)_3$	97	221		278,294, 295
$(C_2H_5)_3B_3N_3(C_2H_5)_3$	89–90			294
$(CH_3C{\equiv}C)_3B_3N_3(CH_3)_3$	187–189			293
$[H_2N]_3B_3N_3(Ph)_3$	255			304
$[CH_3(H)N]_3B_3N_3(Ph)_3$	165			304
$[(CH_3)_2N]_3B_3N_3(Ph)_3$	199			304
$(CH_3)_3B_3N_3(Ph)_3$	240–246		Crude	219,318
$(HC{\equiv}C)_3B_3N_3(Ph)_3$	264–265			340
$(CH_3C{\equiv}C)_3B_3N_3(Ph)_3$	245–246			293
$(CH_3CH{=}CH)_3B_3N_3(Ph)_3$	177–179			293
$(iso\text{-}Am)_3B_3N_3(C_2H_5)_3$	43–45	113–114 (0.06)		299
$(iso\text{-}Am)_3B_3N_3(iso\text{-}C_4H_9)_3$	53–55	126–128 (0.06)		299
$(iso\text{-}Am)_3B_3N_3(Ph)_3$	93.5–95.5	180–181 (0.03)		299
$(Ph)_3B_3N_3(CH_3)_3$	276–277			337
$(Ph)_3B_3N_3(C_2H_5)_3$	208–210			337,338

(continued)

TABLE VIII (*continued*)

Compound	mp, °C	bp (mm), °C	Remarks	References
$(Ph)_3B_3N_3(C_3H_7)_3$	170–171			337
$(Ph)_3B_3N_3(C_4H_9)_3$	131.5–132.5			337
$(Ph)_3B_3N_3(Ph)_3$	380–385			338
$(p\text{-tolyl})_3B_3N_3(Ph)_3$	282–284			338
$(p\text{-tolyl})_3B_3N_3(C_2H_5)_3$	222–225			338
$(PhC{\equiv}C)_3B_3N_3(CH_3)_3$	217–218			293
$(PhC{\equiv}C)_3B_3N_3(Ph)_3$	240–242			293
$[(C_2H_5)_2N]_3B_3N_3(C_2H_5)_3$				320
$[C_2H_5(H)N]_3B_3N_3(C_2H_5)_3$		145–150 (0.1)		272,320,336
$[iso\text{-}C_3H_7(H)N]_3B_3N_3(iso\text{-}C_3H_7)_3$		106 (0.03)		336
$[(C_2H_5)_2N]_2[C_2H_5(H)N]B_3N_3(C_2H_5)_3$				320
$[(CH_3)_3SiCH_2]_3B_3N_3(CH_3)_3$	64			339
$[(CH_3)_2(C_2H_5)SiCH_2]_3B_3N_3(CH_3)_3$		183–184 (1.0)		339
$[(CH_3)_2(C_4H_9)SiCH_2]_3B_3N_3(CH_3)_3$		213–214 (0.9)		339
$[(CH_3)_3SiOSi(CH_3)_2CH_2]_3B_3N_3(CH_3)_3$		175–176 (0.55)		339
$[(CH_3)_3SiCH_2CH_2]_3B_3N_3(Ph)_3$	157–159			340,341
$[(CH_3)_3SiO]_3B_3N_3(CH_3)_3$	22–23	130 (0.85)		339
$[(Ph)_3Si]_3B_3N_3(Ph)_3$	55–58			342
$[(Ph)_3SnCH_2CH_2]_3B_3N_3(Ph)_3$	219–221			341
$[(C_2H_5)_3SnCH_2CH_2]_3B_3N_3(Ph)_3$	87–88			341
$[(Ph)_2PCH_2CH_2]_3B_3N_3(Ph)_3$	160–162.5			343
$[(Ph)_2P(S)CH_2CH_2]_3B_3N_3(Ph)_3$	217–219			343
$[PhSCH_2CH_2]_3B_3N_3Ph_3$	134–135			344
$(BrCH_2CH_2)_3B_3N_3(Ph)_3$	165–166			344
$[Cl_3CCH_2C(H)(Br)]_3B_3N_3Ph_3$	212–213			344
$[Br_3CCH_2C(H)(Br)]_3B_3N_3(Ph)_3$	224–225 (decomp.)			344
$[BrCH_2C(H)(Br)]_3B_3N_3(Ph)_3$	257–258			344

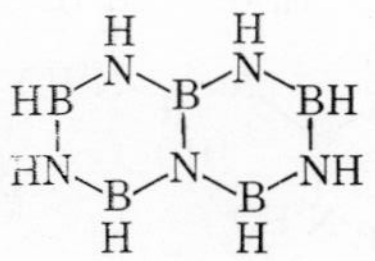 H H HB–N–B–N–BH HN–B–N–B–NH H H	27–30		269,364
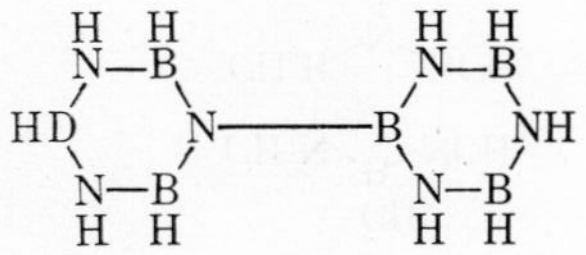 H H H H N–B N–B HD N——B NH N–B N–B H H H H	59–60		269,364
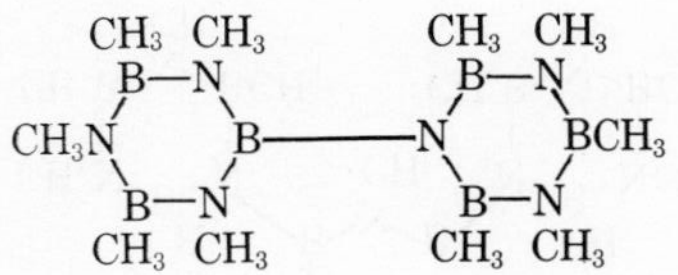 CH_3 CH_3 CH_3 CH_3 B–N B–N CH_3N B——N BCH_3 B–N B–N CH_3 CH_3 CH_3 CH_3	172–174		266
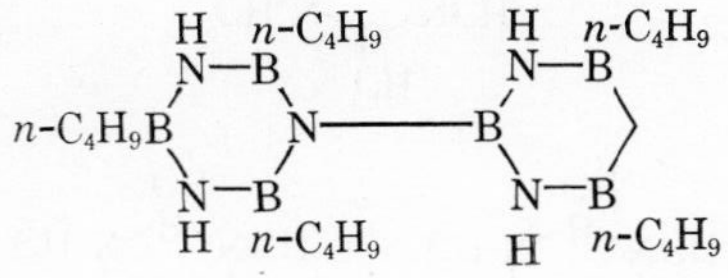 H n-C_4H_9 H n-C_4H_9 N–B N–B n-C_4H_9B N——B N–B N–B H n-C_4H_9 H n-C_4H_9		182–187 (0.6)	267
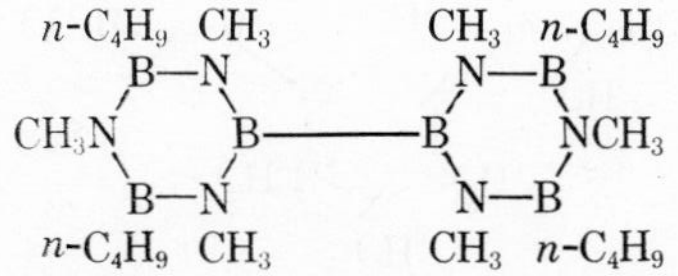 n-C_4H_9 CH_3 CH_3 n-C_4H_9 B–N N–B CH_3N B——B NCH_3 B–N N–B n-C_4H_9 CH_3 CH_3 n-C_4H_9	53	210 (0.001)	271

(continued)

TABLE VIII (*continued*)

Compound	mp, °C	bp (mm), °C	Remarks	References
CH_3 CH_3B–N–BCH_3 CH_3 N–B–N CH_3 CH_3B–N–B CH_3 B–N–BCH_3 CH_3N–B–NCH_3 CH_3N–B–NCH_3 CH_3 CH_3	207–210			266
CH_3 CH_3N–B–NCH_3 CH_3 B–N–B CH_3 CH_3N–B–N CH_3 N–B–NCH_3 CH_3B–N–BCH_3 CH_3B–N–BCH_3 CH_3 CH_3	135–138			266
CH_3 CH_3N–B–NCH_3 CH_3B–N–BCH_3 B CH_3N–B–NCH_3 CH_3 B–N–B CH_3 CH_3N–B–N CH_3 N–B–NCH_3 CH_3B–N–BCH_3 H_3CB–N–BCH_3 CH_3 CH_3	236–245			266

$[n\text{-}C_4H_9B(NCH_3)_3B_2(n\text{-}C_4H_9)]_2NH$	30	214–220 (0.1)	270
$[n\text{-}C_4H_9B(NCH_3)_3B_2(n\text{-}C_4H_9)]_2NC_2H_5$	33	212 (0.08)	270
$[C_2H_5NHB(NC_2H_5)_3B_2(NHC_2H_5)]_2NC_2H_5$			272
$[C_4H_9B(NCH_3)_3B_2C_4H_9]_2NPh$	62	250–260 (0.05)	270
$(CH_3)_3SiCH_2B(NCH_3)_3B[CH_2Si(CH_3)_3]B\text{—}CH_2\text{—}CH_2CH_2CH_2\text{—}B(NCH_3)_3B[CH_2Si(CH_3)_3]BCH_2Si(CH_3)_3$			268

TABLE IX
Tetrameric Borazynes $(RNBX)_4$

Amine used	X	Tetramer mp, °C	References
$(CH_3)_3CNH_2$	Cl	249	274,275
$(CH_3)_3CNH_2$	Br	240	274,275
$CH_3CH_2C(CH_3)_2NH_2$	Cl	162	274,275
$\overline{CH_2(CH_2)_4C}(CH_3)NH_2$	Cl	271	274,275
$CH_3(CH_2)_3C(CH_3)_2NH_2$	Cl	93	274,275
$(CH_3)_2CHCH_2C(CH_3)_2NH_2$	Cl	114	274,275
$(CH_3)_3CCH_2C(CH_3)_2NH_2$	Cl	200	274,275
$(CH_3)_3CCH_2C(CH_3)_2NH_2$	Br	200	274,275

B. Principles of Syntheses

1. Six-Membered Rings

The preparation of borazine is currently best achieved by the reaction of *B*-trichloroborazine with sodium borohydride in diglyme.[347]

$$Cl_3B_3N_3H_3 + 3NaBH_4 \xrightarrow{\text{diglyme}} B_3N_3H_6 + {}^3/_2B_2H_6 + 3NaCl$$

The classical synthesis of borazine is based upon a pyrolysis reaction of a 1:2 mixture of diborane and ammonia.[281] While this procedure is today of little more than historical significance, it is of interest to point out that two schemes have been considered as possible routes to the formation of borazine and substituted borazines in synthetic procedures which involve elimination reactions. The first sequence assumes that H_3NBH_3 is formed initially, followed by elimination of hydrogen in stepwise fashion to form monomeric BHNH, which then condenses as borazine.[295]

$$BH_3NH_3 \xrightarrow{-H_2} BH_2NH_2 \xrightarrow{-H_2} {}^1/_3(BHNH)_3$$

Scheme 1

The second sequence assumes that elimination of hydrogen from ammonia-borane produces cyclotriborazane which then loses hydrogen to form borazine.[345]

$$BH_3NH_3 \xrightarrow{-H_2} {}^1/_3(BH_2NH_2)_3 \xrightarrow{-H_2} {}^1/_3(BHNH)_3$$

Scheme 2

Recent work in this laboratory has shown that pyrolysis of H_3NBH_3 does not yield cyclotriborazane. An amorphous, ill-defined material of composition BH_2NH_2 is formed.[251] Further pyrolysis does not produce borazine, suggesting that neither scheme written above accurately reflects the major steps in the formation of borazine. On the other hand, scheme 2 is consistent with intermediates isolated and identified in the preparation of some of the substituted borazines.

Substituted borazines, in general, can be prepared by a sequence of steps which involve elimination reactions. Three general types of syntheses based upon elimination reactions are indicated below.

$$R_3N + BX_3 \rightarrow R_3NBX_3$$
$$\downarrow$$
$$R_2NBX_2 + RX$$
$$\downarrow$$
$${}^1/_3\,(RNBX)_3 + RX$$

$$R_3NH^+X^- + BR_3' \rightarrow R_3NBR_3' + HX$$
$$\downarrow$$
$$R_2NBR'_2 + RR'$$
$$\downarrow$$
$${}^1/_3(RNBR')_3 + RR'$$

$$R_3NH^+X^- + LiBH_4 \rightarrow R_3NBH_3 + H_2 + LiX$$
$$\downarrow$$
$$R_2NBH_2 + RH$$
$$\downarrow$$
$${}^1/_3(RNBH)_3 + RH$$

where X = Cl or Br, and R and R′ = H, alkyl, or phenyl groups.

The temperatures required for elimination reactions and the state of association of the aminoboranes, which are formed as intermediates, depend upon substitutent groups (see Sect. IV). Elimination reactions which occur most readily are those in which hydrogen or hydrogen halide is given off upon pyrolysis. This can take place in a refluxing solvent such as diglyme, a halobenzene, or triethylamine. The latter solvent may be especially useful since it abstracts hydrogen halide to form insoluble triethylammonium halide. Elimination reactions in which an organohalide or hydrocarbon is given off may require pyrolytic conditions of several hundred degrees.

The synthesis of *B*-trifluoroborazine is best achieved by a metathesis reaction.[287–289,349]

$$4Cl_3B_3N_3H_3 + 3TiF_4 \rightarrow 4F_3B_3N_3H_3 + 3TiCl_4$$

N-Substituted *B*-trifluoroborazines have been prepared from silylaminoborondifluorides under mild pyrolytic conditions.[23]

$$3(SiH_3)(CH_3)NBF_2 \xrightarrow{\Delta} (CH_3)_3N_3B_3F_3 + 3SiH_3F$$

$$3(SiH_3)_2NBF_2 \xrightarrow{\Delta} (SiH_3)_3N_3B_3F_3 + 3SiH_3F$$

The borazine ring has been incorporated into polycyclic ring systems by treating an *ortho*-substituted aniline with boron trichloride or a boron ester in refluxing xylene in the presence of 2,6-lutidine.[350,351]

$$3\ C_6H_4(NH_2)(YR) + 3\,BX_3 \longrightarrow (C_6H_4)_3Y_3B_3N_3 + 6\,HX + 3\,RX$$

where X = Cl or OR; Y = O, S, or NR; and R = H, alkyl.

N-Triorgano-*B*-trichloroborazines have proved to be good starting materials for the preparation of *B*-substituted borazines.

N-Substituted borazines can be prepared from the reaction of an appropriate *B*-trichloroborazine with lithium aluminum hydride[345,346] or a metal borohydride.[282,329,347]

$$4R_3N_3B_3Cl_3 + 3LiAlH_4 \rightarrow 4R_3N_3B_3H_3 + 3LiCl + 3AlCl_3$$

$$2R_3N_3B_3Cl_3 + 6MBH_4 \rightarrow 2R_3N_3B_3H_3 + 3B_2H_6 + 6MCl$$

where M = Li or Na

Protonic substances react readily with the boron–chlorine bond.[332,346,352–354]

$$R_3N_3B_3Cl_3 + 3HNR_2' \rightarrow R_3N_3B_3(NR_2')_3 + 3HCl$$

$$R_3N_3B_3Cl_3 + 3HOH \rightarrow R_3N_3B_3(OH)_3 + 3HCl$$

Reactions with sodium alkoxides produce alkoxyborazines.[339,355,356]

$$R_3N_3B_3Cl_3 + 3NaOR' \rightarrow R_3N_3B_3(OR')_3 + 3NaCl$$

Similarly, it appears as if the CN, CNS, Br, NO_2, and NO_3 groups can displace chlorine from the boron–chlorine bond by reaction with the appropriate alkali metal or silver salt; however, difficulty has been encountered in isolating pure products from some of these reactions.[291]

Grignard reagents and organolithium compounds displace chlorine from the boron–chlorine bond.[291,339,342,357–361]

$$R_3N_3B_3Cl_3 + 3R'MgX \rightarrow R_3N_3B_3R_3' + 3MgXCl$$

$$R_3N_3B_3Cl_3 + 3LiR' \rightarrow R_3N_3B_3R_3' + 3LiCl$$

where R = alkyl or phenyl groups; and R′ = alkyl, phenyl, or silyl groups. Unsymmetrically substituted borazines are obtained from the above reactions when the Grignard reagent or organolithium compound is present in less than the stoichiometric amount required for substitution of all of the B—Cl bonds.[361]

Another method which has been used for preparing unsymmetrically mixed borazines involves the copyrolysis of mixed amine boranes.[362,363] This procedure is not as good as the one described above, because of low yields, for the preparation of borazines with unsymmetrical *B*-substitution. However, it has been used for the preparation of borazines with unsymmetrical *N*-substitution.[265]

$$H_3NB(CH_3)_3 + CH_3H_2NB(CH_3)_3 \xrightarrow{380^\circ} \underset{17.0\%\ \text{yield}}{CH_3H_2N_3B_3(CH_3)_3} + \underset{13.5\%\ \text{yield}}{(CH_3)_2HN_3B_3(CH_3)_3}$$

These borazines with unsymmetrical *N*-substitution have served as starting materials for polycyclic borazines (Sect. V.C.8).[267]

A number of *N*-lithio derivatives of the borazines have been prepared by treating them with methyllithium,[265] e.g.,

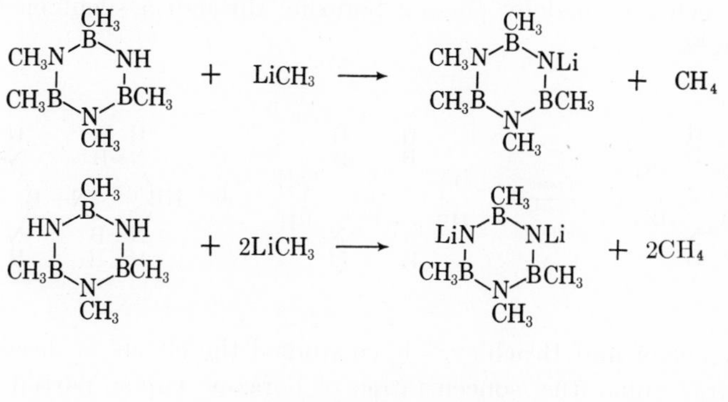

(ring: B-CH₃; N-CH₃, NH; B-CH₃, B-CH₃; N-CH₃) + $LiCH_3$ → (ring: B-CH₃; N-CH₃, NLi; B-CH₃, B-CH₃; N-CH₃) + CH_4

(ring: B-CH₃; HN, NH; B-CH₃, B-CH₃; N-CH₃) + $2LiCH_3$ → (ring: B-CH₃; LiN, NLi; B-CH₃, B-CH₃; N-CH₃) + $2CH_4$

2. *Polycyclic Borazines*

Substituted polycyclic borazines have been prepared from elimination reactions involving *N*-lithio- and *N*-dilithioborazines reacting with appropriately substituted *B*-trichloroborazines,[266]

```
        CH3              CH3
         B                N
  CH3N      NLi    +  ClB    BCH3     ——→
   |         |         |      |
  CH3B      BCH3     CH3N    NCH3
         N                B
        CH3              CH3

                       CH3                  CH3
                        B                    N
                 CH3N      N————————————B       BCH3
                  |        |            |        |        + LiCl
                 CH3B      BCH3      CH3N       NCH3
                        N                    N
                       CH3                  CH3

        CH3                     CH3
         B                       N
  LiN       NLi      +  2   ClB     BCH3
   |         |               |       |
  CH3B      BCH3           CH3N     NCH3
         N                       B
        CH3                     CH3

                    ↓

     CH3                CH3                 CH3
      N                  B                   N
 CH3B    B——————————N       N——————————B       BCH3
  |      |          |       |          |        |      + 2LiCl
 CH3N    NCH3     CH3B      BCH3     CH3N      NCH3
      B                  N                   B
     CH3                CH3                 CH3
```

Unsubstituted, polycyclic borazines have been prepared through the pyrolysis of borazine vapor at 380° to yield small amounts of borazanaphthalene, $B_5N_5H_8$, and diborazinyl, $B_6N_6H_{10}$.[364] The same products have been obtained by passing borazine through a silent electric discharge.[269]

```
      H                        H     H              H H       H H
      B                        B     B              N—B       N—B
  HN     NH     silent     HN     N     NH         /   \     /   \
  |       |    ————————→   |      |      |    +  HB     N—B      NH
  HB     BH     electric   HB     B     BH         \   /     \   /
      N         discharge      N     N              N—B       N—B
      H                        H     H              H H       H H
```

Laubengayer and Beachley[269] have studied the effects of design of the discharge apparatus, concentration of borazine vapor, partial pressure of hydrogen, residence time of borazine and polycyclic borazines in the discharge, and distance of the quenching trap from the discharge region. They were able to repress intermolecular condensations of borazine by dehydrogenation to form $B_6N_6H_{10}$ by adding hydrogen to the discharge tube.

3. Four-Membered Rings

The only reported four-membered B—N ring which is formally an analog of the cyclobutadiene framework has been prepared according to the pyrolysis reactions given below.[273, 365]

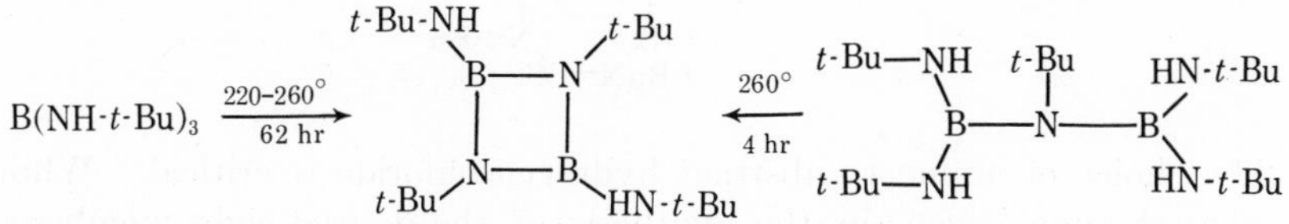

$$\mathrm{B(NH\text{-}}t\mathrm{\text{-}Bu)_3} \xrightarrow[62\ \mathrm{hr}]{220\text{–}260°} \begin{array}{c} t\text{-Bu-NH} \diagdown \quad \diagup t\text{-Bu} \\ \mathrm{B}\text{—}\mathrm{N} \\ | \qquad | \\ \mathrm{N}\text{—}\mathrm{B} \\ t\text{-Bu} \diagup \quad \diagdown \mathrm{HN}\text{-}t\text{-Bu} \end{array} \xleftarrow[4\ \mathrm{hr}]{260°} \begin{array}{c} t\text{-Bu—NH} \quad t\text{-Bu} \qquad \mathrm{HN}\text{-}t\text{-Bu} \\ \mathrm{B}\text{—}\mathrm{N}\text{—}\mathrm{B} \\ t\text{-Bu—NH} \qquad\qquad \mathrm{HN}\text{-}t\text{-Bu} \end{array}$$

Some properties of the product are:

bp	n_D^{20}	d_4^{20}
72–74° at 5 × 10^{-3} mm	1.4582	0.8666

The reactions cited for the preparation of the 4-membered B—N ring appear to take place in a three step process involving:

1. Intermolecular condensation which leads to the formation of a compound having a diborylamine linkage $>\mathrm{B}\text{—}\overset{|}{\mathrm{N}}\text{—}\mathrm{B}<$.

2. Intramolecular 1,3-nucleophilic rearrangement.

3. Dimerization to form the four-membered B—N ring.

These steps are illustrated in the following sequence:

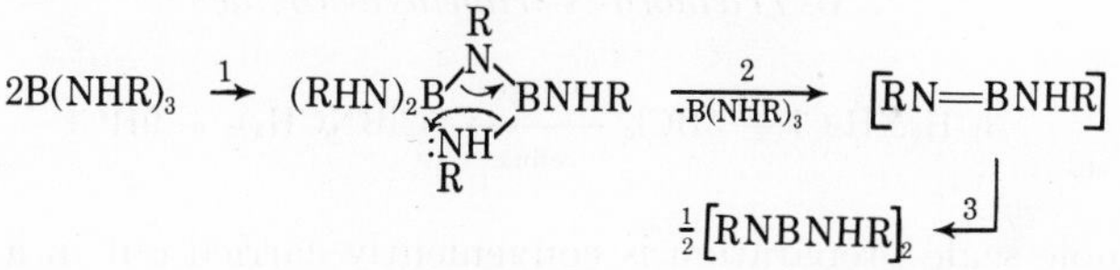

$$2\mathrm{B(NHR)_3} \xrightarrow{1} \mathrm{(RHN)_2B}\begin{array}{c}\mathrm{R}\\ \mathrm{N}\\ \curvearrowright \\ \mathrm{:NH} \\ \mathrm{R}\end{array}\mathrm{BNHR} \xrightarrow[-\mathrm{B(NHR)_3}]{2} [\mathrm{RN{=}BNHR}]$$

$$\xrightarrow{3} \tfrac{1}{2}[\mathrm{RNBNHR}]_2$$

The isolation of the postulated diborylamine in the synthesis of the cyclobutadiene analog provides support for the postulated sequence.[273]

4. Eight-Membered Rings

Turner and Warne[274, 275] have studied elimination reactions analogous to those employed in the syntheses of the *N*-substituted *B*-trihaloborazines (Sect. V.B.1), but have sought to put substituents on nitrogen which minimize the possibility of six-membered borazine ring formation in favor of larger frameworks. A series of eight-membered ring compounds (tetrameric borazynes) was discovered when tertiary alkyl groups were placed on the nitrogen. Table IX lists the known eight-membered ring compounds. A typical pyrolysis reaction for the preparation of a compound in this ring system is given below.

$$t\text{-BuNH}_2 + \text{BCl}_3 \longrightarrow t\text{-BuNHBCl}_2 + t\text{-BuNH}_3\text{BCl}_4$$

$$\swarrow \text{Et}_3\text{N} \qquad \swarrow \text{Et}_3\text{N}$$

$$[\text{ClB—N-}t\text{-Bu}]_4 \text{ (eight-membered ring: ClB—N-}t\text{-Bu, }t\text{-BuN, BCl, ClB, N-}t\text{-Bu, }t\text{-BuN—BCl)}$$

The choice of amine to abstract hydrogen chloride is critical. While triethylamine assists in the synthesis of the desired eight-membered ring, diisopropylethylamine which is highly hindered does not. The use of trimethylamine produces the adduct $(CH_3)_3NBCl_3$.[275]

C. Preparative Procedures

1. Borazine

$$B_3Cl_3N_3H_3 + 3NaBH_4 \xrightarrow[\text{excess N}(n\text{-C}_4\text{H}_9)_3]{\text{diglyme}} B_3H_3N_3H_3 + 3NaCl + {}^3/_2B_2H_6$$

Borazine is most conveniently prepared by the method described in Section IV.C.7 dealing with the synthesis of cyclotriborazane.

2. B-*Trichloro*-N-*trimethylborazine*[361]

$$3CH_3NH_3Cl + 3BCl_3 \xrightarrow[\text{reflux}]{C_6H_5Cl} (ClBNCH_3)_3 + 9HCl$$

A 1 mole scale preparation is conveniently carried out in a two-liter, three-necked flask equipped with a stirrer, a water cooled condenser and a Dry Ice condenser in series, and a gas inlet tube extending nearly to the bottom of the flask. The flask is flushed with dry nitrogen and the gas-inlet tube is connected to a reservoir of trichloroborane. A 1-mole quantity (67.5 g) of methylammonium chloride and about 1 liter of dry chlorobenzene are added to the flask. The contents are refluxed and stirred vigorously, and 1 mole plus a slight excess of trichloroborane is introduced into the reaction flask on a slow stream of nitrogen. After all the trichloroborane has been added, refluxing is continued for about 18 hr until evolution of hydrogen chloride ceases. The reaction mixture is filtered while still hot and the solvent removed from the filtrate under reduced pressure. The residue may be sublimed *in vacuo* or recrystallized from benzene to give pure *B*-trichloro-*N*-trimethylborazine, mp 162–164°, in nearly quantitative yield.

3. N-*Trimethylborazine*[39]

$$3CH_3NH_3Cl + 3LiBH_4 \xrightarrow{Et_2O} (HBNCH_3)_3 + 9H_2 + LiCl$$

A quantity of methylammonium chloride is added to a dry three-necked reaction flask equipped with a stirrer, water cooled condenser, and dropping funnel. An equivalent amount of lithium borohydride as a 0.5*M* solution in ether is slowly added through the dropping funnel. After evolution of hydrogen ceases, the reaction mixture is refluxed for about 3 hr and the ether is removed under reduced pressure. The residue in the reaction flask is heated to 250° and maintained at that temperature for a period of 4 hr. During this time it is vital that the condenser be functioning efficiently to prevent a loss of product in the stream of hydrogen which is evolved. The crude product may be purified by fractional condensation under reduced pressure to give pure *N*-trimethylborazine (bp 132°) in nearly quantitative yield.

4. B-*Triethyl*-N-*trimethylborazine*[361]

$$(ClBNCH_3)_3 + 3Mg + 3C_2H_5Br \rightarrow (C_2H_5BNCH_3)_3 + 3Mg(Cl)Br$$

A 0.1-mole preparation is conveniently carried out in a 250 ml, two-necked flask fitted with a water-cooled condenser and Dry Ice cold-finger condenser in series and a dropping funnel. A calcium chloride drying tube prevents diffusion of moisture into the system.

The flask is charged with 9.0 g (0.37 mole) of magnesium turnings, 25 g (0.11 mole) of *B*-trichloro-*N*-trimethylborazine and about 75 ml of anhydrous diethyl ether for a 0.1-mole scale reaction. Ethyl bromide (0.36 mole) is slowly added over a 1–2 hr period to the stirred reaction mixture after a crystal of iodine has been added to initiate the Grignard reaction. After the alkyl bromide has been added, the contents of the flask are refluxed for another 3–4 hr. The solid precipitate and any unreactive magnesium is removed by filtration under a dry nitrogen atmosphere, and the filtrate is washed several times with dry diethyl ether. The filtrate and washings are combined, and the solvent is removed under reduced pressure. The crude yellow liquid which remains is fractionated under vacuum yielding about 15 g of pure *B*-triethyl-*N*-trimethylborazine, bp 82° (0.65 mm).

5. B-*Tris*(*dimethylamino*)*borazine*[309]

$$(ClBNH)_3 + 6(CH_3)_2NH \rightarrow [(CH_3)_2N]_3B_3N_3H_3 + 3(CH_3)_2NH_2Cl$$

A three-necked flask equipped with stirrer, dropping funnel, and Dry Ice condenser topped by a calcium chloride drying tube is charged with a solution of anhydrous dimethylamine in dry benzene (1 g amine to 10 ml benzene). A solution of the desired amount of *B*-trichloroborazine in dry benzene (1 g borazine to 2 ml benzene) is slowly added by means of the dropping funnel over a 15-min period. After the addition is complete, the reaction mixture is stirred for an additional 90 min and then filtered under a dry nitrogen atmosphere. The precipitate is washed with dry benzene and the combined filtrate and washings are evaporated under reduced pressure. The residue is purified by vacuum sublimation at 95° (2 mm) giving *B*-tris(dimethylamino)borazine (mp 112–113°) in about 70% yield.

6. B-*Trifluoroborazine*[349]

Quantities of *B*-trichloroborazine and titanium tetrafluoride (3:1 molar ratio) are separately powdered, then mixed well and placed in a reaction vessel. The surface of the mixture is covered with a small amount of TiF_4 powder and the vessel is slowly heated until the reaction is self sustaining. Upon completion of the reaction (usually about 10 min), volatile materials are removed under reduced pressure (ca. 70 mm) and the distillate is redistilled at room temperature at approximately 1.0 mm pressure to remove titanium tetrachloride. The residue is purified by further vacuum distillation or sublimation to give *B*-trifluoroborazine, mp 122° (sublimes).

7. N-*Lithio*-B-*trimethylborazine*[265]

$$(CH_3)_3B_3N_3H_3 + CH_3Li \xrightarrow{(C_2H_5)_2O} (CH_3)_3B_3N_3(H)_2Li + CH_4$$

A small quantity (10–20 mmoles) of *B*-trimethylborazine is placed in a glass bomb tube (30–50 ml) in a dry nitrogen atmosphere and the tube is frozen with liquid nitrogen. Using a syringe, an equimolar quantity of methyllithium (about 1*M* solution in diethylether) is carefully added to the bomb which is then sealed under vacuum. The bomb is then allowed to warm slowly to room temperature and considerable effervescence of the mixture should be in evidence. After remaining overnight at room temperature, the tube is opened on a vacuum line and the noncondensable gas (CH_4) produced is pumped off. The ethereal solution of *N*-lithio-*B*-trimethylborazine is then ready to be used as a starting material for further preparations.

8. Decamethyl-N,B-*Biborazyl*[266]

```
       CH3              CH3
        B                N
       / \              / \
  CH3N     NLi      ClB     BCH3
    |       |    +   |       |       ———→
  CH3B     BCH3     CH3N    NCH3
       \ /              \ /
        N                B
       CH3              CH3

                CH3                  CH3
                 B                    N
                / \                  / \
           CH3N     N —————————— B      BCH3
             |      |            |       |
           CH3B    BCH3       CH3N      NCH3
                \ /                  \ /
                 N                    B
                CH3                  CH3
                                   + LiCl
```

A small quantity (10–20 mmoles) of *N*-dimethyl-*B*-trimethylborazine is syringed into a nitrogen-filled 25–50 ml glass bomb tube. The tube is cooled to −196°, the tube is opened on a vacuum line and the non-condensable gas (CH_4) removed. The tube is then warmed to room temperature and an equivalent quantity of pentamethyl-*B*-chloroborazine, dissolved in 1–2 ml of diethylether, is syringed into the *N*-lithiopentamethylborazine solution through a rubber-septum closure on the tube. Gentle agitation of the mixture produces a cloudiness and an evolution of heat. Finally, the tube is shaken vigorously, centrifuged, and the supernatant liquid is withdrawn by a syringe. The residue obtained on evaporation of the ether solution is extracted with 10 ml of petroleum ether (bp 30–60°) and the extracted material is sublimed *in vacuo*, first at 50° to remove unreacted pentamethyl-*B*-chloroborazine, then at 100°. The sublimate obtained at 100° is carefully recrystallized from isopropylamine and then resublimed at 100° giving pure decamethyl-*N*,*B′*-biborazyl, mp 172–174°, in 40–50% yield.

VI. CYCLIC COMPOUNDS CONTAINING EITHER THE AMINE-BORANE LINKAGE OR AMINOBORANE LINKAGE (MONO, BIS, AND TRIS)

A. Introduction

In recent times there has been significant interest in the synthesis and properties of heterocycles which contain one or more boron–nitrogen bonds incorporated in frameworks containing carbon atoms as well. Although a wide variety of compounds have been prepared, they can be classified to some extent according to the types of apparent boron–nitrogen linkage in the cyclic framework. Furthermore, in many respects the linkages show properties similar to those observed in structures which are usually referred to as amine-boranes or amino-boranes.

Thus, for example, structure **20** shows a cyclic compound, cyclo-*N*,*B*-

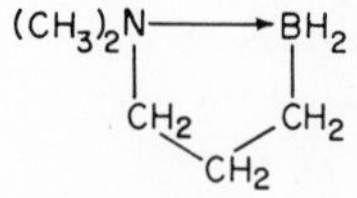

$(CH_3)_2N \rightarrow BH_2$, CH_2, CH_2, CH_2

(**20**)

dimethylaminopropylborane, with an amine-borane linkage. It can be considered to be a cyclic coordination compound formed from the chain-like species $(CH_3)_2NCH_2CH_2CH_2BH_2$.[366]

Structure **21** shows the structure of a derivative of 2,5-diborapipera-

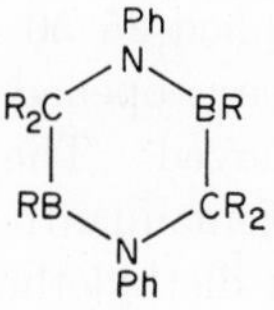

Ph, N, R_2C, BR, RB, CR_2, N, Ph

(**21**)

zine, a compound with aminoborane linkages. Characteristic of amino-boranes, the boron–nitrogen stretching frequency in this compound suggests double bond character.[367] A most interesting compound with an aminoborane linkage is 2-phenyl-1,2-azaborocyclohexane. It can be dehydrogenated to form a heteroaromatic framework.[368]

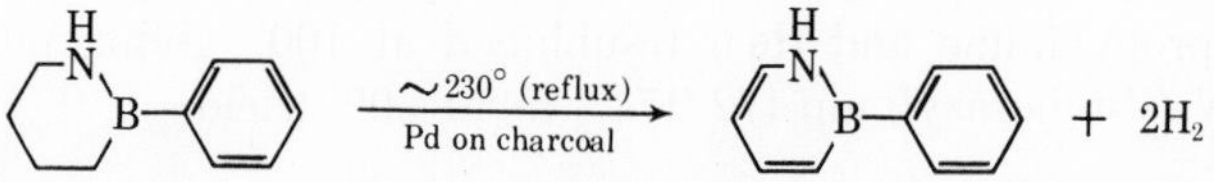

$$\xrightarrow[\text{Pd on charcoal}]{\sim 230^\circ \text{ (reflux)}} \quad + \; 2H_2$$

Typical structures with bis(amino)borane linkages are 2-methyl-1,3,2-diazaborocyclopentane (**22**) and 2-methyl-1,3,2-benzodiazaborolidine

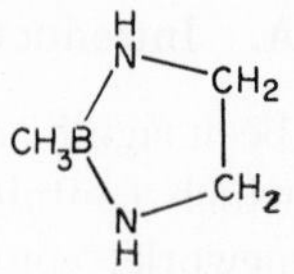

H, N, CH_2, CH_3B, CH_2, N, H

(**22**)

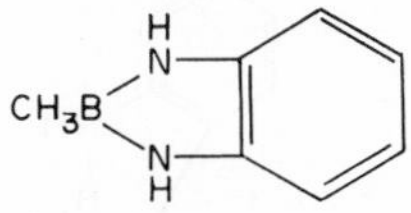

(23)

(**23**). The latter compound is of particular interest because of the potential aromatic character of the heterocyclic framework. It should be recognized that this and several other compounds which are potentially aromatic and appear in this section, could be considered just as appropriately in Section VIII, entitled "Heteroaromatic Boron–Nitrogen Compounds."

Precursors to some of the bis(amino)boranes are novel in the sense that they contain both quaternary and ternary nitrogen in the framework. Upon pyrolysis, the bis(amino)borane is formed.[369]

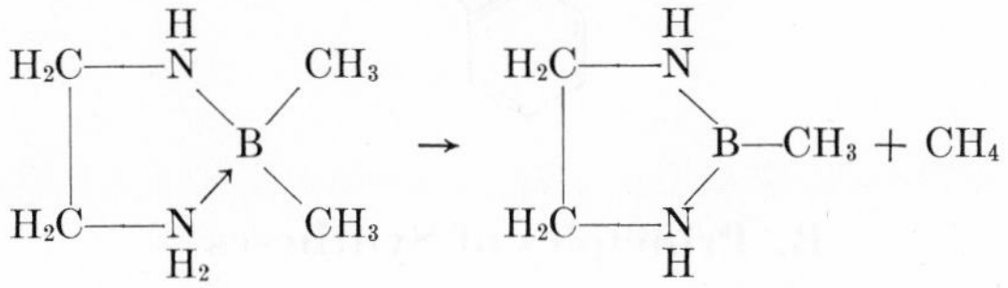

$$\rightarrow \quad B{-}CH_3 + CH_4$$

The 2-bora-1,3-diazaazulenes formally show two types of nitrogen. Significant electron delocalization is suggested, however, by the hydrolytic stability of the heteronuclear framework and proton NMR spectra, so that one might use the following resonance forms to indicate the apparent aromaticity of the structure.[370]

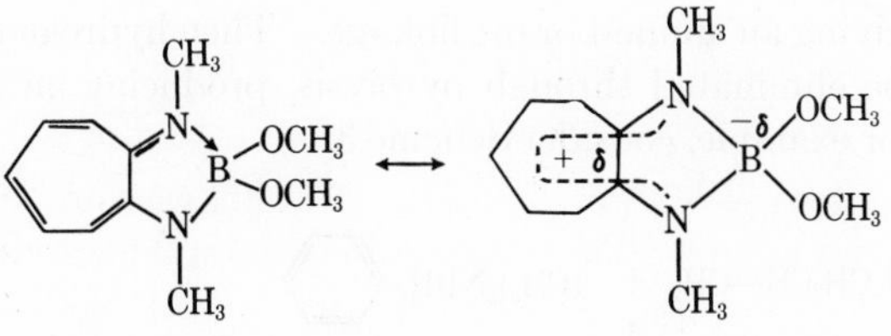

$$\longleftrightarrow$$

The reactions given below indicate that 1,3,2-benzodiazaborolidines and 1,3,2-benzodiheteroborolidines can be precursors in the formation of polycyclic frameworks which contain a borazine ring.[350,351,371] Also see Section V.B.

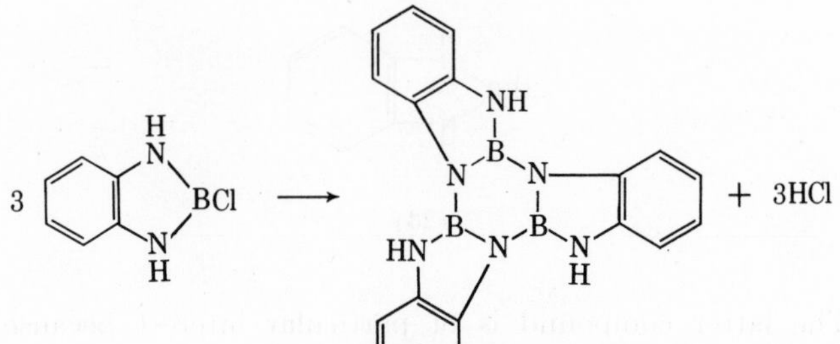

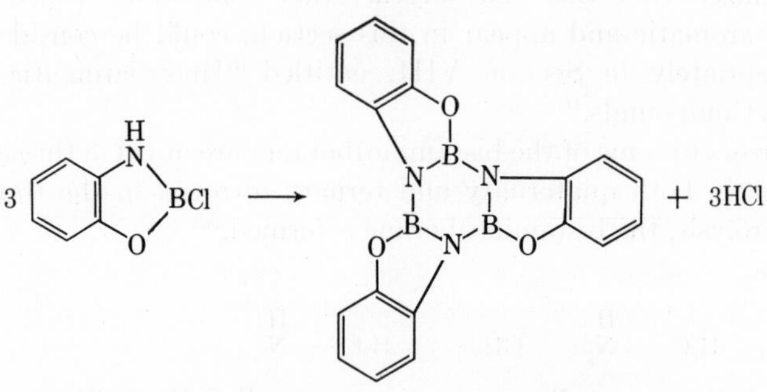

B. Principles of Syntheses

Using a hydroboration procedure, a BH_3 group can be added to an olefinic bond in an amine such as dimethylallylamine, $(CH_3)_2NCH_2$-$CH{=}CH_2$. Cyclization to form a dative bond characteristic of an amine-borane is then possible.[366] See Section VI.C for the procedure.

Two procedures have been developed for the preparation of 1,2-azaborocycloalkanes.[368] The more general procedure will be discussed. It is similar in principle to the one described above in that it involves the hydroboration of an amine containing an olefinic bond, which can lead to cyclization giving an amine-borane linkage. Then hydrogen or hydrogen halide can be eliminated through pyrolysis, producing an aminoborane linkage. For example, consider Scheme 3.

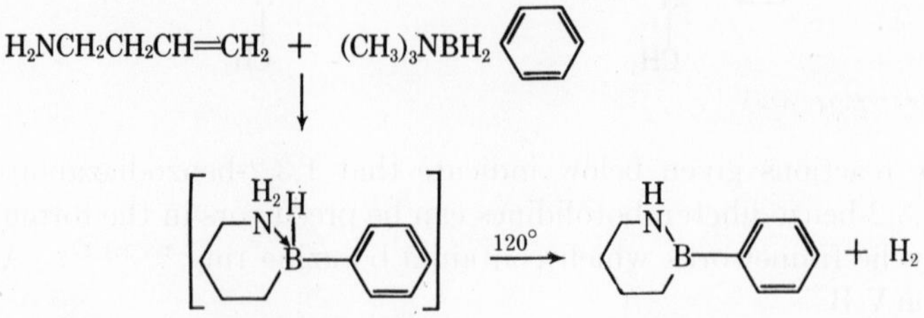

$H_2NCH_2CH_2CH{=}CH_2 + (CH_3)_3NBH_2C_6H_5$ → [cyclic amine-borane] $\xrightarrow{120°}$ cyclic aminoborane $+ H_2$

Scheme 3

Cyclic structures containing bis(amino)borane linkages have been prepared from reactions of diamines with organodihaloboranes, giving 1,3,2-benzodiazaborolidines when the diamine is *ortho*-phenylenediamine.[371–377,382]

$$B(CH_3)_3 + \begin{matrix} H_2NCH_2 \\ | \\ H_2NCH_2 \end{matrix} \xrightarrow{250^\circ} (CH_3)_2B\begin{matrix} NH-CH_2 \\ \leftarrow NH_2-CH_2 \end{matrix} + CH_4$$

$$(CH_3)_2B(NHCH_2CH_2NH_2) \xrightarrow{475^\circ} CH_4 + \begin{matrix} H_2C-NH \\ | \\ H_2C-NH \end{matrix}\!\!\!>B-CH_3$$

$$C_6H_4(NH_2)_2 + CH_3BCl_2 \longrightarrow C_6H_4(NH)_2BCH_3 + 2HCl$$

TABLE X
1,3,2-Diazaboracycloalkanes

Compound	R	mp, °C	bp (mm), °C	References
$HN(CH_2)_2NH$ ring, BR	CH_3	43.5	106	369,378,387
	Ph	157		379
$HN(CH_2)_3NH$ ring, BR	CH_3		132	369,380
	$CH{=}CH_2$		41 (7)	380
	C_2H_5		44–45 (13)	380
	Ph	50–52	94–95 (1)	380
$HN(CH_2)_4NH$ ring, BPh		27–29	102–104 (1)	380
$CH_3N(CH_2)_2NCH_3$ ring, BR	$CH{=}CH_2$		35–36	225
	Ph		73 (3)	227
$C_2H_5N(CH_2)_2NC_2H_5$ ring, B–Ph			95 (8)	227

Table X lists the properties of the known 1,3,2-diazaboracycloalkanes and properties for the 1,3,2-benzodiazaborolidines are given in Table XI.

Appropriately *ortho*-substituted anilines give rise to the formation of 1,3,2-benzodiheteroborolidines.

$$o\text{-}C_6H_4(NH_2)(OH) + CH_3BCl_2 \longrightarrow C_6H_4(NH)(O)BCH_3 + 2HCl$$

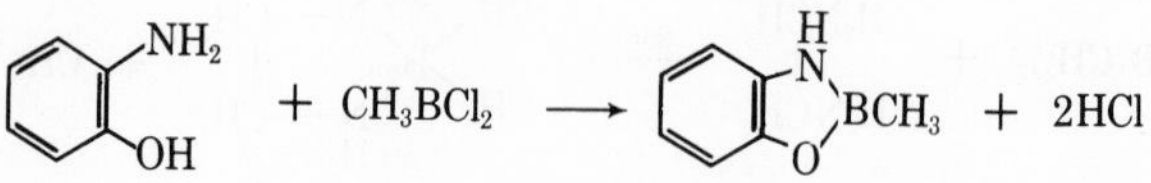

Some physical properties of the 1,3,2-benzodiheteroborolidines are listed in Table XI.

TABLE XI
1,3,2-Benzodiheteroborolidines

Compound	R	mp, °C	References
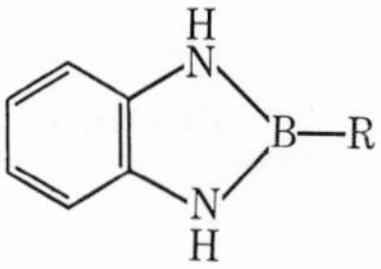 $C_6H_4(NH)_2B\text{—}R$	H	79–80	382
	CH_3	98–99	382,387
	C_3H_7	92–94	384
	Ph	215–216	201,350,371, 372,379 382–385
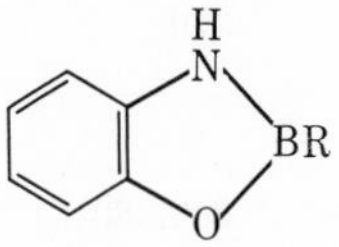 $C_6H_4(NH)(O)BR$	CH_3	32–34	387
	Ph	105–106	201,386
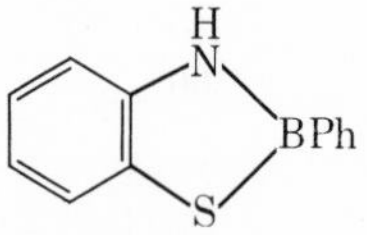 $C_6H_4(NH)(S)BPh$		154–156	201

Transamination reactions of bis(amino)boranes using diamines have proved to be very useful for the syntheses of the 1,3,2-diazaboracycloalkanes.[378]

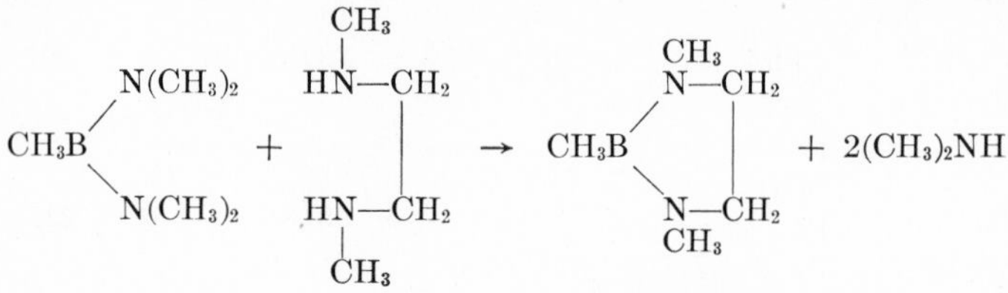

$$CH_3B[N(CH_3)_2]_2 + CH_3HN\text{—}CH_2\text{—}CH_2\text{—}NHCH_3 \rightarrow CH_3B\langle N(CH_3)CH_2CH_2N(CH_3)\rangle + 2(CH_3)_2NH$$

The transamination reaction is probably a better route to the preparation of 1,3,2-diazaboracycloalkanes than the reaction of a chainlike diamine with a triorganoborane.

By treating a tris(amino)borane with 3,3′-diaminodipropylamine, transamination occurs to produce a cyclic structure with a tris(amino)-borane arrangement.[380]

$$[(CH_3)_2N]_2B{-}N(CH_3)_2 + HN(CH_2CH_2NH_2)_2 \rightarrow \text{(bicyclic B–N compound)} + 3\ NH(CH_3)_2$$

1,2-Aminoimino derivatives of cycloheptatriene have been treated with triorganoboranes and organodialkoxyboranes to produce 2-bora-1,3-diazaazulenes.[370]

$$\text{(1-imino-2-aminocycloheptatriene)} + RB(OCH_3)_2 \xrightarrow[\text{toluene}]{\text{5-24hr}} \text{(2-bora-1,3-diazaazulene, } B(OCH_3)_2\text{)} + HR$$

TABLE XII
2-Bora-1,3-diazaazulenes

R_1	R_2	R_3	mp, °C	Remarks	References
H	OCH_3	OCH_3	>300 (decomp.)		370
H	Ph	OC_2H_5	253 (decomp.)		370
H	Ph	OH	>300	Probably impure	370
CH_3	Ph	OH	96–98	Charcoal used in recrystallization	370
			163–164	No charcoal in recrystallization	370
CH_3	F	F	118–119		370
CH_3	OCH_3	OCH_3	127–129		370
CH_3	Ph	OC_2H_5	Indef.		370
p-$CH_3OC_6H_4$	Ph	OC_2H_5	181		370

C. Preparative Procedures

1. *Cyclo*-N,B-*dimethylaminopropylborane*[366]

$$(CH_3)_2N{-}CH_2{-}HC{=}CH_2 + H_3BN(CH_3)_3 \xrightarrow[\text{reflux}]{\text{toluene}} (CH_3)_2N{\rightarrow}BH_2(CH_2)_3 + N(CH_3)_3$$

Equimolar quantities of dimethylallylamine and trimethylamine-borane are mixed in toluene and placed in a reaction flask under an inert atmosphere. The flask is equipped with a water-cooled reflux condenser connected to a mercury or oil bubbler. The toluene solution is refluxed several hours until there is no more trimethylamine evolution. The toluene is removed at atmospheric pressure and the residue is distilled under vacuum. The fraction collected between 80 and 100° (25 mm) is redistilled giving pure cyclo-*N*-*B*-dimethylaminopropylborane, bp 85° (25 mm), in about 25% yield.

2. *1-Methyl-2-phenyl-1,2-azaborolidine*[368]

$$PhH_2BN(CH_3)_3 + CH_2{=}CHCH_2NH(CH_3) \longrightarrow \overline{NCH_3{=}BPh} + N(CH_3)_3 + H_2$$

A quantity of trimethylamine-phenylborane is dissolved in diglyme (about 30 ml diglyme per gram of amine-borane) and the solution transferred to a flask fitted with a mechanical stirrer, dropping funnel, and a reflux condenser connected to a mercury or oil bubbler. The contents of the flask are stirred and gradually heated while an equimolar quantity of a dilute solution of *N*-methylallylamine in diglyme is slowly added through the dropping funnel. The temperature is raised to 135° for a period of several hours during the addition of the amine. After the addition is complete and gas evolution has ceased, a small quantity of trimethylammonium chloride is added to the flask and the diglyme solution is heated to reflux. The diglyme is removed from the reaction mixture at reduced pressure leaving a liquid which is distilled out at 2–4 mm pressure and then redistilled giving pure 1-methyl-2-phenyl-1,2-azaborolidine, bp 78.5–81.5° (2.55 mm), in 30–40% yield.

3. *2-Ethyl-1,3,2-diazaboracyclohexane*[380]

$$C_2H_5B[N(CH_3)_2]_2 + H_2NCH_2CH_2CH_2NH_2 \longrightarrow C_2H_5B\langle NH(CH_2)_3NH\rangle + 2HN(CH_3)_2$$

A quantity of 1,3-diaminopropane is added to a solution of an equimolar quantity of bis(dimethylamino)ethylborane in dry hexane [about 6 ml hexane per gram of bis(amino)borane] under an inert atmosphere. The mixture is refluxed for 2 hr and dimethylamine is evolved, passing out through the water-cooled reflux condenser. The solvent is then stripped off and the residue distilled under reduced pressure to give 2-ethyl-1,3,2-diazaboracyclohexane, bp 44–45° (13 mm), in about 70% yield.

VII. μ-AMINODIBORANES

A. Introduction

The μ-aminodiboranes are structurally analogous to diborane, except that one of the bridge positions is occupied by the nitrogen of an amino group (**24**).[310] The bonding of the nitrogen in the bridge position is

$$H_2B(\mu\text{-}NR_2)(\mu\text{-}H)BH_2$$

(**24**)

unlike that of the bridge hydrogen, since the nitrogen has a sufficient number of valence electrons available to form electron pair bonds with both borons. μ-Aminodiboranes tend to decompose according to the following equation:[21]

$$H_2B(\mu\text{-}NR_2)(\mu\text{-}H)BH_2 \rightarrow {}^1/_2\, B_2H_6 + H_2BNR_2$$

Stability tends to increase with increasing substitution of hydrogen on the nitrogen by alkyl groups. An order of thermal stability is:[169]

$$H_2NB_2H_5 < CH_3NHB_2H_5 < (CH_3)_2NB_2H_5$$

μ-Methylsilylaminodiborane, $(CH_3NSiH_3)B_2H_5$, and μ-disilylaminodiborane, $(SiH_3)_2NB_2H_5$, have also been reported.[21] The order of stability of these μ-aminodiboranes is:[21]

$$(CH_3NSiH_3)B_2H_5 > (SiH_3)_2NB_2H_5$$

Relatively little is known about the μ-aminodiboranes except that they will react with amines. The best characterized of these reactions are the reactions with trimethylamine.[169,310,388]

```
     CH3    CH3                          CH3   CH3
        \  /                                \ /
  H      N      H                            N
   \   /  \   /                            ↙  \
     B      B      + N(CH3)3  →       H3B      BH2
   /  \  /  \                                   ↑
  H     H     H                               N(CH3)3
```

TABLE XIII
μ-Aminodiboranes

Compound	mp, °C	bp (mm), °C	Remarks	References
$H_2NB_2H_5$	−66.5	76.2	B^{11} NMR, t (+44.8 ppm)[a]	276,310, 381
$CH_3(H)NB_2H_5$		66.8	B^{11} NMR, t (+40.8 ppm)[a]	169,381
$(CH_3)_2NB_2H_5$	−54.8 to −54.4	50.3	B^{11} NMR, t (+35.1 ppm)[a]	169,381
$CH_3(SiH_3)NB_2H_5$	−39.0	51		21
$(SiH_3)_2NB_2H_5$	−69.4 to −68.8	54		21
$C_2H_5(H)NB_2H_5$	−96.4	87		55
n-$C_3H_7(H)NB_2H_5$	−146 to −142	121		55
CH_2 / CH_2 ring: CH_2—(CH_2)—CH_2—NB_2H_5 (four-membered ring: CH_2, CH_2, CH_2, NB_2H_5)	−45.4	101		55
CH_2—CH_2 / CH_2—CH_2 ring with NB_2H_5 (five-membered ring)	−63.5	122		55
CH_2—CH_2 / CH_2 / CH_2—CH_2 ring with NB_2H_5 (six-membered ring)		148		55

[a] Chemical shift with respect to trimethylborate, $B(OCH_3)_3$. t = triplet.

TABLE XIV
Amine Adducts of μ-Aminodiboranes

Compound	mp, °C	Remarks	References
$H_3BN(CH_3)_2BH_2NH_3$	96.5–97.5		388
$H_3BN(CH_3)_2BH_2NH_2CH_3$	85–90		388
$H_3BN(CH_3)_2BH_2NH(CH_3)_2$	58–59		388
$H_3BN(CH_3)_2BH_2N(CH_3)_3$	36.8–38	Decomposes completely at 85°	169,388
$H_3BN(H)(CH_3)BH_2N(CH_3)_3$			169
$H_3BNH_2BH_2N(CH_3)_3$			310

Properties of the μ-aminodiboranes and their amine adducts are summarized in Tables XIII and XIV.

B. Principles of Syntheses

By passing diborane over the diammoniate of diborane at 65°, μ-aminodiborane is formed.[310]

$$BH_2(NH_3)_2{}^+BH_4{}^- + B_2H_6 \rightarrow 2B_2H_5NH_2 + 2H_2$$

Alkyl substituted μ-aminodiboranes are prepared essentially by adding diborane to the appropriate aminoborane at elevated temperature.[55,169]

$$R_2NBH_2 + {}^1/_2B_2H_6 \rightarrow B_2H_5NR_2$$

μ-Silylaminodiboranes have been prepared according to the following equations.[21]

$$2CH_3N(SiH_3)_2 + 2B_2H_5Br \rightarrow 2SiH_3Br + 2(CH_3NSiH_3)B_2H_5$$

$$2(SiH_3)_3N + 2B_2H_5Br \rightarrow 2SiH_3Br + 2(SiH_3)_2NB_2H_5$$

C. Preparative Procedures

1. μ-Dimethylaminodiborane[169]

$${}^1/_2B_2H_6 + (CH_3)NH \rightarrow H_3BN(H)(CH_3)_2$$

$$H_3BN(H)(CH_3)_2 \xrightarrow{135°} H_2BN(CH_3)_2 + H_2$$

$$H_2BN(CH_3)_2 + {}^1/_2B_2H_6 \xrightarrow{135°} (CH_3)_2NB_2H_5$$

Diborane is passed into dimethylamine at −42°, in the bottom of tube *A* in Figure 10, then the excess amine is distilled away and the bath temperature is slowly raised to 135°. As the resulting $H_2BN(CH_3)_2$ begins to reflux in the upper part of tube *A*, diborane is bubbled in at the rate of 100–200 cc/min. The product is caught at −196° in trap *B*, from which it is later distilled into a vacuum system and separated from unused diborane and dimethylaminoborane. About 70–80% of the diborane undergoes reaction. The product is obtained by fractional distillation from trap *B*, maintained at −78°, into a second trap at −112°, and finally into a third trap at −196° to catch the more volatile species. The product collected at −112° is refractionated until it exhibits a constant vapor pressure of 101 mm at 0°. Its extrapolated boiling point is 50.3°. Quantities of 25 g or more can be prepared in a 2-hr reaction time depending on the size of the reaction tube.

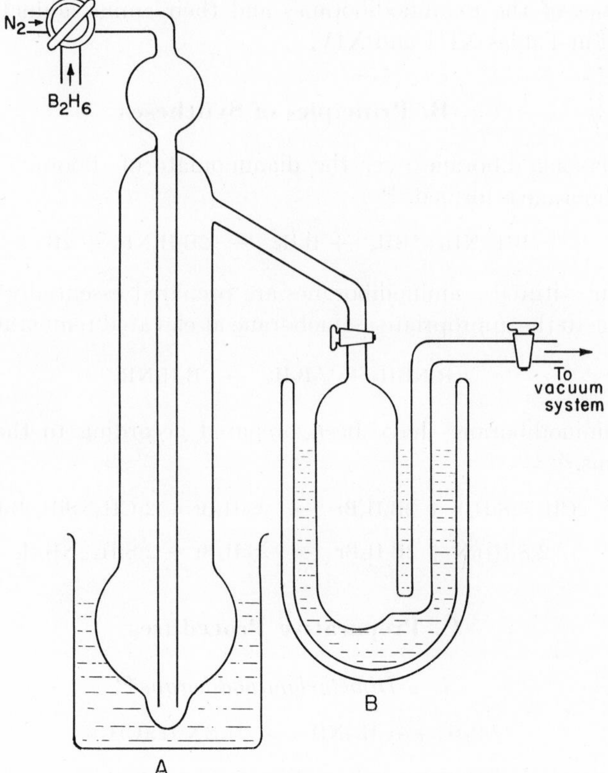

Fig. 10. Apparatus for preparation of μ-aminodiboranes.

VIII. HETEROAROMATIC BORON–NITROGEN COMPOUNDS

A. Introduction

The so-called "boron–nitrogen heteroaromatic ring systems" have been established as a new class of compounds within the past ten years. These species consist of conjugated cyclic frameworks which contain a boron and a nitrogen atom in the ring. Although the possible existence of several types of frameworks (see structures **25**) has been discussed

I II III

(25)

on theoretical grounds, only compounds containing frameworks I and II have been isolated. It should be recognized, however, that structures I and II (**25**) and the borazines, are not the only known boron–nitrogen compounds which are capable, in principle, of possessing aromatic character. There are several other B–N ring systems which could be listed in the heteroaromatic category, but which are listed elsewhere simply because the earlier investigators had not specifically concerned themselves with potential aromatic properties (see Sect. VI).

In general, frameworks I and II have been prepared as part of polycyclic ring systems, the structures of which are shown in Table XV. The only well-characterized monocyclic material which has been reported[368] is 2-phenyl-1,2-borazarobenzene (see structure **13** and Sect. VI.A).

The principle point of interest concerning the heteroaromatic ring systems is that they display some aromatic character.[406,407] This is reflected in their electronic spectra which show points of similarity with analogous aromatic ring systems and in their chemical properties, in particular, unusual hydrolytic stability.[406,407] The aromatic character displayed by these systems is presumed to be more significant than in the borazine ring systems. Properties of most of the known boron–nitrogen compounds which have been classified as heteroaromatics are given in Table XV.

B. Principles of Syntheses

The 2,1-borazarenes can be prepared, in general, through the reaction of a dichloroborane with a primary aromatic amine.[392]

NHR $\xrightarrow{R'BCl_2}$ NHR·BR′Cl_2 $\xrightarrow[-HCl]{AlCl_3}$ $\overset{+}{N}R$ / $\overset{-}{B}R'$

The 4,1-borazarenes are, in general, prepared through the reaction of BCl_3, $RBCl_2$ or a boroxine, $(RBO)_3$, with a 2,2′-dilithiodiphenylamine.[201,391]

CH_3N(Li, Li, CH_3, CH_3) + $RBCl_2$ ⟶ CH_3N BR (CH_3, CH_3) + 2LiCl

TABLE XV

Heteroaromatic Boron–Nitrogen Compounds

Compound	R	mp, °C	bp (mm), °C	Remarks	References
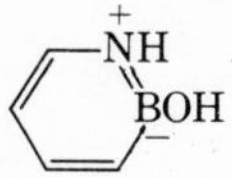 $\overset{+}{N}H$, $\overset{-}{B}OH$				Not characterized completely	390
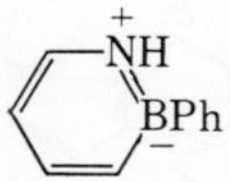 $\overset{+}{N}H$, $\overset{-}{B}Ph$					368
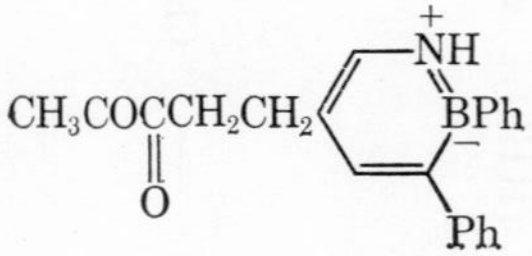 $CH_3COCH_2CH_2$ ($\overset{+}{N}H$, $\overset{-}{B}Ph$, Ph)		110–110.5			393
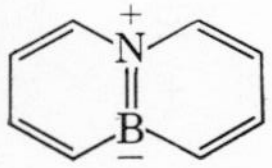 $\overset{+}{N}=\overset{-}{B}$				Not characterized completely	394
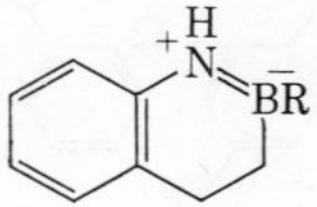 $\overset{+}{N}H=\overset{-}{B}R$	H	100–101			1,395
	CH_3	73–74			1,395
	C_6H_5	138–139			1,395
	Cl	72–74			1
	OCH_3	57–58			395
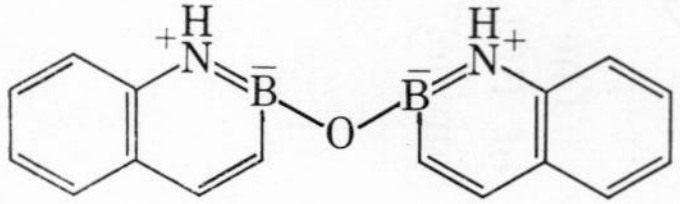 $\overset{+}{N}H=\overset{-}{B}$–O–$\overset{-}{B}=\overset{+}{N}H$					1

Structure	R	M.p.	Ref.
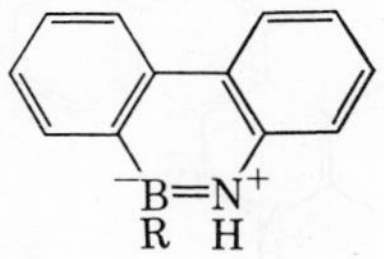 $^{-}B=N^{+}$ R H	Cl	93–94	201
	OH	169–170	201
	CH_3	103—104	201
	C_2H_5	77–78	201
	Ph	110–111.5	201
	H	69–70	201
 $\overset{+}{N}CH_3$ = $\underset{-}{B}R$	CH_3	117–118	396
	C_2H_5		396
	$CH_2{=}CHCH_2$		396
	Ph	122.5–123.5	396
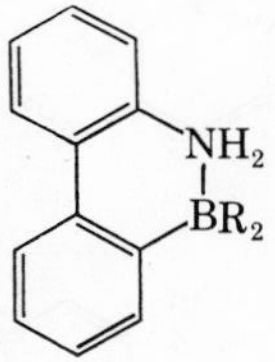 NH_2 – BR_2	CH_3	136	396
	Ph	232	396
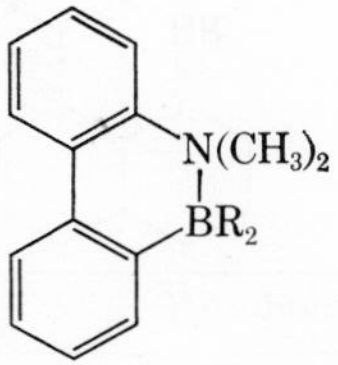 $N(CH_3)_2$ – BR_2	CH_3	108–109	396
	Ph	224–226	396

(*continued*

TABLE XV (*continued*)

Compound	R	mp, °C	bp (mm), °C	Remarks	References
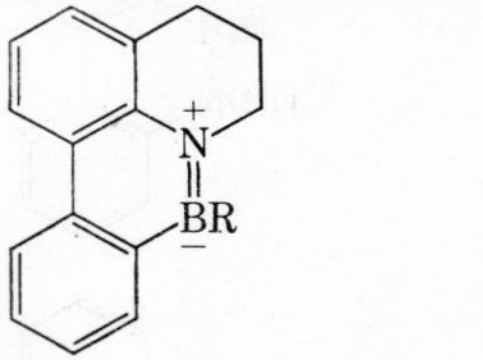 [structure]	Cl				397
	OH				397
	CH_3				397
[structure]	OH				397
	CH_3				397
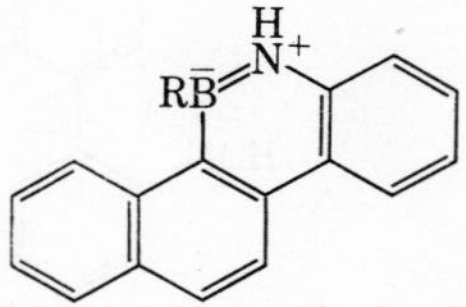 [structure]	OH				398
	CH_3				398
	H				398
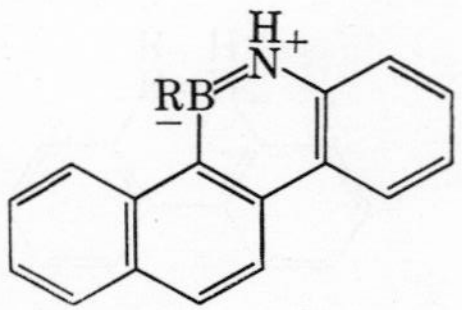 [structure]	OH				398
	CH_3				398
	H				398

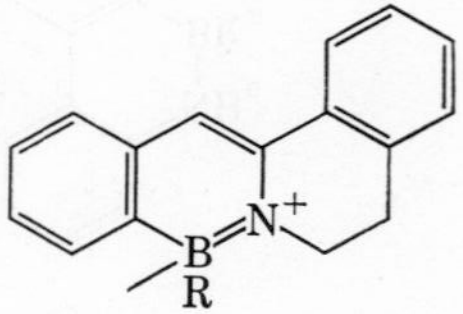

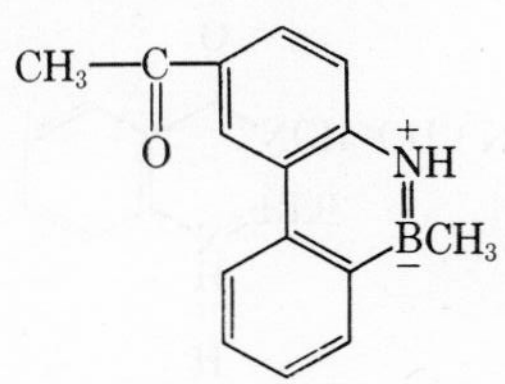 CH_3—C(=O), $\overset{+}{N}H$, $\underset{-}{B}CH_3$		164–165			399
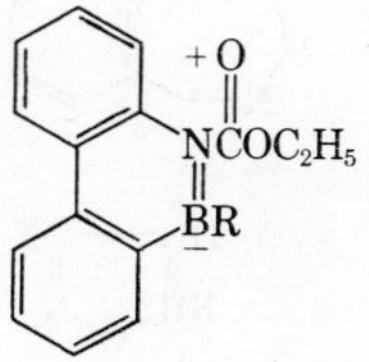 +O, $NCOC_2H_5$, $\underset{-}{B}R$	CH_3		160 (0.3)	$n_D^{21.5}$ 1.6188	400
	C_6H_5	116–117			400
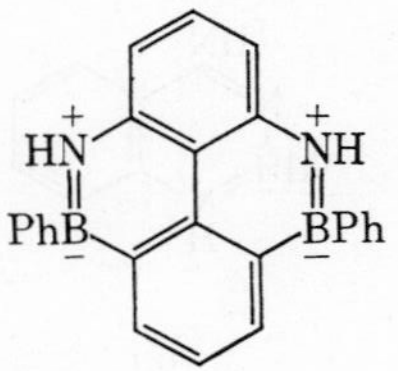 $H\overset{+}{N}$, $Ph\underset{-}{B}$, $\overset{+}{N}H$, $\underset{-}{B}Ph$		200–202			401
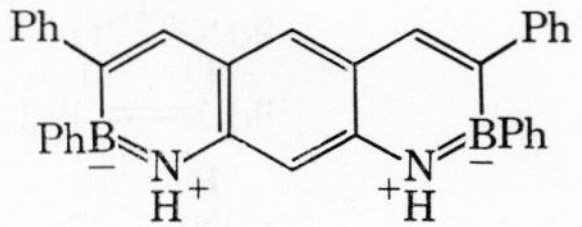 Ph, $Ph\underset{-}{B}$, $N H^+$, Ph, $\underset{-}{B}Ph$, $N {}^+H$		270			401
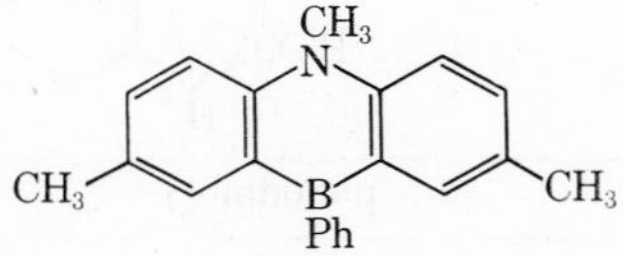 CH_3, N, CH_3, B, Ph, CH_3		114–115			389

(continued)

TABLE XV (*continued*)

Compound	R	mp, °C	bp (mm), °C	Remarks	References
Cyclohexane-fused ring: $\overset{+}{N}H=\bar{B}C_4H_9$–$\bar{B}C_4H_9=\overset{+}{N}H$					402
PhC=CPh, O, $\bar{B}$Ph, $\overset{+}{N}$Ph ring		183–185			403
Benzo ring: $\overset{+}{N}H=\bar{B}Ph$–N=C($NH_2$)		260–263			404
N–O–$\bar{B}$R=$\overset{+}{N}$H–C(X)=N ring	Mesityl (X = 4-pyridyl)	159–160			404
	OH (X = p-ClC_6H_4)	>320			404
Benzo ring: CH=N–O–$\bar{B}$Ph=$\overset{+}{N}$H		249–251			404
Benzo ring: NH–BPh–$NCH_2(CH_2)_2N(CH_3)_2$–C=O		170–172			404

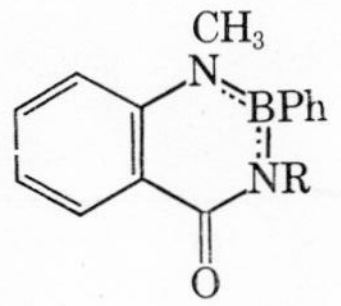 CH_3 N BPh NR O	H	170–172	404
	CH_3	92–94	404
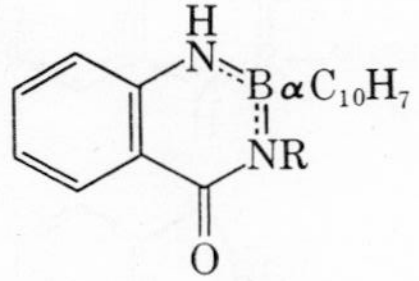 H N B $\alpha C_{10}H_7$ NR O	CH_3	218–220	404
	CH_2Ph	250–252	404
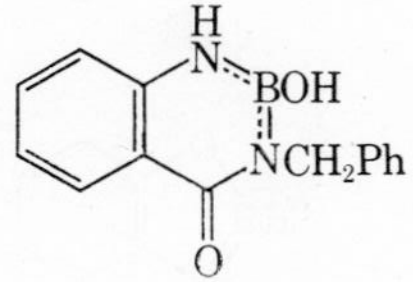 H N BOH NCH_2Ph O		>315	404
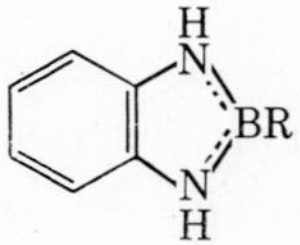 H N BR N H	H		382
	CH_3		382,387
	C_6H_5	215–216	350,372,382, 405
	p-$CH_3OC_6H_4$	258–258.5	372
	p-BrC_6H_4	232–233	372
	p-$CH_2{=}C(CH_3)C_6H_4$	237–238	372
	n-C_4H_9	86–86.5	372
	α-$C_{10}H_7$	149–150	372

(continued)

TABLE XV (*continued*)

Compound	R	mp, °C	bp (mm), °C	Remarks	References
2-Methyl-1,3,2-benzoxazaborole zwitterion ($\overset{+}{N}H=\overset{-}{B}CH_3$, ring O)					387
2-Phenyl-1,3,2-benzoxazaborole zwitterion ($\overset{+}{N}H=\overset{-}{B}Ph$, ring O)		105–106			350,405
2-Phenyl-1,3,2-benzothiazaborole zwitterion ($\overset{+}{N}H=\overset{-}{B}Ph$, ring S)		154–156			405
2-Mesityl-1,3,2-benzodiazaborin-4-one (NH, B—mesityl, NH, C=O)		202–204			404

C. Preparative Procedures

1. 10-Chloro-9-aza-10-boraphenanthrene[201]

$$BCl_3 + C_6H_5{-}C_6H_4NH_2 \longrightarrow C_6H_5{-}C_6H_4NHBCl_2 + HCl \xrightarrow[AlCl_3]{175^\circ}$$

$$\text{(10-chloro-9-aza-10-boraphenanthrene: } {}^{-}B{=}N^{+}\text{, Cl on B, H on N)} + HCl$$

A quantity of boron trichloride dissolved in dry benzene (about 4 ml C_6H_6 per gram BCl_3) is added dropwise with stirring to a solution of an equimolar amount of 2-aminobiphenyl, also in benzene (approximately 20 ml of C_6H_6 per gram of amine), and the mixture is refluxed for 10 hr. The benzene is then distilled off under reduced pressure leaving a residue of 2-aminobiphenylboron dichloride. The crude aminodichloroborane is then heated to 175° for 7 hr in the presence of a catalytic amount (0.5 g) of aluminum trichloride. The resulting solid is sublimed at 160–170° (0.05 mm) giving pure 10-chloro-9-aza-10-boraphenanthrene, mp 93–94°.

The chloro compound is readily converted into alkyl or aryl derivatives by treatment with the appropriate Grignard reagent, or into the parent boron hydride by reduction with lithium aluminum hydride.

IX. DIBORYLAMINES AND TRIBORYLAMINES

A. Introduction

Diborylamines are characterized by the linkage $\begin{matrix} \diagdown & | & \diagup \\ B & {-}N{-} & B \\ \diagup & & \diagdown \end{matrix}$.

The simplest structures in this class are $\begin{matrix} R & H & R \\ \diagdown & | & \diagup \\ B & {-}N{-} & B \\ \diagup & & \diagdown \\ R & & R \end{matrix}$ and $\begin{matrix} R' & H & R' \\ \diagdown & | & \diagup \\ B & {-}N{-} & B \\ \diagup & & \diagdown \\ N(H)R & & N(H)R \end{matrix}$. Cycles which are joined by the diboryl linkage

TABLE XVI
Diborylamines

Compound	mp, °C	bp (mm), °C	Remarks	References
$[(C_3H_7)_2B]_2NH$		80–84 (3)		178
$[(C_4H_9)_2B]_2NH$		75–78 (0.01)		178
$[(C_5H_{11})_2B]_2NH$		86–87 (2)		411
$[(t\text{-}C_4H_9)_2B]_2N(t\text{-}C_4H_9)$		98–100 (0.01)		365
$[t\text{-}C_4H_9(H)NB(Cl)]_2N(t\text{-}C_4H_9)$		82–86 (0.02)		365
$[(CH_3)_2NB(Ph)]_2NH$		158–160 (3)		410
$[CH_3$ … $B]_2NC_2H_5$		121–123 (11.5)		408
$[CH_3$ … $B]_2NPh$		98.5–100 (0.3)		408
$[CH_3$ … $B]_2NCH_2Ph$		137–138 (0.4)		408
[… O, O > B]$_2$NH			Sublimes at 200° (2 mm)	409
[… O, O > B]$_2$N—C(=O)—N(H)(t-C_4H_9)				282

have been reported[408,409] (**26** and **27**). Cycles in which the diboryl linkage is an integral part of the framework have also been reported[408] (**28**).

Ph
B—N—B
CH_3 CH_3

(**26**)

H
O O
B—N—B
O O

(**27**)

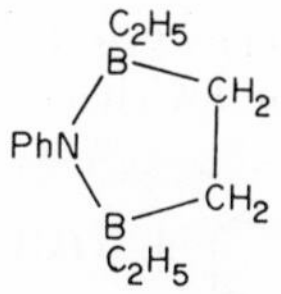

$$\begin{array}{c} C_2H_5 \\ B\!-\!CH_2 \\ PhN \quad\ | \\ B\!-\!CH_2 \\ C_2H_5 \end{array}$$

(**28**)

The only reported triborylamine is tri(1,3,2-benzodioxaborol-2-yl)-amine.[409] (See structure **15**.) Unusual thermal stability is ascribed to this compound based upon the fact that the chelate structure prevents overcrowding around the boron atom and also works against possible rearrangements.

Table XVI lists most of the known diborylamines and some of their properties.

B. Principles of Syntheses

Elimination reactions involving diorganohaloboranes and bis(triogano-silyl)amines have been used to prepare diborylamines.[178,410] Stepwise reaction is involved. An *N*-silylated aminoborane is formed initially.

$$(CH_3)_2BCl + [(CH_3)_3Si]_2NH \rightarrow (CH_3)_2BN(H)Si(CH_3)_3 + (CH_3)_3SiCl$$

The diborylamine is formed when an excess of dimethylchloroborane is used.

$$(CH_3)_2BCl + (CH_3)_2BN(H)Si(CH_3)_3 \rightarrow (CH_3)_2BN(H)B(CH_3)_2 + (CH_3)_3SiCl$$

Iwasaki and Koester[408] have reported the preparation of diborylamines through the elimination of hydrogen in the following reaction.

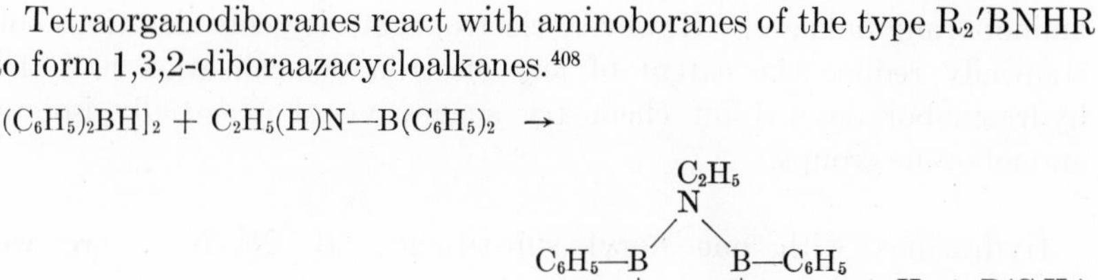

$$CH_3\text{-}C_4H_7B\text{—}N(H)Ph + \tfrac{1}{2}\,[CH_3\text{-}C_4H_7B(\mu\text{-}H)_2BC_4H_7\text{-}CH_3] \xrightarrow[150^\circ]{(C_2H_5)_3N} CH_3\text{-}C_4H_7B\text{—}N(Ph)\text{—}BC_4H_7\text{-}CH_3 + H_2$$

Tetraorganodiboranes react with aminoboranes of the type $R_2'BNHR$ to form 1,3,2-diboraazacycloalkanes.[408]

$$[(C_6H_5)_2BH]_2 + C_2H_5(H)N\text{—}B(C_6H_5)_2 \rightarrow$$

$$\begin{array}{c} C_2H_5 \\ N \\ C_6H_5\text{—}B \qquad B\text{—}C_6H_5 \\ H_2C\text{——}CH_2 \end{array} + H_2 + B(C_6H_5)_3$$

Triborylamine synthesis has been achieved by reacting a diborylamine containing an N—H bond with a chloroborane.[409]

$$[C_6H_4O_2B]_2NH + Cl\text{—}BO_2C_6H_4 + (C_2H_5)_3N \longrightarrow [C_6H_4O_2B]_3N + (C_2H_5)_3NHCl$$

C. Preparative Procedures

1. *Bis(dimethylyaminophenylboryl)amine*[410]

$$2C_6H_5B(Cl)N(CH_3)_2 + [(CH_3)_3Si]_2NH \rightarrow [(CH_3)_2N(C_6H_5)B]_2NH + 2(CH_3)_3SiCl$$

A quantity (14.7 g, 0.088 mole) of (dimethylamino)chlorophenylborane is added slowly, with stirring, to a solution of 7.08 g. (0.044 mole) of bis(trimethylsilyl)amine in 25 cc of toluene, while cooling the reaction flask in an ice bath. After the addition is completed, the reaction mixture is allowed to warm to room temperature and then refluxed for 8 hr before filtering under dry nitrogen to remove the small precipitate of *B*-triphenylborazine. Trimethylchlorosilane and the solvent are removed from the filtrate under reduced pressure and the residue is vacuum distilled. The fraction boiling from 158 to 160° (3 mm) is the product, bis(dimethylaminophenylboryl)amine, in about 50% yield.

X. HYDRAZINOBORANES

A. Introduction

Hydrazinoboranes, $>B\text{—}N(\text{—})\text{—}N(\text{—})\text{—}B<$, represent the inorganic analogs of butadiene, $>C{=}C(\text{—})\text{—}C(\text{—}){=}C<$. In principle, the stability of hydrazinoboranes might be enhanced by conjugative effects between the aminoborane linkages. However, electronegativity considerations substantially reduce the extent of any electron delocalization and thus hydrazinoboranes exhibit chemistry suggestive of essentially isolated aminoborane groups.

Hydrazines with one boryl substituent, $>B\text{—}N(\text{—})\text{—}N<$, are well known where the boron is alkyl or aryl substituted. These species often disproportionate to a hydrazinobisborane and hydrazine when a terminal NH_2 group is present. Substitution of organic groups on

$$2R_2B—NH—NH_2 \rightarrow R_2B—NH—NHBR_2 + N_2H_4$$

the terminal nitrogen reduces the tendency towards disproportionation reactions. In some cases hydrazinomonoboranes form cyclic dimers similar to those formed by sterically unhindered aminoboranes. One example of such a dimer is depicted in structure **29.**[204,227,284]

H H2
N——N
Ph2B BPh2
N——N
H2 H

(**29**)

Bis- and tris(hydrazino)boranes such as $PhB(N(H)N(H)Ph)_2$ and $B[N(H)N(CH_3)_2]_3$ are known as well as the dimethylhydrazino derivative of tetrakis(dimethylamino)diboron,[412]

$$[(CH_3)_2N—N(H)]_2B—B[N(H)—N(CH_3)_2]_2$$

These materials are readily prepared by hydrazinolysis of aminoboranes. (See Sect. X.B.) When bis(dimethylamino)phenylborane is treated with either hydrazine[227,412] or phenylhydrazine[412] under conditions suitable for transamination, derivatives of the 2,3,5,6-tetraza-1,4-diborine ring system are formed. (See structures **30** and **31.**) These

H H
N—N
PhB BPh
N—N
H H

(**30**)

H Ph
N—N
PhB BPh
N—N
Ph H

or

H Ph
N—N
PhB BPh
N—N
H Ph

(**31**)

cyclic species are formally bis(hydrazino)bis(boranes) but ring nomenclature is less cumbersome for locating substituents.

All hydrazinoboranes react readily with HCl and other acids, but the nature of products obtained and number of acid molecules absorbed varies for different hydrazinoboranes. For example, diphenyl(phenyl-

TABLE XVII
Hydrazinoboranes

Compound	mp, °C	bp (mm), °C	Remarks	References
$H_2BN(H)N(H)BH_2$				118
$(CH_3)_2BN(H)N(H)CH_3$		53–55		204
$(CH_3)_2BN(H)N(H)Ph$		101 (11)		204
$(CH_3)_2BN(H)N(H)B(CH_3)_2$		95–97		204
$(C_2H_5)_2BN(H)N(H)B(C_2H_5)_2$		77 (15)		204,412
$(C_3H_7)_2BN(H)N(H)Ph$		94–95 (0.03)	n_D^{20} 1.5165	204,205,412,413
$(C_3H_7)_2BN(H)N(H)B(C_3H_7)_2$		123–125 (11)	n_D^{20} 1.4421	204,205,412,413
$(C_3H_7)_2BN(H)N(Ph)B(C_3H_7)_2$		105–106 (0.04)	$n_D^{21.5}$ 1.4901	205,413
(iso-$C_3H_7)_2BN(H)N(H)Ph$		89–90 (0.035)	n_D^{20} 1.5151	205,413
(iso-$C_3H_7)_2BN(H)N(H)B$-(iso-$C_3H_7)_2$		78–79 (2)	n_D^{20} 1.4430	
$(C_4H_9)_2BN(H)NH_2$	38–39			412
$(C_4H_9)_2BN(H)N(CH_3)_2$		48 (2)	n_D^{20} 1.4122	204,412
$(C_4H_9)_2BN(H)N(H)Ph$		144 (1)		204,412,413
$(C_4H_9)_2BN(H)N(H)B(C_4H_9)_2$		118 (1)	n_D^{20} 1.4510	204,205,412
$(C_4H_9)_2BN(H)N(Ph)B(C_4H_9)_2$		132–3.5 (0.03)	n_D^{20} 1.4883	413
$[Ph_2BN(H)NH_2]_2$	147		Cyclic dimer	204,227,412
$Ph_2BN(H)N(CH_3)_2$		123 (3)		204,227
$Ph_2BN(H)N(H)Ph$	94			412
$HB[N(H)N(CH_3)_2]_2$	33–35			412
$[(CH_3)_2NN(H)]_2B$-B—$[N(H)N(CH_3)_2]_2$	72–75			412
$PhB[N(H)N(CH_3)_2]_2$		76–78 (1)		227,412
$PhB[N(H)N(H)Ph]_2$	122–125			412
$PhB[N(CH_3)_2]N(H)N(H)Ph$	57–58			412

$B[N(H)N(CH_3)_2]_3$	103		412
N(H)—N(H) Ph—B B—Ph N(H)—N(H)	257–258		227,412
N(H)—N(Ph) Ph—B B—Ph N(Ph)—N(H)			412
N(Ph)—N(Ph) H—B B—H N(Ph)—N(Ph)	110–112		412
N(Ph)—N(Ph) Ph—B B—Ph N(Ph)—N(Ph)	156–158		412
$[(CH_3)_2N—N(H)]_3B_3N_3(CH_3)_3$	55–59	134 (3)	325
$[(CH_3)_2N—N(H)]_3B_3N_3(C_2H_5)_3$		140 (3)	325

hydrazino)borane adds 2 moles of HCl resulting in cleavage of the B—N bond,[412]

$$Ph_2BN(H)N(H)Ph + 2HCl \xrightarrow[-40°]{(C_2H_5)_2O} Ph_2BCl + Ph(H)NNH_2 \cdot HCl$$

while $B[N(H)N(CH_3)_2]_3$ reacts with 5 moles of HCl to form an ether-insoluble adduct, $B[N(H)N(CH_3)_2]_3 \cdot 5HCl$.

Table HVII lists most of the known hydrazinoboranes.

B. Principles of Syntheses

Hydrazinolysis of aminoboranes seems to represent the most efficient preparative method for hydrazinoboranes. A typical example is the preparation of tris(dimethylhydrazino)borane[412] (see Sect. X.C).

$$3(CH_3)_2N—NH_2 + B[N(CH_3)_2]_3 \xrightarrow{60\text{–}80°} [(CH_3)_2N—N(H)]_3B + 3HN(CH_3)_2$$

Mono- and bis(hydrazino)boranes may also be obtained by this route.

Diorganochloroboranes react with substituted hydrazine to give reasonable yields of hydrazinoboranes, but similar reactions with

$$R_2BCl + 2H_2N—N(CH_3)_2 \rightarrow R_2B—N(H)—N(CH_3)_2 + (CH_3)_2N—NH_2 \cdot HCl$$

free hydrazine give materials which appear to be saltlike in nature.[412]

$$R_2BCl + 2H_2N—NH_2 \rightarrow R_2B(N_2H_4)_2{}^+Cl^-$$

Derivatives of the 2,3,5,6-tetraza-1,6-diborine ring are prepared by treatment of a bis(amino)borane with hydrazine or a substituted hydrazine, with at least one hydrogen on each nitrogen, at temperatures in excess of 100°.[227,412]

$$2PhB[N(CH_3)_2]_2 + 2H_2N—N(H)R \xrightarrow[\text{toluene}]{\text{refluxing}} PhB\langle{}^{N(H)—N(R)}_{N(R)—N(H)}\rangle B—Ph + 4HN(CH_3)_2$$

Similar compounds have been obtained through the reaction of dilithiodiphenylhydrazine with dichlorophenylborane,[227] and through the

$$2PhBCl_2 + 2Ph(Li)N—N(Li)Ph \rightarrow PhB\langle{}^{N(Ph)—N(Ph)}_{N(Ph)—N(Ph)}\rangle BPh + 4LiCl$$

treatment of azobenzene with diborane,[227]

$$B_2H_6 + PhN{=}NPh \rightarrow HB\begin{matrix} \diagup N(Ph){-}N(Ph) \diagdown \\ \diagdown N(Ph){-}N(Ph) \diagup \end{matrix}BH + 2H_2$$

C. Preparative Procedures

1. *(Dibutyl)dimethylhydrazinoborane*[412]

$$2(CH_3)_2N{-}NH_2 + (C_4H_9)_2BCl \rightarrow (C_4H_9)_2BN(H)N(CH_3)_2 + (CH_3)_2N{-}NH_2\cdot HCl$$

A quantity of $(CH_3)_2N{-}NH_2$ dissolved in anhydrous diethyl ether (8 ml ether per gram of dimethylhydrazine) is placed in a flask of appropriate size under a dry nitrogen atmosphere. A stoichiometric amount of $(C_4H_9)_2BCl$ is added dropwise with stirring and, when the exothermic reaction has ceased, the mixture is refluxed for 1 hr. The solid, $(CH_3)_2N{-}NH_2\cdot HCl$, is filtered off under nitrogen and the ether removed from the filtrate under reduced pressure. The remaining liquid is distilled yielding the product, $(C_4H_9)_2BN(H)N(CH_3)_2$, a clear colorless liquid, bp 47–48° (2 mm).

2. *Tris(dimethylhydrazino)borane*[412]

$$B[N(CH_3)_2]_3 + 3H_2N{-}N(CH_3)_2 \rightarrow B[N(H)N(CH_3)_2]_3 + 3HN(CH_3)_2$$

This is an example of an hydrazinolysis of an aminoborane.

A quantity of tris(dimethylamino)borane is added dropwise to a 4:1 molar excess of $(CH_3)_2N{-}NH_2$ with continuous stirring. When bubbling $[HN(CH_3)_2$ evolution$]$ ceases, the mixture is heated to 80° for 3 hr to complete the reaction. Excess dimethylhydrazine is removed *in vacuo* and the residue is sublimed at 50–60° (1 mm) to yield pure $B[N(H)N(CH_3)_2]_3$, mp 103°.

XI. AMINO-SUBSTITUTED DIBORON COMPOUNDS

A. Introduction

Diboron compounds containing amino groups are among the most stable of the class of compounds containing the $\gt B{-}B\lt$ unit. In principle, the stability of the boron–boron bond is related to the ability of substituent atoms on boron to pi bond with boron. Thus, the follow-

TABLE XVIII
Amino-Derivatives of Diborane(4)

Compound	mp, °C.	bp (mm), °C	Remarks	References
$B_2F_4[N(CH_3)_3]_2$		24.5 (126)	Tetramer	415
$B_2Cl_4[N(H)(CH_3)_2]_2$	204,198 (decomp.)			414,416, 417
$B_2Cl_4[N(CH_3)_3]_2$	228		Tetramer	418
$B_2[N(H)CH_3]_4$		25 (0.5)		253
$B_2[N(H)C_6H_{12}]_4$			n_D^{25} 1.4606	253
$B_2[N(H)Ph]_4$	181–200			253
$B_2[N(CH_3)_2]_4$	−33	56–57 (2)	n_D^{22} 1.4683	253,419–421
$B_2[N(C_2H_5)_2]_4$		88–89 (1)	n_D^{21} 1.4603	419
$B_2[N(Ph)_2]_4$			Impure	422
$B_2[N(CH_3)Ph]_4$			Oil	423
$B_2\left(\begin{matrix}N(CH_3)CH_2\\ \vert \\ N(CH_3)CH_2\end{matrix}\right)_2$	43–44	85 (5)		423
$B_2\left(\begin{matrix}N(C_2H_5)CH_2\\ \vert \\ N(C_2H_5)CH_2\end{matrix}\right)_2$		80 (0.01)		423
$B_2\left(\begin{matrix}N(iso\text{—}C_3H_7)CH_2\\ \vert \\ N(iso\text{—}C_3H_7)CH_2\end{matrix}\right)_2$	130–134			423
$B_2\left(\begin{matrix}N(H)CH_2\\ N(H)CH_2\end{matrix}\!\!>\!CH_2\right)_2$	60–60.5			423
$B_2\left(\begin{matrix}N(CH_3)CH_2\\ N(CH_3)CH_2\end{matrix}\!\!>\!CH_2\right)_2$		74–75 (0.6)		423
$B_2\left(\begin{matrix}N(H)\\ N(H)\end{matrix}\!\!>\!C_6H_4\right)_2$	375–400			422
$\begin{matrix}CH_3\text{—}B\text{—}N(H)\\ \vert \\ CH_3\text{—}B\text{—}N(H)\end{matrix}\!\!>\!C_6H_4$	135			424
$\begin{matrix}C_3H_7\text{—}B\text{—}N(H)\\ \vert \\ C_3H_7\text{—}B\text{—}N(H)\end{matrix}\!\!>\!C_{10}H_6$	184			424

(*continued*)

TABLE XVII (*continued*)

Compound	mp, °C	bp (mm), °C	Remarks	References
C_4H_9—B—N(H) | C_4H_9—B—N(H) (fused to benzene ring)	120–125			424
$B_2[N[H]N(CH_3)_2]_4$	71–72		Sublimes *in vacuo* at 40–50°	253
$B_2(CH_3)_2[N(CH_3)_2]_2$		36–39 (12)	n_D^{20} 1.4405	424
$B_2(C_2H_5)_2[N(CH_3)_2]_2$		32–34 (1.5)	n_D^{20} 1.4460	424
$B_2(C_3H_7)_2[N(H)C_4H_9]_2$		108 (6)	n_D^{20} 1.4416	424
$B_2(C_3H_7)_2[N(CH_3)_2]_2$		48 (1)	n_D^{20} 1.4508	424
$B_2(C_4H_9)_2[N(CH_3)_2]_2$		68–70 (2)	n_D^{20} 1.4521	424
$B_2(Ph)_2[N(CH_3)_2]_2$	101–103			425
$B_2Cl_2[N(CH_3)_2]_2$		34–35 (0.1) 55 (0.2)	n_D^{20} 1.4728	416,426
$B_2Br_2[N(CH_3)_2]_2$		96–97 (1.5)		417
$B_2[N(CH_3)_2]_2[N(H)C_2H_5]_2$		57–58 (0.05)	n_D^{20} 1.4570	417
$B_2Cl[N(CH_3)_2]_3$		28–30 (0.005)		426
$B_2CH_3[N(CH_3)_2]_3$		42–43 (1)		417
$B_2H[N(CH_3)_2]_3$		72–74 (10)	Unstable	417
$B_2C_4H_9[N(CH_3)_2]_3$		87–89 (10)		417
$B_2H_4 \cdot NC_5H_5$				427

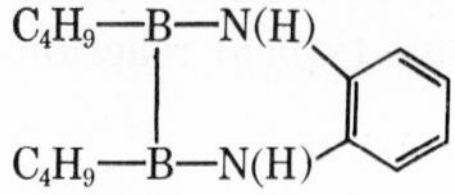

ing order of stability, with respect to disproportionation, has been observed.

$$B_2Cl_4 < B_2F_4 < B_2(OR)_4 < B_2(NR_2)_4$$

Although amino-substituted diboron compounds are thermally stable, and are apparently insensitive to dry air, they do react readily with moisture. Known amino compounds containing the boron–boron bond consist of acyclic frameworks containing simple amino groups and bicyclic structures which are formed with bidentate amines (Table XVIII).

Fused ring structures such as the one depicted in structure **32** have not yet been prepared.

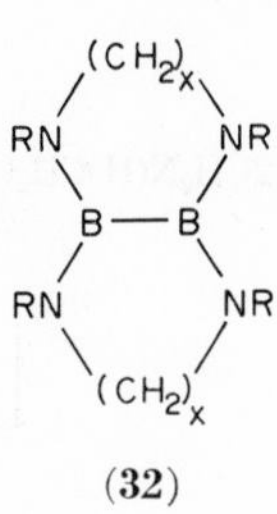

$(CH_2)_x$
RN NR
B—B
RN NR
$(CH_2)_x$

(**32**)

Tetrakis(dimethylamino)diboron, $[(CH_3)_2N]_2B\text{–}B[N(CH_3)_2]_2$, promises to be a very useful reagent, not only as a starting material for the preparation of other amino derivatives of diborane(4) through transamination reactions (see *Principles of Syntheses*), but also for the ready preparation of new derivatives of diborane(4). Some typical reactions are outlined below.[402,414]

$$[(CH_3)_2N]_2B\text{—}B[N(CH_3)_2]_2 + 2H_2S + 4HCl \rightarrow [(CH_3)_2N]B\text{—}B[N(CH_3)_2](\mu\text{-}S)_2[(CH_3)_2N]B\text{—}B[N(CH_3)_2] + 4(CH_3)_2NH_2Cl$$

$$[(CH_3)_2N]_2B\text{—}B[N(CH_3)_2]_2 + 2BR_3 \rightarrow [B_2R_2N(CH_3)_2]_2 + 2R_2BN(CH_3)_2$$

B. Principles of Syntheses

Tetrakis(dimethylamino)diboron is best prepared by means of a coupling reaction in which chloro- or bromobis(dimethylamino)borane is treated with highly dispersed sodium.[253,419]

$$2[(CH_3)_2N]_2BX + 2Na \rightarrow [(CH_3)_2N]_2B\text{—}B[N(CH_3)_2]_2 + 2NaX$$

While this technique has been successful for preparing other amino derivatives, the simplest method for preparing these compounds is to carry out an appropriate transamination[423] reaction, using tetrakis(dimethylamino)diboron as a starting material, since it is commercially available.

$$[(CH_3)_2N]_2B\text{—}B[N(CH_3)_2]_2 + 2CH_3N(H)CH_2CH_2N(H)CH_3 \longrightarrow \overline{CH_2N(CH_3)B(N(CH_3)CH_2)}\text{—}\overline{B(N(CH_3)CH_2)N(CH_3)CH_2} + 4N(CH_3)_2H$$

Although it is possible to prepare amino-substituted diboron compounds using B_2Cl_4 as a starting material, in general, it is inadvisable because of the effort necessary to prepare and store the boron subhalide. The desired amino derivative compound can be much more easily prepared by one of the reactions cited above.

C. Preparative Procedures

1. Tetrakis(dimethylamino)diboron[253]

$$2[(CH_3)_2N]_2BBr + 2Na \xrightarrow[\text{toluene}]{110^\circ} [(CH_3)_2N]_4B_2 + 2NaBr$$

A quantity of bromobis(dimethylamino)borane dissolved in toluene (about 3 g of the borane per milliliter of toluene) is slowly added over a 45-min period to an equimolar quantity of molten sodium dispersed in refluxing toluene (about 5 ml toluene per gram of sodium). The reaction is continued for an additional 2.5 hr at 110°, and the resulting solids are filtered in a dry nitrogen atmosphere. The toluene is removed from the filtrate by vacuum distillation and the residue distilled at 55–57° (2 mm) to give an 80% yield of tetrakis(dimethylamino)diboron.

2. Bi(1,3-dimethyl-1,3,2-diazaborolidin-2-yl)[423]

$$2CH_3(H)NCH_2CH_2N(H)CH_3 + [(CH_3)_2N]_4B_2 \xrightarrow{120^\circ}$$

$$\begin{array}{ccccc} & CH_3 & & CH_3 & \\ CH_2 & \!\!-\!N & & N\!-\! & CH_2 \\ | & & \diagdown \quad \diagup & & | \\ | & & B\!-\!B & & | \\ | & & \diagup \quad \diagdown & & | \\ CH_2 & \!\!-\!N & & N\!-\! & CH_2 \\ & CH_3 & & CH_3 & \end{array} + 4HN(CH_3)_2$$

A mixture of *N,N'*-dimethylethylenediamine and tetrakis(dimethylamino)diboron in a 2:1 molar ratio is placed in a flask equipped with a water-cooled reflux condenser topped by a calcium chloride drying tube. (Alternately the reflux condenser may be connected to a trap maintained at −78° if it is desired to collect the dimethylamine which is evolved.) The contents of the flask are heated at 120° for 5 hr to insure that the reaction be driven to completion. The residue is recrystallized from petroleum ether (bp 40–60°) to give bi(1,3-dimethyl-1,3,2-diazaborolidin-2-yl), mp 43–44°, bp 85° (5 mm), in about 86% yield.

REFERENCES

1. M. J. S. Dewar and R. Dietz, *J. Chem. Soc.*, **1959,** 2728.
2. H. C. Brown, H. I. Schlesinger, and S. Z. Cardon, *J. Am. Chem. Soc.*, **64,** 325 (1942).
3. H. C. Brown, H. Bartholomay, Jr., and M. J. Taylor, *J. Am. Chem. Soc.*, **66,** 435 (944).
4. H. C. Brown, *J. Am. Chem. Soc.*, **67,** 374 (1945).
5. H. C. Brown, *J. Am. Chem. Soc.*, **67,** 1452 (1945).
6. H. C. Brown and H. Pearsall, *J. Am. Chem. Soc.*, **67,** 1765 (1945).
7. H. C. Brown and G. R. Barbaras, *J. Chem. Phys.*, **14,** 114 (1946).
8. H. C. Brown, *Science*, **103,** 385 (1946).
9. M. F. Hawthorne, *J. Am. Chem. Soc.*, **81,** 5836 (1959).
10. M. F. Hawthorne, *J. Am. Chem. Soc.*, **82,** 748 (1960).
11. M. F. Hawthorne, *J. Am. Chem. Soc.*, **83,** 2541 (1961).
12. H. C. Brown and R. R. Holmes, *J. Am. Chem. Soc.*, **78,** 2173 (1956).
13. F. G. A. Stone, *Chem. Rev.*, **58,** 101 (1958).
14. T. D. Coyle and F. G. A. Stone, *Prog. Boron Chem.*, **1,** 83 (1964).
15. N. N. Greenwood and P. G. Perkins, *J. Chem. Soc.*, **1960,** 1141.
16. (a) M. E. Garabedian and S. W. Benson, *J. Am. Chem. Soc.*, **86,** 176 (1964); (b) T. D. Fehler and W. S. Koski, *J. Am. Chem. Soc.*, **87,** 409 (1965); (c) A. B. Burg and Y. C. Fu, *J. Am. Chem. Soc.*, **88,** 1147 (1966).
17. C. A. Kraus and E. H. Brown, *J. Am. Chem. Soc.*, **51,** 2690 (1929).
18. R. W. Parry and T. C. Bissot, *J. Am. Chem. Soc.*, **78,** 1524 (1956).
19. A. B. Burg and H. I. Schlesinger, *J. Am. Chem. Soc.*, **59,** 780 (1937).
20. J. M. Gamboa, *Anales Real Soc. Espan Fis Quim. (Madrid)*, **46B,** 699 (1950).
21. A. B. Burg and E. S. Kulijian, *J. Am. Chem. Soc.*, **72,** 3103 (1950).
22. J. Goubeau and J. Jiminez-Barbera, *Z. Anorg. Allgem. Chem.*, **303,** 217 (1960).
23. S. Suziski and S. Witz, *J. Am. Chem. Soc.*, **79,** 2447 (1957).
24. E. D. Hughes, *J. Am. Chem. Soc.*, **78,** 502 (1956).
25. E. L. Lippert and W. N. Lipscomb, *J. Am. Chem. Soc.*, **78,** 503 (1956).
26. V. P. Sorokin, B. I. Vesnina, and N. S. Klimova, *Zh. Neorgan. Khim*, **8,** No. 1, 66 (1963).
27. S. Geller, R. E. Hughes, and J. L. Hoard, *Acta Cryst.*, **4,** 380 (1951).
28. J. L. Hoard, S. Geller, and W. M. Cashin, *Acta Cryst.*, **4,** 396 (1951).
29. S. G. Shore and R. W. Parry, *J. Am. Chem. Soc.*, **77,** 6084 (1955).
30. R. W. Parry, G. Kodama, and D. R. Schultz, *J. Am. Chem. Soc.*, **80,** 24 (1958).
31. J. R. Bright and W. C. Fernelius, *J. Am. Chem. Soc.*, **65,** 735 (1943).
32. H. C. Kelly and J. O. Edwards, *Inorg. Chem.*, **2,** 226 (1963).
33. H. C. Kelly and J. O. Edwards, *J. Am. Chem. Soc.*, **82,** 4842 (1960).
34. W. J. McDowell and C. W. Keenan, *J. Am. Chem. Soc.*, **78,** 2069 (1956).
35. M. F. Hawthorne, *J. Am. Chem. Soc.*, **80,** 4293 (1958).
36. M. F. Hawthorne, *J. Am. Chem. Soc.*, **83,** 831 (1961).
37. D. T. Hurd and R. C. Osthoff, *Inorg. Syn.*, **5,** 26 (1957).
38. R. T. Sanderson, *Vacuum Manipulation of Volatile Compounds*, Wiley, New York, 1948.
39. G. W. Schaeffer and E. R. Anderson, *J. Am. Chem. Soc.*, **71,** 2143 (1949).
40. H. Noeth and H. Beyer, *Chem. Ber.*, **93,** 928 (1960).
41. S. G. Shore and K. W. Böddeker, *Inorg. Chem.*, **3,** 914 (1964).
42. E. R. Alton, R. D. Brown, J. C. Carter, and R. C. Taylor, *J. Am. Chem. Soc.*, **81,** 3550 (1953).

43. R. S. Tinsley, dissertation, Virginia Polytechnic Institute, 1955.
44. S. G. Shore, C. W. Hickan, Jr., and D. Cowles, *J. Am. Chem. Soc.*, **87**, 2755 (1965).
45. W. H. Schecter (Mine Safety Appliances Co.), Bulletin No. a(s), 9973, Dec. 1, 1950.
46. R. Koester, *Angew. Chem.*, **69**, 94 (1957).
47. L. L. Shchukovskaya, M. G. Vovonkov, and O. V. Pavlova, *Dokl. Akad. Nauk. SSSR*, **143**, 887 (1962).
48. E. C. Ashby and W. E. Foster, *J. Am. Chem. Soc.*, **84**, 3407 (1962).
49. V. I. Mikheeva and E. M. Fedneva, *Zh. Neorg. Khim.*, **1**, 894 (1956).
50. P. F. Winternitz and L. J. Spillane, U.S. Pat. 3,008,988.
51. J. Goubeau and H. Schneider, *Chem. Ber.*, **94**, 816 (1961).
52. H. C. Kelly and J. O. Edwards, *J. Am. Chem. Soc.*, **82**, 4842 (1960).
53. A. K. Holliday and W. Jeffers, *Congr. Intern. Chim. Pure Appl. 16^e, Paris, 1957, Mem. Sect. Chim. Minerale*, 541–544 (1958).
54. F. Klages and H. Sitz, *Chem. Ber.*, **96**, No. 9, 2394 (1963).
55. A. B. Burg and C. D. Good, *J. Inorg. Nucl. Chem.*, **2**, 237 (1956).
56. H. C. Brown and S. Johnson, *J. Am. Chem. Soc.*, **76**, 1978 (1954).
57. L. J. Sowa, U.S. Pat. 2,667,403.
58. C. A. Kraus and E. H. Brown, *J. Am. Chem. Soc.*, **51**, 2690 (1929).
59. A. W. Laubengayer and G. F. Condike, *J. Am. Chem. Soc.*, **70**, 2274 (1948).
60. I. G. Ryss and S. L. Idel's, *Izv. Vysshikh, Uchebn. Zavedenii Khim. Khim. Tekhnol.*, **5**, No. 1, 70 (1962).
61. H. Feichtinger and S. Puschof, Ger. Pat. 1,138,787.
62. I. G. Ryss and S. L. Idel's *Zh. Neorg. Khim.*, **4**, 1990 (1959).
63. C. A. Brown, E. L. Muetterties, and E. G. Rochow, *J. Am. Chem. Soc.*, **76**, 2537 (1954).
64. W. A. G. Graham and F. G. A. Stone, *J. Inorg. Nucl. Chem.*, **3**, 164 (1956).
65. D. T. Hurd and R. C. Osthoff, *Inorg. Syn.*, **5**, 26 (1957).
66. J. R. Bright and W. C. Fernelius, *J. Am. Chem. Soc.*, **65**, 735 (1943).
67. A. B. Burg and Sr. A. A. Green, *J. Am. Chem. Soc.*, **65**, 1838 (1943).
68. I. G. Ryss and S. L. Idel's, *Zh. Neorgan. Khim.*, **7**, 2674 (1962).
69. P. A. van der Meulen and H. A. Heller, *J. Am. Chem. Soc.*, **54**, 4404 (1932).
70. R. Gompper and P. Altreuther, *Z. Anal. Chem.*, **170**, 205 (1959).
71. W. Gerrard, M. Goldstein, C. H. Marsh, and E. F. Mooney, *J. Appl. Chem.*, **13**, 239 (1963).
72. W. G. Patterson and M. Onyszchuk, *Can. J. Chem.*, **39**, 986 (1961).
73. E. L. Meutterties and E. G. Rochow, *J. Am. Chem. Soc.*, **75**, 490 (1953).
74. E. Allenstein and J. Goubeau, *Z. Anorg. Allgem. Chem.*, **322**, 145 (1963).
75. A. W. Laubengayer and D. S. Sears, *J. Am. Chem. Soc.*, **67**, 164 (1945).
76. W. Gerrard, M. F. Lappert and J. W. Wallis, *J. Chem. Soc.*, **1960**, 2141.
77. R. C. Petry, *J. Am. Chem. Soc.*, **82**, 2400 (1960).
78. H. J. Becher, *Z. Anorg. Allgem. Chem.*, **270**, 273 (1952).
79. W. Gerrard, M. F. Lappert, and C. A. Pearce, *J. Chem. Soc.*, **1957**, 381.
80. O. C. Musgrave, *J. Chem. Soc.*, **1956**, 4305.
81. W. Gerrard and M. F. Lappert, *J. Chem. Soc.*, **1951**, 1020.
82. R. D. W. Kemmitt, R. H. Nutall, and D. W. A. Sharp, *J. Chem. Soc.*, **1960**, 46.
83. W. Gerrard, M. F. Lappert, and J. W. Wallis, *J. Chem. Soc.*, **1960**, 2178.
84. H. J. Coerver and C. Curran, *J. Am. Chem. Soc.*, **80**, 3522 (1958).

85. R. C. Osthoff, C. A. Brown, and F. H. Clark, *J. Am. Chem. Soc.*, **73**, 4045 (1951).
86. E. W. Abel, W. Gerrard, and M. F. Lappert, *J. Chem. Soc.*, **1957**, 5051.
87. W. J. Schuele, J. F. Hazel, and W. M. McNabb, *Anal. Chem.*, **28**, 505 (1956).
88. E. Pohland, *Z. Anorg. Allgem. Chem.*, **201**, 282 (1931).
89. S. Ratajczak, *Bull. Soc. Chim. France*, **3**, 487–488 (1960).
90. H. Noeth and H. Beyer, *Chem. Ber.*, **93**, 2251 (1960).
91. J. Dewing and F. M. Taylor, Brit. Pat. 915,579.
92. B. M. Mikhailov and N. S. Fedetov, *Izv. Akad. Nauk SSSR Otd. Khim. Nauk*, **1956**, 1511.
93. B. M. Mikhailov and N. S. Fedetov, *Izvest. Akad. Nauk SSSR Otd. Khim. Nauk*, **1960**, 1590.
94. J. C. Lockhart, *J. Chem. Soc.*, **1962**, 1197.
95. B. M. Mikhailov and N. S. Fedetov, *Izvest. Akad. Nauk SSSR Khim. Nauk*, **1959**, 1482.
96. B. Bartocha, W. A. G. Graham, and F. G. A. Stone, *J. Inorg. Nucl. Chem.*, **6**, 119 (1958).
97. R. D. Chambers and T. Chivers, *Proc. Chem. Soc.*, **1963**, 208.
98. W. Gerrard, M. F. Lappert, and R. Shafferman, *J. Chem. Soc.*, **1957**, 3828.
99. J. Soulie and A. Willemart, *Compt. Rend.*, **251**, 727 (1960).
100. H. I. Schlesinger, N. W. Flodin and A. B. Burg, *J. Am. Chem. Soc.*, **61**, 1078 (1939).
101. A. Stock and L. Zeidler, *Ber.*, **54B**, 531 (1921).
102. E. Kraus and P. Noble, *Ber.*, **63B**, 934 (1930).
103. A. V. Topchiev, A. A. Prokhorova, and M. V. Kurashev, *Dokl. Akad. Nauk SSSR*, **141**, 1386 (1961).
104. B. M. Mikhailov and V. A. Vaver, *Dokl. Akad. Nauk SSSR*, **109**, 94 (1956).
105. D. R. Nielsen, W. E. McEwen, and G. A. Vanderwerf, *Chem. Ind. (London)*, **1957**, 1069.
106. E. Krause, *Ber.*, **57B**, 813 (1924).
107. S. G. Shore and R. W. Parry, *J. Am. Chem. Soc.*, **80**, 8 (1958).
108. S. G. Shore and R. W. Parry, *J. Am. Chem. Soc.*, **77**, 6084 (1955).
109. F. M. Taylor, Brit. Pat. 909,390.
110. G. Kodama and R. W. Parry, *Inorg. Chem.*, **4**, 410 (1965).
111. B. M. Mikhailov and V. A. Dorokhov, *Izv. Akad. Nauk SSSR, Otd. Khim. Nauk*, **1961**, 2084.
112. R. C. Osthoff and F. H. Clark, *J. Am. Chem. Soc.*, **74**, 1361 (1952).
113. Kali-Chemie A. G., Brit. Pat. 830,768.
114. A. B. Burg and H. I. Schlesinger, *J. Am. Chem. Soc.*, **59**, 870 (1937).
115. R. E. Davis, E. Bromels, and C. L. Kibby, *J. Am. Chem. Soc.*, **84**, 885 (1962).
116. F. Schubert and K. Lang, Ger. Pat. 1,138,397.
117. F. C. Gunderloy, Jr., *Inorg. Chem.*, **2**, 221 (1963).
118. J. Goubeau and E. Richter, *Z. Anorg. Allgem. Chem.*, **310**, 123 (1961).
119. J. A. Bigot, Th. J. deBoar, and F. L. J. Sixma, *Rec. Trav. Chim.*, **76**, 996 (1957).
120. E. L. Muetterties, *Z. Naturforsch.*, **12B**, 265 (1957).
121. T. D. Coyle, *Proc. Chem. Soc.*, **1963**, 172.
122. H. S. Turner and R. J. Warne, *Chem. Ind. (London)*, **1958**, 526.
123. W. Gerrard and M. F. Lappert, *J. Chem. Soc.*, **1955**, 3084.
124. B. M. Mikhailov and V. A. Dorokhov, *Dokl. Akad. Nauk SSSR*, **130**, 782 (1960).
125. M. F. Hawthorne, *Chem. Ind. (London)*, **1957**, 1242.

126. M. F. Hawthorne, *J. Am. Chem. Soc.*, **80**, 4291 (1958).
127. M. F. Hawthorne, *J. Org. Chem.*, **23**, 1579 (1958).
128. K. Borer and J. Dewing, Brit. Pat. 899,557.
129. M. F. Hawthorne, *J. Am. Chem. Soc.*, **80**, 4293 (1958).
130. B. M. Mikhailov and V. A. Vaver, *Izv. Akad. Nauk SSSR Otd. Khim. Nauk*, **1957**, 812.
131. W. D. Phillips, H. C. Miller, and E. L. Muetterties, *J. Am. Chem. Soc.*, **81**, 4496 (1959).
132. H. I. Schlesinger and A. B. Burg, *J. Am. Chem. Soc.*, **60**, 290 (1938).
133. A. B. Burg and R. I. Wagner, *J. Am. Chem. Soc.*, **76**, 3307 (1954).
134. A. B. Burg and R. I. Wagner, *J. Am. Chem. Soc.*, **75**, 3872 (1953).
135. G. E. McAchran and S. G. Shore, *Inorg. Chem.*, **4**, 125 (1965).
136. A. Stock and E. Kuss, *Ber. Deut. Keram. Ges.*, **56**, 789 (1923).
137. A. Stock and E. Pohland, *Ber.*, **59B**, 2210 (1925).
138. H. I. Schlesinger and A. B. Burg, *J. Am. Chem. Soc.*, **60**, 290 (1938).
139. E. Wiberg, *Ber. Deut. Keram Ges.*, **69**, 2816 (1936).
140. W. L. Jolly, University of California Radiation Laboratory Report No. 4504, May 1955.
141. G. W. Schaeffer, M. D. Adams, and F. J. Koenig, *J. Am. Chem. Soc.*, **78**, 725 (1956).
142. R. W. Parry and S. G. Shore, *J. Am. Chem. Soc.*, **80**, 15 (1958).
143. D. R. Schultz and R. W. Parry, *J. Am. Chem. Soc.*, **80**, 4 (1958).
144. B. Z. Egan and S. G. Shore, *J. Am. Chem. Soc.*, **83**, 4717 (1961).
145. E. Wiberg, A. Bolz, and P. Buckheit, *Z. Anorg. Chem.*, **256**, 285 (1948).
146. E. Wiberg, K. Hertwig, and A. Bolz, *Z. Anorg. Chem.*, **256**, 177 (1948).
147. S. G. Shore and C. Hall, *J. Am. Chem. Soc.*, **88**, 5346 (1966).
148. H. C. Brown, P. F. Stehle, and P. A. Tierney, *J. Am. Chem. Soc.*, **79**, 2020 (1957).
149. R. W. Parry and L. J. Edwards, *J. Am. Chem. Soc.*, **81**, 3554 (1959).
150. L. J. Edwards, W. V. Hough, and M. D. Ford, *Congr. Intern. Chim. Pure Appl., 16e Paris, 1957, Mem. Sect. Chim. Minerale*, 475–481 (1958); Meeting Am. Chem. Soc., 132nd, New York, Sept. 1960.
151. R. W. Parry and G. Kodama, *J. Am. Chem. Soc.*, **82**, 6250 (1960).
152. J. A. Pople, W. G. Schneider, and H. J. Bernstein, *High-Resolution Nuclear Magnetic Resonance*, McGraw-Hill, New York, 1959.
153. R. Schaeffer, *Prog. Boron Chem.*, **1**, 417 (1964).
154. E. L. Muetterties and W. D. Phillips, *Advan. Inorg. Chem. Radiochem.*, **4**, 231 (1962).
155. D. R. Schultz and C. Ring, unpublished results.
156. N. E. Miller and E. L. Muetterties, *J. Am. Chem. Soc.*, **86**, 1033 (1964).
157. H. Noeth, H. Beyer, and H. Vetter, *Ber.*, **97**, 110 (1964).
158. H. Noeth, *Angew. Chem.*, **72**, 638 (1960).
159. H. Noeth and H. Beyer, *Angew. Chem.*, **71**, 383 (1959).
160. R. W. Parry, R. C. Taylor, C. E. Nordman, G. Kodama, and S. G. Shore, WADC Tech. Rept. 59-207, The University of Michigan Research Institute, May, 1959.
161. G. Kodama, Ph.D. dissertation, University of Michigan (1957).
162. R. W. Parry and G. Kodama, Proc. XVI Congress, IUPAC, Inorganic Section, Paris, 483, 1957.
163. C. Heitsch, Ph.D. dissertation, University of Michigan, 1959.

164. R. W. Parry, R. C. Taylor, C. E. Nordman, H. Schumacher, E. R. Alton, R. Amster, J. C. Carter, C. Cluff, C. W. Heitsch, C. R. Peters, D. E. Shriver, J. R. Weaver, and M. Yamauchi, WADD Tech. Rept. 60–262, The University of Michigan Research Institute, 1960.
165. W. S. Brey, Jr., M. E. Fuller, II, G. E. Ryschkewitsch, and A. S. Marshall, *Advan. Chem. Ser.*, **42**, 100 (1964).
166. R. Hoffman, *Advan. Chem. Ser.*, **42**, 78 (1964).
167. C. W. Hickam, Ph.D. dissertation, The Ohio State University (1964).
168. G. W. Schaeffer and L. J. Basil, *J. Am. Chem. Soc.*, **77**, 331 (1955).
169. A. B. Burg and C. L. Randolf, Jr., *J. Am. Chem. Soc.*, **71**, 3451 (1949).
170. K. W. Boeddeker, S. G. Shore, and R. K. Bunting, *J. Am. Chem. Soc.*, **88**, 4396 (1966).
171. H. J. Becher, *Z. Anorg. Allgem. Chem.*, **288**, 235 (1956).
172. C. E. Erikson and F. C. Gunderloy, *J. Org. Chem.*, **24**, 1161 (1959).
173. F. C. Gunderloy, Ph.D. dissertation, Rutgers University (1958).
174. E. Wiberg and K. Schuster, *Z. Anorg. Allgem. Chem.*, **213**, 77 (1933).
175. G. H. Dahl and R. Schaeffer, *J. Am. Chem. Soc.*, **83**, 3032 (1961).
176. R. O. Buttlar, Ph.D. dissertation, Indiana University (1962).
177. S. G. Shore and C. W. Hickam, Jr., *Inorg. Chem.*, **2**, 638 (1963).
178. H. Noeth, *Z. Naturforsch.*, **16B**, 618 (1961).
179. H. Noeth, *Z. Naturforsch.*, **15B**, 327 (1960).
180. J. L. Boone and A. B. Burg, *J. Am. Chem. Soc.*, **80**, 1519 (1958).
181. B. M. Mikhailov and V. A. Dorokhov, *Dokl. Akad. Nauk SSSR*, **136**, 356 (1961).
182. H. Jenker, Ger. Pat. 1,133,393.
183. A. F. Zhigach, E. B. Kazakova, and I. S. Antonov, *Zh. Obshch. Khim.*, **27**, 1655 (1957).
184. T. C. Bissot and R. W. Parry, *J. Am. Chem. Soc.*, **77**, 3481 (1955).
185. D. F. Gaines and R. Schaeffer, *J. Am. Chem. Soc.*, **85**, 395 (1963).
186. J. K. Ruff, *J. Org. Chem.*, **27**, 1020 (1962).
187. D. W. Aubrey, M. F. Lappert, and M. K. Majumdar, *J. Chem. Soc.*, **1962**, 4088.
188. W. A. Jenkins, *J. Am. Chem. Soc.*, **78**, 5500 (1956).
189. B. M. Mikhailov and Yu. N. Bubnov, *Zh. Obshch. Khim.*, **31**, 577 (1961).
190. B. M. Mikhailov and Yu. N. Bubnov, *Izv. Akad. Nauk SSSR*, **1960**, 1872.
191. J. P. Laurent, *Bull. Soc. Chim. France*, **1963**, 558.
192. B. M. Mikhailov and Yu. N. Bubnov, *Zh. Obshch. Khim.*, **32**, 1969 (1962).
193. B. M. Mikhailov and F. B. Tutorskaya, *Izv. Akad. Nauk SSSR Otd Khim. Nauk*, **1961**, 1158.
194. G. E. Coates and J. G. Livingston, *J. Chem. Soc.*, **1961**, 1000.
195. G. E. Coates and J. G. Livingston, *J. Chem. Soc.*, **1961**, 4909.
196. J. Goubeau and H. Grabner, *Chem. Ber.*, **93**, 1379 (1960).
197. H. Noeth, *Z. Naturforsch.*, **16B**, 470 (1961).
198. E. Wiberg and K. Hertwig, *Z. Anorg. Chem.*, **257**, 138 (1948).
199. K. Niedenzu, P. Fritz, and J. Dawson, *Inorg. Chem.*, **3**, 778 (1964).
200. W. Gerrard and E. F. Mooney, *Chem. Ind. (London)*, **1958**, 1259.
201. M. J. S. Dewar, V. P. Kubba, and R. Pettit, *J. Chem. Soc.*, **1958**, 3073.
202. B. M. Mikhailov, V. A. Vaver, and Yu. N. Bubnov, *Dokl. Akad. Nauk SSSR*, **126**, 575 (1959).
203. E. M. Horn, Belg. Pat. 626,034.
204. H. Noeth, *Z. Naturforsch.*, **16B**, 471 (1961).
205. B. M. Mikhailov and Yu. N. Bubnov, *Izv. Akad. Nauk SSSR, Otd. Khim. Nauk*, **1960**, 370.

206. B. M. Mikhailov and Yu. N. Bubnov, *Izv. Akad. Nauk SSSR Otd. Khim. Nauk*, **1959,** 172.
207. B. M. Mikhailov and Yu. N. Bubnov, *Zh. Obshch. Khim.*, **29,** 1648 (1959).
208. B. M. Mikhailov and P. M. Aronovich, *Zh. Obshch. Khim.*, **29,** 3124 (1959).
209. B. M. Mikhailov and F. B. Tutorskaya, *Dokl. Akad. Nauk SSSR,* **123,** 479 (1958).
210. J. F. Brown, Jr., *J. Am. Chem. Soc.*, **74,** 1219 (1952).
211. A. B. Burg and J. Banus, *J. Am. Chem. Soc.*, **76,** 3903 (1954).
212. C. A. Brown and R. C. Osthoff, *J. Am. Chem. Soc.*, **74,** 2340 (1952).
213. J. Goubeau, M. Rahtz, and H. J. Becher, *Z. Anorg. Allgem. Chem.*, **275,** 161 (1954).
214. K. Niedenzu and J. W. Dawson, *J. Am. Chem. Soc.*, **81,** 5553 (1959).
215. W. Gerrard, M. F. Lappert, and C. A. Pearce, *J. Chem. Soc.*, **1957,** 381.
216. W. Gerrard, H. R. Hudson, and E. F. Mooney, *Chem. Ind.* (*London*), **1959,** 432.
217. H. Watanabe, K. Nagasawa, T. Totani, T. Yoshizaki, and T. Nakagawa, *Advan. Chem. Ser.*, **42,** 108 (1964).
218. K. Niedenzu, H. Beyer, J. W. Dawson, and H. Jenne, *Ber.*, **96,** 2653 (1963).
219. H. J. Becher, *Z. Anorg. Allgem. Chem.*, **289,** 262 (1957).
220. C. A. Brown and A. W. Laubengayer, *J. Am. Chem. Soc.*, **77,** 3699 (1955).
221. G. H. Dahl and R. Schaeffer, *J. Inorg. Nucl. Chem.*, **12,** 380 (1960).
222. K. Niedenzu, D. H. Harrelson, W. George, and J. W. Dawson, *J. Org. Chem.*, **26,** 3037 (1961).
223. U. S. Borax and Chemical Corp. Brit. Pat. 913,862.
224. J. Braun, *Compt. Rend.*, **256,** 2422 (1963).
225. P. Fritz, K. Niedenzu, and J. W. Dawson, *Inorg. Chem.*, **3,** 626 (1964).
226. L. L. Patterson, R. J. Brotherton, G. Wellcockson, and A. L. McCloskey, U. S. Pat. 3,079,432.
227. K. Niedenzu, H. Beyer, and J. W. Dawson, *Inorg. Chem.*, **1,** 738 (1962).
228. B. M. Mikhailov and V. A. Dorokhov, *Izv. Akad. Nauk SSSR, Otd. Khim. Nauk*, **1961,** 1163.
229. B. M. Mikhailov and V. A. Dorokhov, *Zh. Obshch. Khim.*, **32,** 1511 (1962).
230. V. I. Mikheeva and E. M. Fedneva, *Zh. Neorg. Khim.*, **2,** 604 (1957).
231. R. J. Brotherton and L. L. Patterson, U.S. Pat. 3,024,279.
232. H. Noeth, W. A. Dorokhov, P. Fritz, and F. Pfab, *Z. Anorg. Allgem. Chem.*, **318,** 293 (1962).
233. A. Dornow and H. H. Gehrt, *Z. Anorg. Allgem. Chem.*, **294,** 81 (1958).
234. B. M. Mikhailov and T. A. Shchegoleva, *Izv. Akad. Nauk SSSR Otd. Khim. Nauk*, **1958,** 777.
235. B. M. Mikhailov and T. K. Kozminskaya, *Zh. Obshch. Khim.*, **30,** 3619 (1960).
236. M. F. Hawthorne, *J. Am. Chem. Soc.*, **83,** 2671 (1961).
237. B. M. Mikhailov and P. M. Aronovich, *Izv. Akad. SSSR Otd. Khim. Nauk*, **1957,** 1123.
238. W. Gerrard, M. F. Lappert, and C. A. Pearce, *J. Chem. Soc.*, **1957,** 381.
239. D. W. Aubrey, W. Gerrard, and E. F. Mooney, *J. Chem. Soc.*, **1962,** 1786.
240. H. Noeth and P. Fritz, *Z. Anorg. Allgem. Chem.*, **322,** 297 (1963).
241. M. Norton, Ital. Pat. 526,303.
242. W. J. McDowell and C. W. Keenan, *J. Am. Chem. Soc.*, **78,** 2065 (1956).
243. W. D. English, H. Steinberg, and A. L. McCloskey, U. S. Pat. 3,068,182.
244. W. D. English, A. L. McCloskey, and H. Steinberg, *J. Am. Chem. Soc.*, **83,** 2122 (1961).

245. C. A. Kraus and E. H. Brown, *J. Am. Chem. Soc.*, **52**, 4414 (1930).
246. A. Dornow and H. H. Gehrt, *Angew. Chem.*, **68**, 619 (1956).
247. A. K. Holliday, H. J. Marsden, and A. G. Massey, *J. Chem. Soc.*, **1961**, 3348.
248. W. D. English, U. S. Pat. 3,052,718.
249. R. J. Brotherton and T. Buckman, *Inorg. Chem.*, **2**, 424 (1963).
250. P. Fritz, K. Niedenzu, and J. W. Dawson, *Inorg. Chem.*, **4**, 886 (1965).
251. S. G. Shore, unpublished results.
252. J. Crist and S. G. Shore, unpublished results.
253. R. J. Brotherton, A. L. McCloskey, L. L. Patterson, and H. Steinberg, *J. Am. Chem. Soc.*, **82**, 6242 (1960).
254. G. W. Campbell and L. Johnson, *J. Am. Chem. Soc.*, **81**, 3800 (1959).
255. E. Wiberg and W. Sturm, *Z. Naturforsch.*, **8B**, 689 (1953).
256. E. K. Mellon and J. J. Lagowski, *Advan. Inorg. Chem. Radiochem.*, **5**, 259 (1963).
257. J. R. Platt, H. B. Klevens, and G. W. Schaeffer, *J. Chem. Phys.*, **15**, 598 (1947).
258. L. E. Jacobs, J. R. Platt, and G. W. Schaeffer, *J. Chem. Physics*, **16**, 116 (1948).
259. C. W. Rector, G. W. Schaeffer, and J. R. Platt, *J. Chem. Phys.*, **17**, 460 (1949).
260. O. Chalvet, R. Daudel, and J. J. Kaufman, *Advan. Chem. Ser.*, **42**, 251 (1964).
261. H. Watanabe, K. Ito, and M. Kubo, *J. Am. Chem. Soc.*, **82**, 3294 (1960).
262. R. A. Spurr and S. Chang, *J. Chem. Phys.*, **19**, 518 (1951).
263. E. Wiberg and A. Bolz, *Chem. Ber.*, **73**, 209 (1940).
264. K. Niedenzu and J. W. Dawson, *Boron–Nitrogen Compounds*, Academic Press, New York, 1965, p. 92, ref. 5.
265. R. I. Wagner and J. L. Bradford, *Inorg. Chem.*, **1**, 93 (1962).
266. R. I. Wagner and J. L. Bradford, *Inorg. Chem.*, **1**, 99 (1962).
267. J. J. Harris, *J. Org. Chem.*, **26**, 2155 (1961).
268. D. Seyferth, W. R. Freyer, and M. Takamizawa, *Inorg. Chem.*, **1**, 710 (1962).
269. A. W. Laubengayer and O. T. Beachley, Jr., *Advan. Chem. Ser.*, **42**, 281 (1964).
270. V. Gutmann, A. Meller, and R. Schlegel, *Mh. Chem.*, **94**, 1071 (1963).
271. V. Gutmann, A. Meller, and R. Schlegel, *Mh. Chem.*, **95**, 314 (1964).
272. M. F. Lappert, *Proc. Chem. Soc.*, **1959**, 59.
273. M. F. Lappert and M. K. Majumdar, *Advan. Chem. Ser.*, **42**, 208 (1964).
274. H. S. Turner and R. J. Warne, *Proc. Chem. Soc.*, **1962**, 69.
275. H. S. Turner and R. J. Warne, *Advan. Chem. Ser.*, **42**, 290 (1964).
276. S. H. Bauer, *J. Am. Chem. Soc.*, **60**, 524 (1938).
277. G. H. Dahl, dissertation, Iowa State University of Science and Technology, 1960.
278. E. Wiberg and K. Hertwig, *Z. Anorg. Chem.*, **255**, 141 (1947).
279. A. W. Laubengayer, O. T. Beachley, Jr., and R. F. Porter, *Inorg. Chem.*, **4**, 578 (1965).
280. A. Stock and E. Pohland, *Ber.*, **59 B**,2210 (1926).
281. A. Stock and E. Pohland, *Ber. Deut. Keram. Ges.*, **59**, 2215 (1926).
282. E. Wiberg and A. Bolz, *Ber.*, **73B**, 209 (1940).
283. H. I. Schlesinger, R. Schaeffer, T. Wartik et al., University of Chicago Final Report, Navy Contract N6 ori-20 T.O. 10 (1947–1948).
284. G. W. Schaeffer, R. Schaeffer, and H. I. Schlesinger, *J. Am. Chem. Soc.*, **73**, 1612 (1951).
285. V. I. Mikheeva and V. Yu. Markina, *Zh. Neorg. Khim.*, **1**, 2700 (1956).
286. H. J. Emeleus and G. J. Videla, *J. Chem. Soc.*, **1959**, 1306.
287. R. K. Pearson and J. W. Frazer, *J. Inorg. and Nuclear Chem.*, **21**, 188 (1961).
288. K. Niedenzu, *Inorg. Chem.*, **1**, 943 (1962).

289. A. W. Laubengayer, K. Watterson, D. R. Bidinosti, and R. F. Porter, *Inorg. Chem.*, **2,** 519 (1963).
290. H. Noeth, *Z. Naturforsch.*, **16B,** 618 (1961).
291. G. L. Brenan, G. H. Dahl and R. Schaeffer, *J. Am. Chem. Soc.*, **82,** 6248 (1960).
292. K. Niedenzu and J. W. Dawson, *Boron–Nitrogen Compounds*, Academic Press, New York, 1965, p. 103, ref. 8.
293. H. Watanabe, T. Totani, and T. Yoshizaki, *Inorg. Chem.*, **4,** 657 (1965).
294. D. T. Hawthorn and L. F. Hohnstedt, *J. Am. Chem. Soc.*, **82,** 3860 (1960).
295. E. Wiberg, *Naturwissenschaften*, **35,** 182, 212 (1948).
296. A. F. Zhigach, E. B. Kazakova, and E. S. Krongauz, *Dokl. Akad. Nauk SSSR* **111,** 1029 (1956).
297. R. Koester, G. Bruno, and P. Binger, *Ann. Chem.*, **644,** 1 (1961).
298. W. L. Ruigh, W. R. Dunnavant, F. C. Gunderloy, Jr., N. G. Steinberg, M. Sedlak, and A. D. Olin, *Advan. Chem. Ser.*, **32,** 241 (1961).
299. B. M. Mikhailov and T. K. Kozminskaya, *Dokl. Akad. Nauk SSSR*, **121,** 656 (1958).
300. B. M. Mikhailov, T. K. Kozminskaya, N. S. Fedtov, and V. A. Dorokhov, *Dokl. Akad. Nauk SSSR*, **127,** 1023 (1959).
301. H. Goldsmith, Ger. Pat. 131,672.
302. P. C. Moews, Jr. and A. W. Laubengayer, *Inorg. Chem.*, **2,** 1072 (1963).
303. H. Goldsmith and W. G. Woods, Fr. Pat. 321,257.
304. R. H. Toeniskoetter and F. R. Hall, *Inorg. Chem.*, **2,** 29 (1963).
305. B. M. Mikhailov, A. N. Blokhina, and T. V. Kostroma, *Zh. Obshch. Khim.*, **29,** 1483 (1959).
306. J. R. Gould, U.S. Pat. 2,754,177.
307. K. Niedenzu and J. W. Dawson, *Angew. Chem.*, **73,** 433 (1961).
308. W. Gerrard, H. R. Hudson, and E. F. Mooney, *J. Chem. Soc.*, **1962,** 113.
309. K. Niedenzu and J. W. Dawson, *J. Am. Chem. Soc.*, **81,** 3561 (1959).
310. H. I. Schlesinger, D. M. Ritter, and A. B. Burg, *J. Am. Chem. Soc.*, **60,** 1296 (1938).
311. W. V. Hough, G. W. Schaeffer, M. Dzurus, and A. C. Stewart, *J. Am. Chem. Soc.*, **77,** 864 (1955).
312. B. M. Mikhailov and V. A. Dorokhov, *Izv. Akad. Nauk SSSR Otd. Khim. Nauk,* **1961,** 1346.
313. H. Noeth and G. Mikulashek, *Z. Anorg. Allgem. Chem.*, **311,** 241 (1961).
314. E. M. Horn and K. Lang, Ger. Pat. 1,147,944.
315. A. J. Leffler, *Inorg. Chem.*, **3,** 145 (1964).
316. E. M. Horn and K. Lang, Fr. Pat. 1,321,235.
317. H. Jenker, Ger. Pat. 1,142,589.
318. S. F. Stafiej, U. S. Pat. 2,998,449.
319. P. A. Chopard and R. F. Hudson, *J. Inorg. Nucl. Chem.*, **25,** 801 (1963).
320. M. F. Lappert and M. K. Majumdar, *Proc. Chem. Soc.*, **1961,** 425.
321. W. Gerrard, *Soc. Chem. Ind.* (*London*), *Monograph*, **13,** 328 (1961).
322. H. Jenker, Ger. Pat. 1,138,052.
323. H. C. Newsom, W. G. Woods, and A. L. McCloskey, U. S. Pat. 3,072,718.
324. R. K. Bartlett, H. S. Turner, R. J. Warne, M. A. Young, and W. S. McDonald, *Proc. Chem. Soc.*, **1962,** 153.
325. K. Niedenzu, D. H. Harrelson, and J. W. Dawson, *Chem. Ber.*, **94,** 671 (1961).
326. E. Wiberg and G. Horeld, *Z. Naturforsch.*, **6B,** 338 (1951).
327. K. Niedenzu, H. Beyer, and H. Jenne, *Chem. Ber.*, **96,** 2649 (1963).

328. K. A. Muszkat, L. Hill, and B. Kirson, *Israel J. Chem.*, **1**, 27 (1963).
329. L. F. Hohnstedt and D. T. Haworth, *J. Am. Chem. Soc.*, **82**, 89 (1960).
330. M. F. Lappert and H. Pyszora, *J. Chem. Soc.*, **1963**, 1744.
331. W. Gerrard and E. F. Mooney, *J. Chem. Soc.*, **1960**, 4028.
332. R. G. Jones and C. Kinney, *J. Am. Chem. Soc.*, **61**, 1378 (1939).
333. W. Gerrard, E. F. Mooney, and D. E. Pratt, *J. Appl. Chem.*, **13**, 127 (1963).
334. B. M. Mikhailov and T. V. Kostroma, *J. Gen. Chem. USSR*, **29**, 1483 (1959).
335. K. A. Muszkat and B. Kirson, *Israel J. Chem.*, **1**, 150 (1963).
336. D. W. Aubrey and M. F. Lappert, *J. Chem. Soc.*, **1959**, 2927.
337. J. E. Burch, W. Gerrard, and E. F. Mooney, *J. Chem. Soc.*, **1962**, 2200.
338. B. M. Mikhailov and T. V. Kostroma, *Zh. Obshch. Khim.*, **29**, 1477 (1959).
339. D. Seyferth and H. P. Koegler, *J. Inorg. Nucl. Chem.*, **15**, 99 (1960).
340. D. Seyferth, H. Yamasaki, and Y. Sato, *Inorg. Chem.*, **2**, 734 (1963).
341. D. Seyferth and M. Takamizawa, *Inorg. Chem.*, **2**, 731 (1963).
342. A. H. Cowley, H. H. Sisler, and G. E. Ryschkewitsch, *J. Am. Chem. Soc.*, **82**, 501 (1960).
343. D. Seyferth, H. P. Koegler, W. R. Freyer, M. Takamizawa, H. Yamazaki, and Y. Sato, *Advan. Chem. Ser.*, **42**, 259 (1964), ref. 10.
344. D. Seyferth and M. Takamizawa, *J. Org. Chem.*, **28**, 1142 (1963).
345. R. Schaeffer, M. Steindler, L. Hohnstedt, S. H. Smith, Jr., L. P. Eddy, and H. I. Schlesinger, *J. Am. Chem. Soc.*, **76**, 3303 (1954).
346. J. H. Smalley and S. F. Stafiej, *J. Am. Chem. Soc.*, **81**, 582 (1952).
347. G. H. Dahl and R. Schaeffer, *J. Inorg. Nucl. Chem.*, **12**, 380 (1960).
348. G. W. Schaeffer, R. Schaeffer, and H. I. Schlesinger, *J. Am. Chem. Soc.*, **73**, 1612 (1951).
349. H. Beyer, H. Jenne, J. B. Hynes, and K. Niedenzu, *Advan. Chem. Ser.*, **42**, 266 (1964).
350. R. J. Brotherton and H. Steinberg, *J. Org. Chem.*, **26**, 4632 (1961).
351. B. Rudner and J. J. Harris, Abstrs. 138th Meeting, Am. Chem. Soc., New York, September 1960, p. 61.
352. W. Gerrard, H. R. Hudson, and E. F. Mooney, *J. Chem. Soc.*, **1962**, 113.
353. K. Niedenzu and J. W. Dawson, *J. Am. Chem. Soc.*, **81**, 3561 (1959).
354. C. R. Kinney and M. J. Kolbezen, *J. Am. Chem. Soc.*, **64**, 1584 (1942).
355. M. J. Bradley, G. E. Ryschkewitsch and H. H. Sisler, *J. Am. Chem. Soc.*, **81**, 2635 (1959).
356. D. T. Haworth and L. F. Hohnstedt, *J. Am. Chem. Soc.*, **81**, 842 (1959).
357. H. J. Becher and S. Frick, *Z. Anorg. Chem.*, **295**, 83 (1958).
358. W. D. English and A. L. McCloskey, U. S. Pat. 3,000,937; *Chem. Abstr.*, **56**, 1479h (1962).
359. S. J. Groszos and S. F. Stafiej, *J. Am. Chem. Soc.*, **80**, 1357 (1958).
360. D. T. Haworth and L. F. Hohnstedt, *J. Am. Chem. Soc.*, **82**, 3860 (1960).
361. G. E. Ryschkewitsch, J. J. Harris, and H. H. Sisler, *J. Am. Chem. Soc.*, **80**, 4515 (1958).
362. H. I. Schlesinger, L. Horvitz, and A. B. Burg, *J. Am. Chem. Soc.*, **58**, 409 (1936).
363. H. I. Schlesinger, D. M. Ritter, and A. B. Burg, *J. Am. Chem. Soc.*, **60**, 1296 (1938).
364. A. W. Laubengayer, P. C. Moews, and R. F. Porter, *J. Am. Chem. Soc.*, **83**, 1337 (1961).
365. M. F. Lappert and M. K. Majumdar, *Proc. Chem. Soc.*, **1963**, 88.
366. R. M. Adams and F. D. Poholsky, *Inorg. Chem.*, **2**, 640 (1963).

367. G. Hesse and H. Witte, *Angew. Chem.*, **75**, 791 (1963).
368. D. G. White, *J. Am. Chem. Soc.*, **85**, 3634 (1963).
369. J. Goubeau and A. Zappel, *Z. Anorg. Allgem. Chem.*, **279**, 38 (1955).
370. H. E. Holmquist and R. E. Benson, *J. Am. Chem. Soc.*, **84**, 4720 (1962).
371. H. Beyer, K. Niedenzu, and J. W. Dawson, *J. Org. Chem.*, **27**, 4701 (1962).
372. R. L. Letsinger and S. B. Hamilton, *J. Am. Chem. Soc.*, **80**, 5411 (1958).
373. H. Weidmann and H. K. Zimmerman, *Liebigs Ann. Chem.*, **619**, 28 (1958).
374. R. L. Letsinger and S. H. Dandegaonker, *J. Am. Chem. Soc.*, **81**, 498 (1959).
375. R. T. Hawkins and H. R. Snyder, *J. Am. Chem. Soc.*, **82**, 3863 (1960).
376. S. S. Chissick, M. J. S. Dewar, and P. M. Maitlis, *J. Am. Chem. Soc.*, **81**, 6329 (1959).
377. R. T. Hawkins, W. J. Lennarz, and H. R. Snyder, *J. Am. Chem. Soc.*, **82**, 3053 (1960).
378. H. Noeth, *Z. Naturforsch.*, **16B**, 470 (1961).
379. M. Pailer and W. Fenzl, *Mh. Chem.*, **92**, 1294 (1961).
380. K. Niedenzu, P. Fritz, and J. W. Dawson, *Inorg. Chem.*, **3**, 1077 (1964).
381. D. F. Gaines and R. Schaeffer, *J. Am. Chem. Soc.*, **86**, 1505 (1964).
382. L. F. Hohnstedt and A. M. Pellicciotto, Abstr. of Papers, 137th National Meeting, American Chemical Society, Cleveland, 1960, sect. 0, p. 7.
383. R. Neu, *Tetrahedron Letters*, **20**, 917 (1962).
384. E. Nyilas and A. H. Soloway, *J. Am. Chem. Soc.*, **81**, 2681 (1959).
385. J. M. Sugihara and C. M. Bowman, *J. Am. Chem. Soc.*, **80**, 2443 (1958).
386. E. E. Van Tamelen, G. Brieger, and K. G. Untch, *Tetrahedron Letters*, **8**, 14 (1960).
387. D. Ulmschneider and J. Goubeau, *Chem. Ber.*, **90**, 2733 (1957).
388. G. A. Hahn and R. Schaeffer, *J. Am. Chem. Soc.*, **86**, 1503 (1964).
389. P. M. Maitlis, *J. Chem. Soc.*, **1961**, 425.
390. M. J. S. Dewar, *Advan. Chem. Ser.*, **42**, 227 (1964), C. G. Culling, unpublished results.
391. K. Niedenzu and J. W. Dawson, *Boron–Nitrogen Compounds*, Academic Press, New York, 1965, p. 145.
392. M. J. S. Dewar, V. P. Kubba, and R. Pettit, *J. Chem. Soc.*, **1958**, 3073.
393. M. J. S. Dewar and P. Marr, *J. Am. Chem. Soc.*, **84**, 3782 (1962).
394. M. J. S. Dewar, *Advan. Chem. Ser.*, **42**, 227 (1964), ref. 3.
395. M. J. S. Dewar, R. Dietz, V. P. Kubba, and A. R. Lepley, *J. Am. Chem. Soc.*, **83**, 1754 (1961).
396. M. J. S. Dewar and P. M. Maitlis, *J. Am. Chem. Soc.*, **83**, 187 (1961).
397. M. J. S. Dewar, *Prog. Boron Chem.*, **1**, 235 (1964), ref. 16.
398. M. J. S. Dewar, *Prog. Boron. Chem.*, **1**, 235 (1964), ref. 28.
399. M. J. S. Dewar and V. P. Kubba, *J. Am. Chem. Soc.*, **83**, 1757 (1961).
400. M. J. S. Dewar and P. M. Maitlis, *Tetrahedron*, **15**, 35 (1961).
401. S. S. Chissick, M. J. S. Dewar, and P. M. Maitlis, *Tetrahedron Letters* **23**, 8 (1960).
402. H. Noeth, P. Fritz, and W. Meister, *Angew. Chem.*, **73**, 762 (1961).
403. R. L. Letsinger and S. B. Hamilton, *J. Org. Chem.*, **25**, 592 (1960).
404. H. L. Yale, F. H. Bergeim, F. A. Sowinsky, F. A. Bernstein, and J. Fried, *J. Am. Chem. Soc.*, **84**, 689 (1962).
405. M. J. S. Dewar, V. P. Kubba, and R. Pettit, *J. Chem. Soc.*, **1958**, 3076.
406. M. J. S. Dewar, *Advan. Chem. Ser.*, **42**, 227 (1964).
407. M. J. S. Dewar, *Prog. Boron Chem.*, **1**, 235 (1964).

408. R. Koester and K. Iwasaki, *Advan. Chem. Ser.*, **42**, 148 (1964).
409. M. F. Lappert and G. Srivastava, *Proc. Chem. Soc.*, **1964**, 120.
410. H. Jenne and K. Niedenzu, *Inorg. Chem.*, **3**, 68 (1964).
411. K. Niedenzu and J. W. Dawson, *Boron–Nitrogen Compounds,* Academic Press, New York., 1965, p. 75, ref. 6.
412. H. Noeth and W. Regnet, *Advan. Chem. Ser.*, **42**, 166 (1964).
413. B. M. Mikhailov and Yu. N. Bubnov, *Izv. Akad. Nauk SSSR, Otd. Khim. Nauk*, **1960**, 370.
414. S. C. Malhotra, *Inorg. Chem.*, **3**, 862 (1964).
415. A. Finch and H. I. Schlesinger, *J. Am. Chem. Soc.*, **80**, 3573 (1958).
416. M. P. Brown and H. B. Silver, *Chem. Ind.* (*London*), **1963**, 85.
417. R. J. Brotherton, *Prog. Boron Chem.*, **1**, 1 (1964), H. Noeth, private communication.
418. G. Urry, T. Wartik, R. E. Moore, and H. I. Schlesinger, *J. Am. Chem. Soc.*, **76**, 5293 (1954).
419. H. Noeth and W. Meister, *Ber.*, **94**, 509 (1961).
420. H. J. Becher, W. Sawodny, H. Noeth, and W. Meister, *Z. Anorg. Allgem. Chem.*, **314**, 226 (1962).
421. R. J. Brotherton, *Prog. Boron Chem.*, **1**, 1 (1964), ref. 31.
422. R. J. Brotherton, *Prog. Boron Chem.*, **1**, 1 (1964), ref. 34.
423. M. P. Brown, A. E. Dann, D. W. Hunt, and H. B. Silver, *J. Chem. Soc.*, **1962**, 4648.
424. H. Noeth and P. Fritz, *Z. Anorg. Allgem. Chem.*, **324**, 129 (1963).
425. R. J. Brotherton, *Prog. Boron Chem.*, **1**, 1 (1964), ref. 25.
426. H. Noeth and W. Meister, *Z. Naturforsch.*, **17B**, 714 (1962).
427. V. I. Mikheeva and V. Yu. Markina, *Zh. Neorg. Khim*, **5**, 1977 (1960).
428. A. B. Burg and C. L. Randolf, Jr., *J. Am. Chem. Soc.*, **73**, 953 (1951).

AUTHOR INDEX*

* *Italic* numbers indicate reference pages.

H

S

T

Y

Z

SUBJECT INDEX

CUMULATIVE INDEX, VOLUMES 1–3